Contents

1

On the Continuance of an Analytical Solution across the Elastic–Plastic Boundary of a Mode I Fracture Mechanics Problem

2

Plastic Zone Transitions

3

Environmental Cracking

4

Small-Scale Yielding versus Exact Linear
Elastic Solutions

Preface

This book is designed to supplement existing textbooks on fracture mechanics with material related to the analytical solution of partial differential equations that pertain to its theory. It concentrates mainly on the near crack-tip region, on which most current research is being focused. Further, it contains a collection of problems that are drawn from recent research in the fields of elastoplastic and environmentally assisted fracture mechanics. In the course of solving these problems, several different solution techniques are demonstrated.

The Introduction presents a systematic development of fracture mechanics theory. It begins with the equations of continuum mechanics and follows with descriptions of general elastic and plastic theory. Subsequent to these general topics, linear elastic fracture mechanics, plastic strip models, and mode III elastoplastic solutions are presented. Following these, failure criteria, slip line theory, and finite element solutions of the mode I problem are discussed. The Introduction provides the necessary background for understanding the subjects covered in the remainder of the book.

In Chapter 1, an initial value problem for the plastic stress function is solved and corresponding displacements of a mode I elastoplastic problem under plane stress loading conditions are obtained. The prescribed elastic–plastic boundary is found by substituting the elastic small-scale-yielding stresses into the Tresca yield condition. If the properties of the governing Monge–Ampere equation (a second-order and nonlinear partial differential equation) are exploited, then it is possible to reduce the problem to a nonlinear, first-order partial differential equation. The plastic stress function is subsequently obtained through the use of differential geometry theory by finding an integral surface that circumscribes the known elastic (Airy) stress function. Unlike in the analogous mode III problem (Hult and McClintock, [HM 56]), whose solution is also presented, a disequilibrated stress discontinuity is found in the trailing portion of the plastic zone of the mode I problem. This discontinuity indicates that an elastic unloading and a redistribution of stress must occur if equilibrium is to be established. Despite the appearance of the stress discontinuity, this solution might still approximate the plastic stress field ahead of the crack tip, where unloading is likely to be minimal. Currently, there are no other analytical elastoplastic solutions available for mode I problems involving finite-dimensional plastic zones.

In Chapter 2, an elastoplastic solution is obtained for a mode III problem that is related to a transition in plastic zone shape through changes in the eccentricity of the elliptical plastic region. One can recover from this solution, as special cases, the Cherepanov plastic strip solution and the Hult and McClintock small-scale-yielding solution. Also discussed in this chapter, in connection with the transition model, are an equivalent crack length, energy dissipation rate, and fracture assessment diagram. This model has important implications regarding failure curves on the fracture assessment diagram.

Chapter 3 investigates two different mathematical models that are related to environmentally assisted crack growth. The first model is an incremental approach to crack growth, whereas the second model assumes a continuous growth process. Both series and asymptotic expansions are employed in the solution of the equations of the first model for the onset of hydrogen-assisted cracking. Numerical solutions for the secondary and tertiary phases of environmental crack propagation are then examined. In connection with the second model, a modified Stefan problem is proposed and solved for a certain class of transport-controlled stress corrosion cracking problems. Of particular note is the elegant mathematical solution of the moving boundary value problem that is associated with this problem. This solution resolves the seemingly paradoxical situation that external transport of corrodant can lead to uniform rather than decreasing crack growth rates. The decreasing crack growth rates that are predicted by the conventional Stefan problem are not observed experimentally. This explains why this classic moving boundary value problem for diffusion-controlled phenomena has not been applied previously to fracture problems.

In Chapter 4, a Westergaard formulation of the three principal modes of fracture is provided. Exact linear elastic solutions are presented for infinite plates subject to remote tractions. A quantitative comparison between the exact linear elastic solutions and the small-scale-yielding approximations for stresses, displacements, and elastic–plastic boundaries is then given. Chapter 4 is designed to provide insight into the assumptions and limitations of small-scale yielding.

Acknowledgments

The author acknowledges the support of the National Science Foundation (U.S.A.) under Grant MEA-8404065 for the research reported in Chapter 3 on environmental cracking phenomena. Additional support has been provided by the Center for Mechanics of Materials and Instabilities at the Michigan Technological University and the Office of Research and Graduate Studies at the Ohio State University.

Further thanks are given to Pergamon Press Ltd., Headington Hill Hall, Oxford OX3 OBW, UK, for their kind permission to freely adapt text and figures reprinted from Refs. [Ung 90a, Ung 89b, Ung 92a, LU 88, Ung 89a, Ung 90c, UGA 83] in Sections 1.1, 2.1, 2.2, 3.1, 3.2, 3.3, 4.1, and 4.2. Gratitude is also expressed to Kluwer Academic Publishers, Spuiboulevard 50, P.O. Box 17, 3300 AA Dordrecht, The Netherlands, for their permission to incorporate text and figures reprinted from Refs. [Ung 91, Ung 90b, Ung 92b, Ung 93] in Sections 1.2, 2.3, 2.4, and 4.3.

Section 3.1 of this text contains material from an article coauthored with S. L. Lee [LU 88]. Section 3.1 also contains supplementary computations and figures produced jointly with Y. Seo [SU 88] where indicated. The figures and analyses in Chapter 4 (less Section 4.3) were published originally with W. W. Gerberich and E. C. Aifantis as [UGA 83] or by Aifantis and Gerberich in [AG 78] where noted.

Thanks are also given to J. D. McBrayer for his assistance in the production of the color plates.

Special thanks are extended to my former doctoral thesis adviser, E. C. Aifantis, for guidance and for inspiring my love of research.

Lastly, thanks are given to my wife Carolyn for the love and support she has given to me over the years.

Introduction

The purpose of this introduction is to acquaint the reader with some of the fundamental equations and theorems of mechanics that govern elastic and plastic material behavior. Some fundamental problems pertaining to fracture mechanics, along with their associated partial differential equations and solution techniques, will also be discussed.

I.1 EQUATIONS OF CONTINUUM MECHANICS

The term *continuum* in this section's title refers to a body that is continuous at an infinitesimal scale as opposed to a discretized model, i.e., one that is represented by a collection of individual masses with space between them, as in an atomic lattice. Other terms that one commonly encounters in mechanics literature are *homogeneous* and *isotropic*. A homogeneous body is one whose material properties do not change abruptly, as in an aggregate such as concrete, which is composed of cement and gravel. An isotropic body is one whose material properties do not vary with direction, as in wood, whose properties change with the orientation of the grain. We will restrict our discussion to isotropic and homogeneous bodies.

Equilibrium
All of the problems discussed in this text will neglect inertia (i.e., high acceleration) and the effects of body forces (e.g., weight is negligible in comparison to applied forces on the body). Thus the body will be in a state of equilibrium such that the following system of equations are satisfied for

1

an isotropic, homogeneous body when expressed in a rectangular Cartesian coordinate system (x, y, z):

$$\sigma_{x,x} + \tau_{yx,y} + \tau_{zx,z} = 0 \tag{I.1-1}$$

$$\sigma_{y,y} + \tau_{xy,x} + \tau_{zy,z} = 0 \tag{I.1-2}$$

$$\sigma_{z,z} + \tau_{xz,x} + \tau_{yz,y} = 0 \tag{I.1-3}$$

where σ_i represents a normal stress in the i direction $(i = x, y, z)$, τ_{ij} represents a shear stress in the ij plane $(j = x, y, z)$, and the variables following a comma designate partial differentiation with respect to those variables; e.g.,

$$\sigma_{i,i} \equiv \frac{\partial \sigma_i}{\partial i}, \text{etc.} \tag{I.1-4}$$

(Note, as in (I.1-4) that the commonly used Einstein summation convention for repeated index $(j = i)$ on an arbitrary second-order tensor A_{ij} will not be employed in this text; i.e., $A_{ii} \neq A_{xx} + A_{yy} + A_{zz}$.)

Equilibrium also requires that shear stresses be symmetrical in the absence of a body couple (true in most applications, with the exception of strong magnetic fields); i.e.,

$$\tau_{ij} = \tau_{ji}. \tag{I.1-5}$$

This assumption reduces the number of stresses to be determined in (I.1-1)–(I.1-3) from nine to six.

The actions of individual stresses on a cube of material are shown pictorially in Fig. I.1-1.

On the surface of a body, the stresses produce a force per unit area called traction t_i $(i = x, y, z)$. The components of the traction may be expressed in matrix form as follows:

$$\begin{Bmatrix} t_x \\ t_y \\ t_z \end{Bmatrix} = \begin{bmatrix} \sigma_x & \tau_{xy} & \tau_{xz} \\ \tau_{xy} & \sigma_y & \tau_{yz} \\ \tau_{xz} & \tau_{yz} & \sigma_z \end{bmatrix} \begin{Bmatrix} n_x \\ n_y \\ n_z \end{Bmatrix} \tag{I.1-6}$$

where n_i $(i = x, y, z)$ are the components of an outward normal unit vector of the surface. The directions of the vectors relative to the inclined surface of a tetrahedron are shown in Fig. I.1-2.

The axes of the Cartesian coordinate system can always be rotated at any point of a body such that all shear stresses disappear from the surface

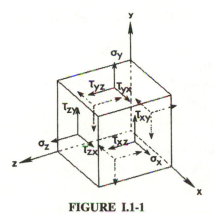

FIGURE I.1-1

Positive stresses acting on various planes of a cube of material in equilibrium.

of the stress cube. The magnitude of stress at this given point is then characterized by three normal stresses $(\sigma_1, \sigma_2, \sigma_3)$, which are referred to as the principal stresses.

The magnitude of the maximum shear stress $|\tau_{max}|$ that a body sustains at a point is related to the principal stresses by the formula

$$|\tau_{max}| = \max|\sigma_\alpha - \sigma_\beta|/2, \qquad (I.1\text{-}7)$$

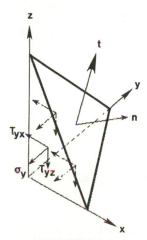

FIGURE I.1-2

Normal and traction vectors on the inclined surface of a tetrahedron.

where $\max|\sigma_\alpha - \sigma_\beta|$ represents the greatest difference between the principal stresses σ_α ($\alpha = 1, 2, 3$) and σ_β ($\beta = 1, 2, 3$).

Strain–Displacement

Small geometric changes of a deforming body are assumed in this text. Consequently, the familiar linearized strain–displacement relationships hold true:

$$\epsilon_x = u_{x,x}, \qquad \epsilon_y = u_{y,y}, \qquad \epsilon_z = u_{z,z} \tag{I.1-8}$$

$$\gamma_{xy} = 2\epsilon_{xy} = u_{x,y} + u_{y,x} \tag{I.1-9}$$

$$\gamma_{xz} = 2\epsilon_{xz} = u_{x,z} + u_{z,x} \tag{I.1-10}$$

$$\gamma_{yz} = 2\varepsilon_{yz} = u_{y,z} + u_{z,y}, \tag{I.1-11}$$

where u_i is the displacement in the i direction, ϵ_i is the normal strain in the i direction, γ_{ij} is the engineering shear strain in the ij plane, and ϵ_{ij} is the shear strain in the ij plane.

Shear strains are symmetrical with respect to the coordinates, i.e.,

$$\gamma_{ij} = \gamma_{ji}, \qquad \epsilon_{ij} = \epsilon_{ji}, \qquad i = x, y, z, j = x, y, z, i \neq j, \tag{I.1-12}$$

as can be seen from their relationships with displacement (I.1-9)–(I.1-11).

Analogous to shear stresses, it is always possible to rotate the orientation of the Cartesian axes at a given point in the body so that all shear strains (I.1-12) vanish. The normal strains that remain at this point in the body after this rotation of axes are called the principal strains ϵ_1, ϵ_2, and ϵ_3, where the subscripts $1, 2, 3$ denote the new Cartesian axes.

Change of Volume

The change of volume of a material, ΔV per unit volume of material V, is referred to as the dilatation θ. The dilatation is related to the normal strains as follows:

$$\theta = \Delta V/V = \epsilon_x + \epsilon_y + \epsilon_z = \epsilon_1 + \epsilon_2 + \epsilon_3. \tag{I.1-13}$$

Compatibility of Strains

In general, six equations of strain compatibility must be satisfied in order to obtain a single-valued displacement field. Mathematically, this situation occurs because specifying strain without restriction overdetermines the possible displacement field. These compatibility relationships are

$$\epsilon_{x,\,yz} = \epsilon_{xy,\,xz} + \epsilon_{zx,\,xy} - \epsilon_{yz,\,xx} \tag{I.1-14}$$

$$\epsilon_{y,\,xz} = \epsilon_{yx,\,yz} + \epsilon_{yz,\,xy} - \epsilon_{zx,\,yy} \tag{I.1-15}$$

$$\epsilon_{z,\,xy} = \epsilon_{zx,\,yz} + \epsilon_{yz,\,xz} - \epsilon_{xy,\,zz} \tag{I.1-16}$$

$$\gamma_{xy,\,xy} = \epsilon_{x,\,yy} + \epsilon_{y,\,xx} \tag{I.1-17}$$

$$\gamma_{xz,\,xz} = \epsilon_{z,\,xx} + \epsilon_{x,\,zz} \tag{I.1-18}$$

$$\gamma_{yz,\,yz} = \epsilon_{y,\,zz} + \epsilon_{z,\,yy}. \tag{I.1-19}$$

I.2 EQUATIONS OF ELASTICITY

The following stress–strain relationships hold true for linear elasticity:

$$\sigma_x = \{E/[(1 + \nu)(1 - 2\nu)]\}\big[(1 - \nu)\epsilon_x + \nu(\epsilon_y + \epsilon_z)\big] \tag{I.2-1}$$

$$\sigma_y = \{E/[(1 + \nu)(1 - 2\nu)]\}\big[(1 - \nu)\epsilon_y + \nu(\epsilon_x + \epsilon_z)\big] \tag{I.2-2}$$

$$\sigma_z = \{E/[(1 + \nu)(1 - 2\nu)]\}\big[(1 - \nu)\epsilon_z + \nu(\epsilon_x + \epsilon_y)\big], \tag{I.2-3}$$

where E is Young's modulus and ν is Poisson's ratio (both assumed constant).

Alternatively, we may write strain in terms of stress as

$$\epsilon_x = (1/E)\big[\sigma_x - \nu(\sigma_y + \sigma_z)\big] \tag{I.2-4}$$

$$\epsilon_y = (1/E)\big[\sigma_y - \nu(\sigma_x + \sigma_z)\big] \tag{I.2-5}$$

$$\epsilon_z = (1/E)\big[\sigma_z - \nu(\sigma_x + \sigma_y)\big]. \tag{I.2-6}$$

There are only two independent parameters of linear elasticity for an isotropic material. One alternative parameter, called the shear modulus G, is related to Young's modulus and Poisson's ratio as follows:

$$G = E/[2(1 + \nu)]. \tag{I.2-7}$$

This parameter is useful in describing the elastic shear stress and shear strain relationships compactly:

$$\tau_{ij} = G\gamma_{ij}, \qquad i = x, y, z, j = x, y, z, i \neq j. \tag{I.2-8}$$

For an incompressible material Poisson's ratio $\nu = 1/2$.

I.3 EQUATIONS OF PLASTICITY

The two most commonly applied criteria of plastic yield for the modeling of metals are the Mises yield condition and the Tresca yield condition. The Mises yield condition predicts that plastic behavior is initiated in a material when its maximum distortion energy reaches a critical value (see [Men 68]). On the other hand, the Tresca yield condition predicts yield when the maximum shear stress reaches a critical value.

In Cartesian coordinates, the Mises yield condition for incipient plastic flow assumes the form

$$(\sigma_x - \sigma_y)^2 + (\sigma_y - \sigma_z)^2 + (\sigma_z - \sigma_x)^2$$
$$+ 6(\tau_{xy}^2 + \tau_{xz}^2 + \tau_{yz}^2) = 2\sigma_0^2, \tag{I.3-1}$$

where σ_0 is the yield stress in simple tension. The relationship between σ_0 and the yield stress in pure shear k for the Mises criterion is

Mises: $$\sigma_0 = 3^{1/2}k \rightarrow k \approx 0.577\sigma_0. \tag{I.3-2}$$

This can be deduced from (I.3-1) by setting all of the stresses equal to zero —save one shear stress, which is given the symbol k.

The Mises yield condition can also be expressed in terms of the three principal stresses $(\sigma_1, \sigma_2, \sigma_3)$ by an equivalent form (4.2-1). One advantage of using (4.2-1) instead of (I.3-2) is that a surface representing (4.2-1) can be visualized in conventional three-dimensional space, with the principal stresses serving as Cartesian coordinates whose base vectors point in the direction of the principal stresses (the Haigh–Westergaard space), whereas (I.3-2) can be visualized only in a generalized sense—as a surface in six-dimensional hyperspace $(\sigma_x, \sigma_y, \sigma_z, \tau_{xy}, \tau_{xz}, \tau_{yz})$.

In the Haigh–Westergaard principal stress space $(\sigma_1, \sigma_2, \sigma_3)$, the Mises yield criterion appears as a cylindrical surface of radius $R = (2/3)^{1/2}\sigma_0$ by virtue of a geometric interpretation of Eq. (4.2-1). However, this surface appears as a circle in Fig. I.3-1, as the line of sight is along the central axis; i.e., the generators of the cylinder are perpendicular to the plane of the paper.

In contrast to the Mises yield condition, the Tresca yield condition can be deduced from (I.1-7) as

$$\max|\sigma_\alpha - \sigma_\beta|/2 = k, \qquad \alpha = 1, 2, 3, \ \beta = 1, 2, 3, \tag{I.3-3}$$

where k is again defined as the yield stress in pure shear, as it was for the Mises yield condition. Using (I.3-3), by setting all but one of the principal stresses equal to zero and setting one principal stress equal to σ_0, we come to the conclusion that

Tresca: $$k = 0.5\sigma_0. \qquad (I.3\text{-}4)$$

Notice the difference in the relationships between the tensile yield stress and the yield stress in pure shear, (I.3-2) and (I.3-4), that occurs between the two yield criteria.

The planes that define the Tresca yield condition in the Haigh–West-ergaard space are, by (I.3-3) and (I.3-4),

$$\sigma_1 - \sigma_2 = \pm\sigma_0, \qquad \sigma_2 - \sigma_3 = \pm\sigma_0, \qquad \sigma_3 - \sigma_1 = \pm\sigma_0. \quad (I.3\text{-}5)$$

Equations (I.3-5) define six planes, which intersect to form the sides of a hexagonal prism whose sides comprise the yield surface of the Tresca yield condition. They appear edge-on in Fig. I.3-1 as a regular hexagon because they are viewed from the vantage point of the prism's centerline.

For both the Mises and Tresca yield conditions, the addition of an arbitrary pressure p to all the normal stresses of a given stress state $(\sigma_x, \sigma_y, \sigma_z, \tau_{xy}, \tau_{xz}, \tau_{yz})$ to yield a new stress state $(\sigma_x^+, \sigma_y^+, \sigma_z^+, \tau_{xy}, \tau_{xz}, \tau_{yz})$, i.e.,

$$\sigma_x^+ = \sigma_x + p, \qquad \sigma_y^+ = \sigma_y + p, \qquad \sigma_z^+ = \sigma_z + p, \qquad (I.3\text{-}6)$$

does not affect the yield status. This reflects the experimental observation that pressure p has little effect on the yielding of metals, except at extremely high levels. This is not necessarily true of other materials, such as soils, which are modeled by different yield criteria (Mohr–Coulomb, Drucker–Prager) that incorporate pressure dependence into the yield condition.

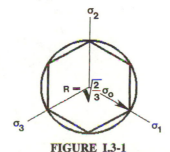

FIGURE I.3-1
Mises and Tresca yield conditions.

We will assume that total strain in a body is always decomposable into the sum of elastic components and plastic components as follows:

$$\epsilon_i = \epsilon_i^E + \epsilon_i^P, \qquad i = x, y, z, \tag{I.3-7}$$

$$\gamma_{ij} = \gamma_{ij}^E + \gamma_{ij}^P, \qquad i = x, y, z, j = x, y, z, i \neq j, \tag{I.3-8}$$

where ϵ_i is the total normal strain, γ_{ij} is the total engineering shear strain, and the superscripts E and P on strain tensors denote the elastic and plastic components of the total strain tensor, respectively. The relationship between ϵ_i^E and γ_{ij}^E will be related to the stresses as in (I.2-4)–(I.2-6), where ϵ_i^E and γ_{ij}^E take the place of ϵ_i and γ_{ij}. General relationships between plastic strains and stresses cannot be given, as plastic strains are path-dependent. Special relationships between incremental plastic strain and stress will be derived later for the Mises and Tresca yield criteria. Under special circumstances, called proportional loading, relationships between stress and strain can be given for materials that have undergone yield. These will also be discussed later.

In Fig. I.3-2, idealized stress–strain behavior is shown for a bar of material subject to a tensile load. In the elastic range, $\epsilon < \epsilon_0$, the slope of the stress–strain curve has the value of Young's modulus E. Three different responses are depicted for materials that have experienced yield at the stress level σ_0, with corresponding strain ϵ_0 in the direction of the load.

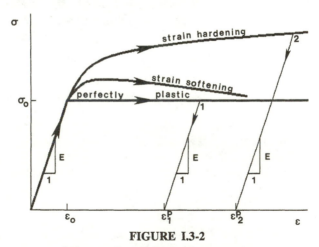

FIGURE I.3-2

Stress versus strain for tensile test specimens.

If the slope of the stress–strain curve remains positive at strains beyond ϵ_0, the material is said to harden. If the slope becomes negative, the material is said to soften. A horizontal line beyond the strain level ϵ_0 is a perfectly plastic response.

Strain softening is exhibited only by unstable plastic materials, and they will not be considered. However, typical structural materials may exhibit what appears to be strain softening when softening does not, in fact, occur. This is due to plotting nominal stress versus strain, instead of true stress versus strain. Nominal stress uses the original cross-section of the test specimen, rather than the reduced cross-section under load, which may be significantly smaller due to necking. When the nominal stresses are converted to true stresses, stable material properties are observed [GT 84, pp. 10–12].

If the load is reduced on the specimen, the material will unload elastically along a stress–strain line with slope E. The residual strain that remains when $\sigma = 0$ ($\epsilon^E = 0$) is the plastic strain ϵ^P attained at the maximum elongation of the test specimen. Two different unloadings are shown in Fig. I.3-2. One is associated with point 1 of the perfectly plastic response and the other is associated with point 2 of the strain hardening curve. The residual strains ϵ_1^P and ϵ_2^P for $\sigma = 0$ may also be interpreted as the plastic strains at points 1 and 2, respectively.

Strain Hardening

Post-yield behavior of a material is characterized by what is called strain or work hardening. When increased stress is required for increased plastic strain to occur, the material is said to harden. Another measure of material hardening is the amount of plastic work (per unit volume) U^P,

$$U^P = \int \sigma_x \, d\epsilon_x^P + \int \sigma_y \, d\epsilon_y^P + \int \sigma_z \, d\epsilon_z^P$$

$$+ \int \tau_{xy} \, d\gamma_{xy}^P + \int \tau_{xz} \, d\gamma_{xz}^P + \int \tau_{yz} \, d\gamma_{yz}^P, \qquad (I.3\text{-}9)$$

that the specimen undergoes. Only for special cases can these two different hardening criteria be shown to be equivalent. When the yield criterion on stress does not change at all with respect to the amount of plastic strain or work that the material undergoes, the material is considered a perfectly plastic or non–work-hardening material.

Two principal types of strain or work hardening exist: isotropic hardening and kinematic hardening. Real materials often exhibit both types of hardening.

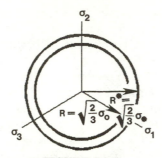

FIGURE I.3-3

Isotropic hardening for the Mises yield condition.

Isotropic hardening involves a simple expansion of the yield surface with plastic strain or work, as shown in Fig. I.3-3 for the Mises yield criterion. In this figure, the yield surface expands for the radius $R = (2/3)^{1/2}\sigma_0$ to the larger radius $R^* = (2/3)^{1/2}\sigma_*$, where $\sigma_* > \sigma_0$. In the case of isotropic hardening for the Tresca yield condition, a larger regular hexagon with the same center and the same orientation relative to the principal stress axes would be obtained. Figure I.3-2 shows a mechanical response to isotropic hardening for a specimen subject to uniaxial tension; see the curve labeled *strain hardening*.

Kinematic hardening involves a translation of the yield surface with plastic strain or work, as shown in Fig. I.3-4 for the Mises yield condition. (No rotation of the yield surface is permitted for cases such as the Tresca yield condition.) This local anisotropy induced in the material by plastic strain is called the Bauschinger effect in materials science literature. Kinematic hardening is very important for modeling material behavior under cyclic loads.

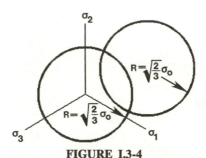

FIGURE I.3-4

Kinematic hardening for the Mises yield condition.

FIGURE I.3-5
Convex surface.

Material Stability

Convexity of the yield surface in Haigh–Westergaard space is a necessary requirement of Drucker's criteria (see [Men 68, Kac 74]) for modeling stable plastic materials (real materials). Materials that exhibit strain softening (see Fig. I.3-2) are not considered, as they are unstable where the slope of the stress–strain curve becomes negative.

A typical convex surface is shown in Fig. I.3-5. The heavy line drawn across the surface represents a test of convexity. Nowhere will this line cross the boundary of the surface, regardless of where the two endpoints are positioned. In Fig. I.3-6, a concavity of that particular surface is demonstrated by the intersection of the heavy line with the boundary of that surface.

A second consequence of Drucker's definition of a stable plastic material is the normality of differential plastic strain relative to the yield surface in the Haigh–Westergaard stress space. This situation is represented in Fig. I.3-7 by the symbol $d\epsilon^P$, which always points in the outward normal direction at a given point on the yield surface. Notice at point A of

FIGURE I.3-6
Concavity on a surface.

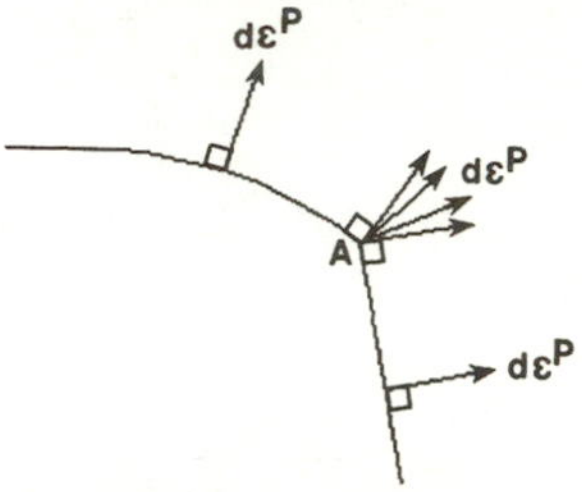

FIGURE I.3-7
Orthogonality of plastic strains to yield surface.

the yield surface in Fig. I.3-7 that the outward normal is indeterminate, as the yield surface is not smooth at this particular point. In such cases, as at the corners of the Tresca yield condition, the direction of the plastic strain is not unique, but is instead bounded by the two outward normal directions of the adjacent smooth sides of the yield surface.

Incremental Strain–Stress Relationships

The normality of the differential strain relative to the yield surface imposes certain conditions on the increment of plastic strain and the state of stress. Let us define a function $h(\sigma_\alpha)$, which represents the equation of a yield surface in the Haigh–Westergaard principal stress space for a perfectly plastic material response

$$h(\sigma_\alpha) = C, \qquad\qquad (\text{I.3-10})$$

where argument σ_α denotes that h is a function of the principal stresses, and C is a constant. By taking the gradient of (I.3-10), where σ_α are treated as Cartesian coordinates, we obtain a vector in the Haigh–Westergaard space that is orthogonal to the yield surface in the outward direction. Since Drucker's postulate on stable plastic materials requires that the differential strain in the principal stress directions be orthogonal to the yield surface in the outward sense, we may infer that

$$d\epsilon_\alpha^{\text{P}} = (\partial h/\partial \sigma_\alpha)\, d\lambda, \qquad \alpha = 1, 2, 3, \qquad (\text{I.3-11})$$

where $d\lambda$ is an incremental loading function to be determined.

A basic property of plasticity in metals is that the incremental change in volume for plastic strains is zero. Since strain is simply a geometric relationship, equation (I.1-13) holds independently of the material response.

This imposes the additional condition on $h(\sigma_\alpha)$ for metals that the dilatation (I.1-13) of plastic strain is zero ($d\theta^P = 0$), or

$$d\epsilon_1^P + d\epsilon_2^P + d\epsilon_3^P = 0 \rightarrow d\lambda(\partial h/\partial\sigma_1 + \partial h/\partial\sigma_2 + \partial h/\partial\sigma_3) = 0$$

$$\text{(I.3-12)}$$

by way of (I.1-13).

Let us now associate the Mises yield condition for a perfectly plastic material with relationship (I.3-10). For this particular yield condition, we may identify $h(\sigma_\alpha)$ and C as follows:

Mises: $$h(\sigma_\alpha) = (\sigma_1 - \sigma_2)^2 + (\sigma_2 - \sigma_3)^2 + (\sigma_3 - \sigma_1)^2, \quad \text{(I.3-13)}$$

$$C = 2\sigma_0^2, \quad \text{(I.3-14)}$$

through the use of (4.2-1). Thus by (I.3-11), we obtain

Mises: $$d\epsilon_1^P = 2\,d\lambda[2\sigma_1 - (\sigma_2 + \sigma_3)] \quad \text{(I.3-15)}$$

$$d\epsilon_2^P = 2\,d\lambda[2\sigma_2 - (\sigma_1 + \sigma_3)] \quad \text{(I.3-16)}$$

$$d\epsilon_3^P = 2\,d\lambda[2\sigma_3 - (\sigma_1 + \sigma_2)]. \quad \text{(I.3-17)}$$

Equations (I.3-15)–(I.3-16) are referred to collectively as a plastic flow rule.

One may readily determine that the incompressibility relationship (I.3-13) is satisfied by (I.3-15)–(I.3-17) without further restriction. This occurs geometrically because in the Haigh–Westergaard principal stress space, the circular cylindrical surface of the Mises yield condition has its generators parallel to the line through points $(0, 0, 0)$ and $(1, 1, 1)$. (A generator is a straight line whose motion traces out the surface of a ruled surface, e.g., a cylinder). We can also generalize this statement to include all cylinders (those with different shapes for cross-sections) having the same orientation of generators. This includes the prismatic yield surface of the Tresca yield condition.

In Fig. I.3-8, we observe the motion of a point P to P' along a generator of the Tresca yield surface. This motion corresponds to a change of the stress state from $(\sigma_1, \sigma_2, \sigma_3)$ to $(\sigma_1^+, \sigma_2^+, \sigma_3^+)$, while maintaining yield, due to a change in pressure p; i.e.,

$$\sigma_1^+ = \sigma_1 + p, \qquad \sigma_2^+ = \sigma_2 + p, \qquad \sigma_3^+ = \sigma_3 + p. \quad \text{(I.3-18)}$$

The reason point P stays on the yield surface despite the increase in pressure is that the Tresca yield equations (I.3-6) involve only differences in the principal stresses, and the common pressure term added to all

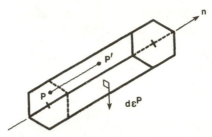

FIGURE I.3-8

Pressure-induced motion of point P to P' along generator of the Tresca yield surface.

principal stresses in (I.3-18) cancels out. Viewed from the perspective of Fig. I.3-1, the point P on the Tresca yield surface would not appear to move at all.

To prove that the plastic strain incompressibility equation is satisfied for the Tresca yield condition, let us define a unit vector $\mathbf{n}$ that is parallel to the line through $(0,0,0)$ and $(1,1,1)$. Elementary analytical geometry gives this unit vector as

$$\mathbf{n} = (\mathbf{i}_1 + \mathbf{i}_2 + \mathbf{i}_3)/3^{1/2}, \tag{I.3-19}$$

where $\mathbf{i}_1$, $\mathbf{i}_2$, and $\mathbf{i}_3$ are defined as unit base vectors in the principal stress directions (σ_1, σ_2, and σ_3, respectively). Referring to Fig. I.3-8, we see that $\mathbf{n}$ is perpendicular to the plastic strain vector $d\boldsymbol{\epsilon}^P$,

$$d\boldsymbol{\epsilon}^P = d\epsilon_1^P \mathbf{i}_1 + d\epsilon_2^P \mathbf{i}_2 + d\epsilon_3^P \mathbf{i}_3, \tag{I.3-20}$$

as $\mathbf{n}$ is parallel to the generators of the cylinder. Thus the inner product between $\mathbf{n}$ and $d\boldsymbol{\epsilon}^P$ is zero; i.e.,

$$\mathbf{n} \cdot d\boldsymbol{\epsilon}^P = 0 \rightarrow d\epsilon_1^P + d\epsilon_2^P + d\epsilon_3^P = 0. \tag{I.3-21}$$

This proves that the incompressibility equation (I.3-12) is satisfied for plastic strains related to the Tresca yield surface. This result can easily be extended to the arbitrary convex cylinder, as $\mathbf{n}$ will remain parallel to the generators and $d\boldsymbol{\epsilon}^P$ will remain perpendicular to them. One should also note that the incompressibility equation holds true even at sharp corners of yield surfaces. Although a unique strain vector does not exist in these cases (see Fig. I.3-7), all of the possible strains remain perpendicular to $\mathbf{n}$. Therefore, the inner product of (I.3-21) remains zero.

The concept of the gradient of the yield surface can be generalized to include the six-dimensional hyperspace ($\sigma_x, \sigma_y, \sigma_z, \tau_{xy}, \tau_{xz}, \tau_{yz}$) such that

Drucker's definition of a stable plastic material implies the following flow rule:

$$d\epsilon_i^P = (\partial H/\partial\sigma_i)\,d\lambda, \qquad i = x, y, z, \tag{I.3-22}$$

$$d\gamma_{ij}^P = (\partial H/\partial\tau_{ij})\,d\lambda, \qquad i = x, y, z, j = x, y, z, i \neq j, \tag{I.3-23}$$

where $d\lambda$ is a differential of a loading function. In (I.3-22) and (I.3-23) the yield surface is represented by the function

$$H = H(\sigma_{ij}) = C, \tag{I.3-24}$$

where C is a constant, and the argument σ_{ij} denotes an arbitrary stress in the Cartesian coordinate system (x, y, z). Because it is a function only of the stresses and not the plastic strains or plastic work, we have limited $H(\sigma_{ij})$ in our discussion to perfectly plastic materials.

The incompressibility condition is, by (I.1-13),

$$d\epsilon_x^P + d\epsilon_y^P + d\epsilon_z^P = 0 \rightarrow d\lambda(\partial H/\partial\sigma_x + \partial H/\partial\sigma_y + \partial H/\partial\sigma_z) = 0. \tag{I.3-25}$$

For use with (I.3-22) and (I.3-23), the alternative form of the Mises yield condition (I.3-1) should be used to give

$$H(\sigma_{ij}) = (\sigma_x - \sigma_y)^2 + (\sigma_y - \sigma_z)^2 + (\sigma_z - \sigma_x)^2$$
$$+ 6(\tau_{xy}^2 + \tau_{xz}^2 + \tau_{yz}^2), \tag{I.3-26}$$

$$C = 2\sigma_0^2. \tag{I.3-27}$$

By taking partial derivatives of $H(\sigma_{ij})$ as in (I.3-22) and (I.3-23), we find

Prandtl–Reuss:

$$d\epsilon_x^P = 2\,d\lambda\left[2\sigma_x - (\sigma_y + \sigma_z)\right] \tag{I.3-28}$$

$$d\epsilon_y^P = 2\,d\lambda\left[2\sigma_y - (\sigma_x + \sigma_z)\right] \tag{I.3-29}$$

$$d\epsilon_z^P = 2\,d\lambda\left[2\sigma_z - (\sigma_x + \sigma_y)\right] \tag{I.3-30}$$

$$d\gamma_{xy}^P = 12\,d\lambda\,\tau_{xy} \tag{I.3-31}$$

$$d\gamma_{xz}^P = 12\,d\lambda\,\tau_{xz} \tag{I.3-32}$$

$$d\gamma_{yz}^P = 12\,d\lambda\,\tau_{yz}. \tag{I.3-33}$$

The differential relationships (I.3-30)–(I.3-33) are called the Prandtl–Reuss equations. By dropping the superscript P on the Prandtl–Reuss equations and by interpreting the differential strains as total strain increments, i.e., neglecting elastic deformations, we obtain the equations of the Saint Venant–von Mises theory of plasticity.

Flow Theory versus Deformation Theory

There are two distinct approaches to modeling plastic strains—flow (incremental) theories and deformation theories. The former is a path-dependent theory and the latter is a path-independent theory. Flow theories account for the loss of energy due to plastic deformation which is nonrecoverable. Deformation theories do not.

The flow rules for a perfectly plastic material under the Mises yield condition have already been derived for plastic strain increments in the principal directions (I.3-15)–(I.3-17) and for plastic strain increments in Cartesian coordinates (I.3-28)–(I.3-33). In the principal strain derivation there are no shear strains and hence no incremental rules for shear. In the Cartesian system shear strains exist and shear strain increments are derived. Plastic strain increments for the Tresca yield condition in the principal directions are given later as equations (1.3-5)–(1.3-7).

Under conditions termed proportional or radial loading, the Prandtl–Reuss equations may be integrated to yield

Hencky:
$$\epsilon_x^P = \Lambda\left[2\sigma_x - (\sigma_y + \sigma_z)\right] \qquad (I.3\text{-}34)$$

$$\epsilon_y^P = \Lambda\left[2\sigma_y - (\sigma_x + \sigma_z)\right] \qquad (I.3\text{-}35)$$

$$\epsilon_z^P = \Lambda\left[2\sigma_z - (\sigma_x + \sigma_y)\right] \qquad (I.3\text{-}36)$$

$$\gamma_{xy}^P = 6\Lambda\tau_{xy} \qquad (I.3\text{-}37)$$

$$\gamma_{xz}^P = 6\Lambda\tau_{xz} \qquad (I.3\text{-}38)$$

$$\gamma_{yz}^P = 6\Lambda\tau_{yz}, \qquad (I.3\text{-}39)$$

where $\Lambda = \Lambda(x, y, z)$. The above plastic relationships between stress and strain, together with the linear elastic relationships between stress and strain, the Mises yield condition, and the total strain relationships (I.3-7)–(I.3-8), constitute what is termed the Hencky deformation theory. The Hencky deformation theory of plasticity represents a nonlinearly "elastic" material.

I.4 PLANE PROBLEMS OF ELASTICITY THEORY

The plane problems of elasticity [TG 70, Sok 56] are generally designated as plane strain problems and generalized plane stress problems.

Plane strain conditions are typically met by thick plates that are loaded in the plane; generalized plane stress conditions are typically met by thin plates. In all of our plane problems, the coordinate z will be perpendicular to the plane of symmetry, be it Cartesian (x, y), polar (r, θ), or some other orthogonal two-dimensional system (u, v). Generalized plane stress problems require an averaging of stress and displacement across the plate thickness so that they become truly two-dimensional [Lov 44, Lit 73]. We will henceforth refer to them simply as plane stress problems in this text.

Cartesian Coordinates

Common to both plane problems is the stress function $\phi(x, y)$, whose second partial derivatives are related to an equilibrated state of stress. This function can be interpreted as a surface

$$z = \phi(x, y) \tag{I.4-1}$$

in the Cartesian system (x, y, z). The second derivatives of $\phi(x, y)$ will be related to the stresses as follows [TG 70]:

$$\sigma_x = \phi_{,yy}, \qquad \sigma_y = \phi_{,xx}, \qquad \tau_{xy} = -\phi_{,xy}. \tag{I.4-2}$$

The two remaining shear stresses are zero for both plane problems:

$$\tau_{xz} = \tau_{yz} = 0. \tag{I.4-3}$$

The normal stress in the z direction σ_z differs between the two classes of plane problems; namely,

$$\sigma_z = 0 \quad \text{for plane stress,} \qquad \sigma_z = \nu(\sigma_x + \sigma_y) \quad \text{for plane strain,} \tag{I.4-4}$$

where ν is Poisson's ratio. In light of the simplified stress states the equilibrium equations (I.1-1)–(I.1-3) reduce to

$$\sigma_{x,x} + \tau_{xy,y} = 0, \qquad \sigma_{y,y} + \tau_{xy,x} = 0, \tag{I.4-5}$$

which are satisfied automatically by stresses (I.4-2) derived from the stress function $\phi(x, y)$. In (I.4-5), body forces have been neglected.

The compatibility equation of strain for both plane problems is

$$\epsilon^{E}_{x,yy} + \epsilon^{E}_{y,xx} = \gamma^{E}_{xy,xy} = 2\epsilon^{E}_{xy,xy}, \tag{I.4-6}$$

where the superscript E denotes an elastic state.

The stress–strain relationships for *plane stress* [HG 64] are

$$\sigma_x = [E/(1 - \nu^2)]\left(\epsilon_x^E + \nu\epsilon_y^E\right) \qquad \text{(I.4-7)}$$

$$\sigma_y = [E/(1 - \nu^2)]\left(\epsilon_y^E + \nu\epsilon_x^E\right) \qquad \text{(I.4-8)}$$

$$\tau_{xy} = G\gamma_{xy}^E \qquad \text{(I.4-9)}$$

$$\sigma_z = \tau_{xz} = \tau_{yz} = 0, \qquad \text{(I.4-10)}$$

or

$$\epsilon_x^E = (1/E)(\sigma_x - \nu\sigma_y) \qquad \text{(I4-11)}$$

$$\epsilon_y^E = (1/E)(\sigma_y - \nu\sigma_x) \qquad \text{(I.4-12)}$$

$$\epsilon_z^E = -(\nu/E)(\sigma_x + \sigma_y) \qquad \text{(I.4-13)}$$

$$\gamma_{xy}^E = (1/G)\tau_{xy} \qquad \text{(I.4-14)}$$

$$\gamma_{xz}^E = \gamma_{yz}^E = 0. \qquad \text{(I.4-15)}$$

The stress–strain relationships for *plane strain* are

$$\sigma_x = \{E/[(1 + \nu)(1 - 2\nu)]\}\left[(1 - \nu)\epsilon_x^E + \nu\epsilon_y^E\right] \qquad \text{(I.4-16)}$$

$$\sigma_y = \{E/[(1 + \nu)(1 - 2\nu)]\}\left[(1 - \nu)\epsilon_y^E + \nu\epsilon_x^E\right] \qquad \text{(I.4-17)}$$

$$\sigma_z = \{\nu E/[(1 + \nu)(1 - 2\nu)]\}\left[\epsilon_x^E + \epsilon_y^E\right] \qquad \text{(I.4-18)}$$

$$\tau_{xy} = G\gamma_{xy}^E \qquad \text{(I.4-19)}$$

$$\tau_{xz} = \tau_{yz} = 0, \qquad \text{(I.4-20)}$$

or

$$\epsilon_x^E = [(1 + \nu)/E]\left[(1 - \nu)\sigma_x - \nu\sigma_y\right] \qquad \text{(I.4-21)}$$

$$\epsilon_y^E = [(1 + \nu)/E]\left[(1 - \nu)\sigma_y - \nu\sigma_x\right] \qquad \text{(I.4-22)}$$

$$\gamma_{xy}^E = (1/G)\tau_{xy} \qquad \text{(I.4-23)}$$

$$\epsilon_z^E = \gamma_{xz}^E = \gamma_{yz}^E = 0. \qquad \text{(I.4-24)}$$

By substituting the relationships for stress in terms of the function $\phi(x, y)$ into the relationships for strain and then substituting the resulting equations for strain into the compatibility equation, we obtain for either plane stress or plane strain the same governing equation:

$$\phi,_{xxxx} + 2\phi,_{xxyy} + \phi,_{yyyy} = 0. \tag{I.4-25}$$

This is called the biharmonic equation and is represented symbolically by

$$\nabla^4 \phi = 0 \tag{I.4-26}$$

where

$$\nabla^4(\ ) \equiv \nabla^2(\nabla^2(\ )), \tag{I.4-27}$$

with $\nabla^2(\ )$ being the usual Laplacian operator

$$\nabla^2(\ ) \equiv (\ ),_{xx} + (\ ),_{yy}. \tag{I.4-28}$$

A stress function $\phi(x, y)$ that satisfies the biharmonic equation is called an Airy stress function. This function $\phi(x, y)$ represents a plane solution that satisfies both equilibrium (I.4-5) and the compatibility equation (I.4-6).

Polar Coordinates

The standard transformation between Cartesian (x, y) and polar coordinates (r, θ) is

$$x = r \cos \theta, \qquad y = r \sin \theta. \tag{I.4-29}$$

Some useful partial derivatives between the two systems are [TG 70]

$$r,_x = \cos \theta, \qquad r,_y = \sin \theta \tag{I.4-30}$$

$$\theta,_x = -\sin \theta / r, \qquad \theta,_y = \cos \theta / r. \tag{I.4-31}$$

These can be used to generate the following relationships between the first and second partial derivatives between the two coordinate systems for an arbitrary function ϕ (such as the Airy stress function).

For the first partial derivative with respect to x, we have

$$\phi,_x = \phi,_r r,_x + \phi,_\theta \theta,_x \tag{I.4-32}$$

$$= \phi,_r \cos \theta - \phi,_\theta \sin \theta / r. \tag{I.4-33}$$

Similarly, for y we find

$$\phi,_y = \phi,_r \sin \theta + \phi,_\theta \cos \theta / r. \tag{I.4-34}$$

For the second partial derivative with respect to x, we have

$$\phi_{,xx} = (\phi_{,x})_{,r} r_{,x} + (\phi_{,x})_{,\theta} \theta_{,x} \tag{I.4-35}$$

$$= (\phi_{,r}\cos\theta - \phi_{,\theta}\sin\theta/r)_{,r} r_{,x} + (\phi_{,r}\cos\theta - \phi_{,\theta}\sin\theta/r)_{,\theta} \theta_{,x} \tag{I.4-36}$$

$$= \phi_{,rr}\cos^2\theta + \phi_{,\theta} 2\sin\theta\cos\theta/r^2$$
$$- \phi_{,r\theta} 2\sin\theta\cos\theta/r + \phi_{,r}\sin^2\theta/r + \phi_{,\theta\theta}\sin^2\theta/r^2 \tag{I.4-37}$$

$$= \phi_{,rr}\cos^2\theta + \left[\phi_{,\theta\theta}/r^2 + \phi_{,r}/r\right]\sin^2\theta$$
$$+ 2\sin\theta\cos\theta\left[\phi_{,\theta}/r^2 - \phi_{,r\theta}/r\right]. \tag{I.4-38}$$

Similarly,

$$\phi_{,xy} = \sin\theta\cos\theta\left[\phi_{,rr} - \phi_{,r}/r - \phi_{,\theta\theta}/r^2\right]$$
$$+ (\cos^2\theta - \sin^2\theta)\left[\phi_{,r\theta}/r - \phi_{,\theta}/r^2\right], \tag{I.4-39}$$

$$\phi_{,yy} = \phi_{,rr}\sin^2\theta + \cos^2\theta\left[\phi_{,r}/r + \phi_{,\theta\theta}/r^2\right]$$
$$+ 2\sin\theta\cos\theta\left[\phi_{,r\theta}/r - \phi_{,\theta}/r^2\right]. \tag{I.4-40}$$

The sign conventions for stresses expressed in a polar coordinate system are shown in Fig. I.4-1. The formulas between a stress function $\phi(r, \theta)$ and the stresses in polar coordinates are [TG 70]

$$\sigma_r = \phi_{,\theta\theta}/r^2 + \phi_{,r}/r \tag{I.4-41}$$

$$\sigma_\theta = \phi_{,rr} \tag{I.4-42}$$

$$\tau_{r\theta} = -(\phi_{,\theta}/r)_{,r} = -\phi_{,\theta r}/r + \phi_{,\theta}/r^2. \tag{I.4-43}$$

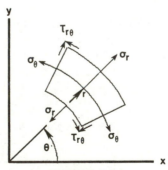

FIGURE I.4-1

Polar coordinates and sign conventions for stresses.

The conversion of stresses between the two coordinate systems is

$$\sigma_x = \sigma_r\cos^2\theta + \sigma_\theta\sin^2\theta - 2\sin\theta\cos\theta\tau_{r\theta} \qquad (I.4\text{-}44)$$

$$\sigma_y = \sigma_r\sin^2\theta + \sigma_\theta\cos^2\theta + 2\sin\theta\cos\theta\tau_{r\theta} \qquad (I.4\text{-}45)$$

$$\tau_{xy} = [\sigma_r - \sigma_\theta]\sin\theta\cos\theta + [\cos^2\theta - \sin^2\theta]\tau_{r\theta} \qquad (I.4\text{-}46)$$

or

$$\sigma_r = \sigma_x\cos^2\theta + \sigma_y\sin^2\theta + 2\sin\theta\cos\theta\tau_{xy} \qquad (I.4\text{-}47)$$

$$\sigma_\theta = \sigma_x\sin^2\theta + \sigma_y\cos^2\theta - 2\sin\theta\cos\theta\tau_{xy} \qquad (I.4\text{-}48)$$

$$\tau_{r\theta} = [\sigma_y - \sigma_x]\sin\theta\cos\theta + [\cos^2\theta - \sin^2\theta]\tau_{xy}. \qquad (I.4\text{-}49)$$

The equilibrium equations in polar coordinates [TG 70] are

$$\sigma_{r,r} + \tau_{r\theta,\theta}/r + (\sigma_r - \sigma_\theta)/r = 0 \qquad (I.4\text{-}50)$$

$$\sigma_{\theta,\theta}/r + \tau_{r\theta,r} + 2\tau_{r\theta}/r = 0. \qquad (I.4\text{-}51)$$

The Laplacian operator $\nabla^2(\ )$ in polar coordinates is expressible as

$$\nabla^2(\ ) = (\ )_{,rr} + (\ )_{,r}/r + (\ )_{,\theta\theta}/r^2. \qquad (I.4\text{-}52)$$

Equation (I.4-52) can be used successively as in (I.4-27) to generate the biharmonic operator in polar coordinates.

Strain–displacement relationships in polar coordinates for small geometric changes are [TG 70]

$$\epsilon_r = u_{r,r} \qquad (I.4\text{-}53)$$

$$\epsilon_\theta = (u_{\theta,\theta} + u_r)/r \qquad (I.4\text{-}54)$$

$$\gamma_{r\theta} = 2\epsilon_{r\theta} = (u_{r,\theta} - u_\theta)/r + u_{\theta,r}, \qquad (I.4\text{-}55)$$

where ϵ_r and ϵ_θ are normal strains in the r and θ directions, respectively, and $\gamma_{r\theta}$ and $\epsilon_{r\theta}$ are the engineering shear strain and the shear strain, respectively, in the $r\theta$ plane. These equations are applicable to both elastic strains and total strains.

Kolosov Equations

The Kolosov formulation of plane problems of elasticity [Sok 56, TG 70] follows:

$$\sigma_x + \sigma_y = 2\left[\Phi'(z) + \overline{\Phi'(\bar{z})}\right] \qquad (I.4\text{-}56)$$

$$\sigma_y - \sigma_x + 2i\tau_{xy} = 2[\bar{z}\Phi''(z) + \Psi'(z)] \qquad (I.4\text{-}57)$$

$$2G(u_x + iu_y) = \kappa\Phi(z) - z\overline{\Phi'(\bar{z})} - \overline{\Psi(\bar{z})} \qquad (I.4\text{-}58)$$

where the complex variable z and its complex conjugate $\bar{z}$ are defined by

$$z = x + iy \qquad \text{and} \qquad \bar{z} = x - iy, \tag{I.4-59}$$

where i is the imaginary number $(-1)^{1/2}$. The functions $\Phi(z)$ and $\Psi(z)$ in (I.4-56)–(I.4-58) and their first $(\ )'$ and second derivatives $(\ )''$ are arbitrary complex functions of z. The functions $\overline{\Phi(\bar{z})}$ and $\overline{\Psi(\bar{z})}$ are determined from $\Phi(z)$ and $\Psi(z)$ by replacing i by $-i$ [TG 70], e.g.,

$$\Phi(z) = i \sin z = i \sin(x + iy) \to \overline{\Phi(\bar{z})} = -i \sin(x - iy) = -i \sin \bar{z}. \tag{I.4-60}$$

The material parameter κ (kappa) is a function of Poisson's ratio ν and the type of plane problem addressed, as designated below [Sok 56]:

$$\kappa = \begin{cases} (3 - \nu)/(1 + \nu) & \text{plane stress} \\ 3 - 4\nu & \text{plane strain.} \end{cases} \tag{I.4-61}$$

The Kolosov equations result from the integrability of the biharmonic equation (I.4-26), after a coordinate transformation is performed from Cartesian coordinates (x, y) to complex variables $(z, \bar{z})$, i.e.,

$$x = (z + \bar{z})/2, \qquad y = (z - \bar{z})/(2i). \tag{I.4-62}$$

The biharmonic operator and the biharmonic equation become, respectively,

$$\nabla^4 \phi = 8\phi_{,z\bar{z}z\bar{z}}, \qquad \nabla^4 \phi = 0 \to \phi_{,z\bar{z}z\bar{z}} = 0. \tag{I.4-63}$$

The fourth-order partial differential equation in (I.4-63) can now be integrated to yield a real function ϕ of the form

$$\phi(z, \bar{z}) = \bar{z}F(z) + z\overline{F(\bar{z})} + G(z) + \overline{G(\bar{z})}, \tag{I.4-64}$$

where $F(z)$ and $G(z)$ are arbitrary functions. This result was first obtained by E. Goursat in 1898 [Sok 56].

    In terms of the Kolosov potentials of (I.4-56)–(I.4-58), $F(z)$ and $G(z)$ of (I.4-64) are

$$F(z) = \tfrac{1}{2}\Phi(z), \qquad G(z) = \tfrac{1}{2}\int \Psi(z)\, dz. \tag{I.4-65}$$

A related representation of a solution of the biharmonic equation in Cartesian coordinates is [Sne 57]

$$\phi(x, y) = x\phi_1(x, y) + y\phi_2(x, y) + \phi_3(x, y) \qquad (I.4\text{-}66)$$

where $\phi_1(x, y)$, $\phi_2(x, y)$, and $\phi_3(x, y)$ are harmonic functions, i.e.,

$$\nabla^2\phi_i(x, y) = 0, \qquad i = 1, 2, 3. \qquad (I.4\text{-}67)$$

Boundary Conditions

There are two fundamental types of boundary value problems in elasticity. The first is specifying traction on the boundary, and the second is specifying displacement on the boundary.

With respect to the Airy stress function $\phi(x, y)$ and the accompanying solution of the biharmonic equation, one finds that prescribing traction on a boundary $\partial\Omega$ requires specifying either both partial derivatives [Sok 56]

$$\phi_{,x}(s) \qquad \text{and} \qquad \phi_{,y}(s) \quad \text{on} \quad \partial\Omega, \qquad (I.4\text{-}68)$$

where s is a parameter defining the functions on $\partial\Omega$, or specifying the stress function itself and its partial derivative normal to the boundary $\partial\phi/\partial n$, i.e.,

$$\phi(s) \qquad \text{and} \qquad (\partial\phi/\partial n)|_s \equiv (\nabla\phi \cdot \mathbf{n})|_s \quad \text{on} \quad \partial\Omega, \qquad (I.4\text{-}69)$$

where $\mathbf{n}$ is an outward unit vector to the boundary and $\nabla(\ )$ is the gradient operator. These two methods may be shown to be equivalent.

I.5 LINEAR ELASTIC FRACTURE MECHANICS

There are three distinct ways of loading a plate containing a crack, and each load orientation has its own designation. The problems associated with these different loading configurations are commonly referred to as modes I, II, and III. Mode I is the principal mode of fracture that occurs when two surfaces of a crack are being separated by tensile forces which are applied perpendicularly to the plane of the crack. This type of loading is shown in Fig. I.5-1a. Mode II is sometimes called the sliding mode of fracture and occurs when in-plane shear forces are applied to a body containing a crack as in Fig. I.5-1b. Mode III is often referred to as the tearing mode of fracture or the antiplane crack problem. This mode of fracture has out-of-plane shear forces acting on a plate the same manner that one uses to tear a sheet of paper. This mode's load orientation is shown in Fig. I.5-1c.

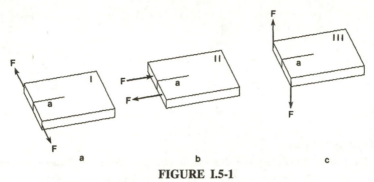

FIGURE I.5-1

Three principal modes of fracture with applied forces F.

We will now investigate linear elastic solutions corresponding to the three fundamental modes of fracture for infinite plates. The Cartesian coordinate system to be used is shown in Fig. I.5-2. the origin of the coordinates 0 is located at the center of the crack. The length of the crack is $2a$, which spans from $-a$ to $+a$ along the x-axis. The plate has an arbitrary thickness. The crack width, i.e., the distance between the crack's parallel surfaces, is mathematically idealized to be zero before loading.

The boundary condition along the crack surfaces for all three modes of fracture is that they are traction-free. The implications of these traction-

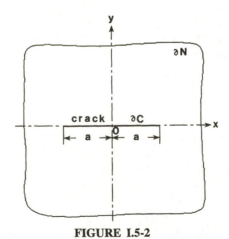

FIGURE I.5-2

Infinite plate coordinates, boundaries, and crack (length $2a$).

less surfaces on the in-plane stresses along the crack faces ∂C (Fig. I.5-2) are for the plane modes of fracture (I and II):

$$\partial C: \quad -a \le x \le a, \quad y = 0, \tag{I.5-1}$$

$$t_x = t_y = 0 \rightarrow \sigma_y = 0, \quad \tau_{xy} = 0. \tag{I.5-2}$$

The implications of the traction-free crack surfaces on stresses for the antiplane crack problem (mode III) are given as (I.5-64)–(I.5-65).

The boundary condition at infinity depends on the mode of fracture to be investigated. The far-field tractions of the three principal modes of fracture are shown in Figs I.5-3a to I.5-3c.

Mode I

For mode I we will assign a biaxial tensile traction σ_∞ at infinity ∂N:

$$\partial N: \begin{cases} x \rightarrow \pm\infty, & t_x = \sigma_\infty, & t_y = 0 \rightarrow \sigma_x = \sigma_\infty, & \tau_{xy} = 0 \quad (I.5\text{-}3) \\ y \rightarrow \pm\infty, & t_x = 0, & t_y = \sigma_\infty \rightarrow \sigma_y = \sigma_\infty, & \tau_{xy} = 0. \quad (I.5\text{-}4) \end{cases}$$

Notice that we have applied a constant tensile load in the x direction at infinity, which has no corresponding forces in Fig. I.5-1a. This particular traction is introduced to simplify the boundary condition at infinity to a uniform state of tension σ_∞. An additional stress σ_∞ will be produced in the x direction by this specific traction. This stress is constant because it acts in the plane of the crack and is therefore unaffected by the internal boundary condition that the crack surfaces would otherwise impose. This extraneous stress can be subtracted out of the solution later if desired.

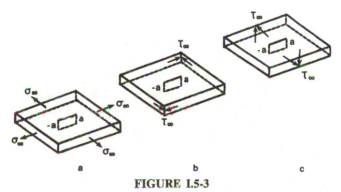

FIGURE I.5-3

Far-field tractions for the three principal modes of fracture.

The elastic solution to the mode I problem can be obtained by substituting the following complex functions into the Kolosov equations (I.4-56)–(I.4-58) [Sne 57, PM 78]:

$$\Phi'(z) = \tfrac{1}{2}Z_I(z), \qquad \Psi'(z) = -\tfrac{1}{2}zZ_I'(z), \qquad (I.5\text{-}5)$$

where $Z_I(z)$ is given by (4.1-6) and called a Westergaard function.

Note that the following relationship results from integrating (I.5-5) by parts:

$$\Psi(z) = \tfrac{1}{2}Z_I^*(z) - \tfrac{1}{2}zZ_I(z) \qquad (I.5\text{-}6)$$

where $Z_I^*(z)$ is the integral of $Z_I(z)$ with respect to z, as given by (4.1-8).

These substitutions result in the following linear elastic solution, which meets the boundary conditions (I.5-1)–(I.5-4):

$$\sigma_x + \sigma_y = Z_I(z) + \overline{Z_I(\bar{z})} = 2\,\mathrm{Re}\,Z_I(z) \qquad (I.5\text{-}7)$$

$$\sigma_y - \sigma_x + 2i\tau_{xy} = (\bar{z} - z)Z_I'(z) = -2yiZ_I'(z)$$

$$= 2y[\mathrm{Im}\,Z_I'(z) - i\,\mathrm{Re}\,Z_I'(z)] \qquad (I.5\text{-}8)$$

$$2G(u_x + iu_y) = \tfrac{1}{2}(\kappa - 1)\mathrm{Re}\,Z_I^* - y\,\mathrm{Im}\,Z_I$$

$$+ i[\tfrac{1}{2}(\kappa + 1)\mathrm{Im}\,Z_I^* - y\,\mathrm{Re}\,Z_I], \qquad (I.5\text{-}9)$$

where Re and Im denote the real and imaginary parts of a complex function, and the parameter κ is defined individually for plane stress and plane strain by (I.4-61).

Notice that this particular Westergaard formulation restricts solutions to those that have the property $\sigma_x = \sigma_y$ and $\tau_{xy} = 0$ along the x-axis ($y = 0$). Thus the boundary condition of biaxial tension at infinity $\sigma_x = \sigma_y = \sigma_\infty$ (see Fig. I.5-3a) is a necessity in order to apply the Westergaard technique to the mode I problem.

The exact linear elastic solution for the stresses and the displacements for plane strain which meet the boundary conditions at infinity are given in Chapter 4. Around the crack tip $x = a$, $y = 0$, the functions Z_I, Z_I', and Z_I^* assume the asymptotic forms (4.1-26), (4.1-29), and (4.1-32), respectively, where r and θ are redefined about the crack tip as shown in Fig. 4.1-1a. The associated asymptotic solution for stresses, which is valid for both plane stress and plane strain for mode I, is

$$\sigma_x = \left[K_I/(2\pi r)^{1/2}\right]\cos(\theta/2)\{1 - \sin(\theta/2)\sin(3\theta/2)\} \quad (I.5\text{-}10)$$

$$\sigma_y = \left[K_I/(2\pi r)^{1/2}\right]\cos(\theta/2)\{1 + \sin(\theta/2)\sin(3\theta/2)\} \quad (I.5\text{-}11)$$

$$\tau_{xy} = \left[K_I/(2\pi r)^{1/2}\right]\cos(\theta/2)\sin(\theta/2)\cos(3\theta/2), \quad (I.5\text{-}12)$$

where the parameter K_I, called the mode I stress intensity factor, is for the infinite plate with an internal crack of length $2a$ subject to a remotely applied uniform tensile traction σ_∞:

$$K_I = \sigma_\infty(\pi a)^{1/2}. \tag{I.5-13}$$

We can now subtract the constant stress σ_∞ from the σ_x stress distribution (I.5-10) in order to eliminate the extraneous boundary condition at infinity in the x direction of $t_x = \sigma_\infty$ that we had introduced earlier to facilitate solution. However, since σ_x and all of the other stresses have a $1/r^{1/2}$ singularity at the crack tip, this extraneous stress has little effect near the crack tip and as such is usually neglected from the mode I asymptotic solution for the infinite plate.

Similarly, the asymptotic displacements around the crack tip for mode I plane stress and plane strain are found from (I.5-9) to be [KP 85]

$$u_x = [K_I/(2G)][r/(2\pi)]^{1/2}\cos(\theta/2)\{\kappa - 1 + 2\sin^2(\theta/2)\} \tag{I.5-14}$$

$$u_y = [K_I/(2G)][r/(2\pi)]^{1/2}\sin(\theta/2)\{\kappa + 1 - 2\cos^2(\theta/2)\}, \tag{I.5-15}$$

where κ is defined as in (I.4-61).

Under plane stress loading conditions, the mode I displacements are explicitly

$$u_x = (K_I/E)(2r/\pi)^{1/2}\cos(\theta/2)\{2 - (1 + \nu)\cos^2(\theta/2)\} \tag{I.5-16}$$

$$u_y = (K_I/E)(2r/\pi)^{1/2}\sin(\theta/2)\{2 - (1 + \nu)\cos^2(\theta/2)\}, \tag{I.5-17}$$

where relationship (I.2-7) was used to relate G to E.

The mode I plane strain asymptotic displacements for an infinite plate are given explicitly as (4.1-36) and (4.1-37), and the exact mode I displacements for an infinite plate are given by (4.1-19) and (4.1-20). These exact solutions are fairly complicated algebraically, unlike the asymptotic (first-term) solutions.

For geometries other than the infinite plate, and for different types of loads, only the stress intensity factor K_I changes from the form (I.5-13).

For example, the stress intensity factor for an edge crack of length a in a semi-infinite plate with a remotely applied tensile stress σ_∞ is approximately [Koi 65]

$$K_I = 1.12\,\sigma_\infty(\pi a)^{1/2}. \tag{I.5-18}$$

An edge crack in a plate of finite dimensions with concentrated forces is illustrated in Fig. I.5-1a.

The state under which the stress intensity factor is sufficient to characterize the stress distribution around the neighborhood of the crack tip is called small-scale yielding.

Regardless of the geometry of the specimen or the type of load, the strength of the singularity for all stresses at the crack tip ($r = 0$) remain $1/r^{1/2}$ for all linear elastic problems. This is not true, however, for deformation theories of plasticity, which may be interpreted as nonlinear elastic theories. We will examine crack problems for these types of nonlinear materials later.

Mode II

Like the mode I solution, the elastic solution to the mode II problem can be obtained by substituting the Westergaard function (4.1-44) into the Kolosov equations (I.4-56)–(I.4-58) [Sne 57, PM 78]:

$$\Phi'(z) = -\tfrac{1}{2}iZ_{II}(z), \qquad \Psi'(z) = \tfrac{1}{2}izZ'_{II}(z) + iZ_{II}(z). \quad (I.5\text{-}19)$$

These Westergaard potentials differ from the previous functions (I.5-5) in that they generate solutions that have the property $\sigma_y = 0$ and $\tau_{xy} = 0$ along the x-axis, and satisfy the following boundary conditions at infinity (Fig. I.5-3):

$$\partial N: \begin{cases} x \to \pm\infty, & t_x = 0, & t_y = \tau_\infty \to \sigma_x = 0, & \tau_{xy} = \tau_\infty & (I.5\text{-}20) \\ y \to \pm\infty, & t_x = \tau_\infty, & t_y = 0 \to \sigma_y = 0, & \tau_{xy} = \tau_\infty. & (I.5\text{-}21) \end{cases}$$

The potentials (I.5-19) also satisfy the boundary conditions (I.5-1) and (I.5-2) and produce the linear elastic solution

$$\sigma_x + \sigma_y = \tfrac{1}{2}i\left[\overline{Z_{II}(\bar{z})} - Z_{II}(z)\right] = 2\,\mathrm{Im}\,Z_{II}(z) \quad (I.5\text{-}22)$$

$$\sigma_y - \sigma_x + 2i\tau_{xy} = i(z - \bar{z})Z'_{II}(z) + 2iZ_{II}(z)$$

$$= -2y\,\mathrm{Re}\,Z'_{II}(z) - 2\,\mathrm{Im}\,Z_{II}(z)$$

$$+ 2i[-y\,\mathrm{Im}\,Z'_{II}(z) + \mathrm{Re}\,Z_{II}(z)] \quad (I.5\text{-}23)$$

$$2G(u_x + iu_y) = \tfrac{1}{2}(\kappa + 1)\mathrm{Im}\,Z_{II}^* + y\,\mathrm{Re}\,Z_{II}$$

$$- i[\tfrac{1}{2}(\kappa - 1)\mathrm{Re}\,Z_{II}^* + y\,\mathrm{Im}\,Z_{II}], \quad (I.5\text{-}24)$$

where parameter κ is defined individually by (I.4-61) for plane stress and plane strain. The exact linear elastic solution for the stresses and the displacements for plane strain that meet the boundary conditions at infinity are given in Chapter 4. Around the crack tip $x = a$, $y = 0$ the function Z_{II} assumes the from (4.1-52). The functions Z'_{II} and Z^*_{II} follow analogously from (4.1-29) and (4.1-32) by replacing σ_∞ with τ_∞.

The asymptotic solution for stresses near the crack tip are for mode II under plane stress or plane strain loading conditions:

$$\sigma_x = -\left[K_{II}/(2\pi r)^{1/2}\right]\sin(\theta/2)\{2 + \cos(\theta/2)\cos(3\theta/2)\} \quad (I.5\text{-}25)$$

$$\sigma_y = \left[K_{II}/(2\pi r)^{1/2}\right]\cos(\theta/2)\sin(\theta/2)\cos(3\theta/2) \quad (I.5\text{-}26)$$

$$\tau_{xy} = \left[K_{II}/(2\pi r)^{1/2}\right]\cos(\theta/2)\{1 - \sin(\theta/2)\sin(3\theta/2)\}, \quad (I.5\text{-}27)$$

where the parameter K_{II} is called the mode II stress intensity factor.

For an infinite plate with an internal crack of length $2a$ subject to a remotely applied in-plane shear traction τ_∞ (see, Fig. I.5-3b), the stress intensity factor is

$$K_{II} = \tau_\infty(\pi a)^{1/2}. \quad (I.5\text{-}28)$$

Similarly, the asymptotic displacements around the crack tip for mode II plane stress and plane strain loading conditions are [KP 85]

$$u_x = [K_{II}/(2G)][r/(2\pi)]^{1/2}\sin(\theta/2)\{\kappa + 1 + 2\cos^2(\theta/2)\} \quad (I.5\text{-}29)$$

$$u_y = [K_{II}/(2G)][r/(2\pi)]^{1/2}\cos(\theta/2)\{1 - \kappa + 2\sin^2(\theta/2)\} \quad (I.5\text{-}30)$$

where κ is again defined by (I.4-61).

For plane stress loading conditions, the mode II displacements are

$$u_x = (K_{II}/E)(2r/\pi)^{1/2}\sin(\theta/2)\{2 + (1 + \nu)\cos^2(\theta/2)\} \quad (I.5\text{-}31)$$

$$u_y = (K_{II}/E)(2r/\pi)^{1/2}\cos(\theta/2)\{2\nu - (1 + \nu)\cos^2(\theta/2)\}. \quad (I.5\text{-}32)$$

The plane strain mode II asymptotic displacements for an infinite plate are given explicitly as (4.1-56) and (4.1-57). Exact mode II displacements for an infinite plate are given by (4.1-48) and (4.1-49).

A general method of solving plane problems through a complex variable mapping scheme and the Kolosov equations was developed by N. I. Muskhelishvili [Mus 63]. This method of solution is very powerful for solving linear elastic fracture mechanics problems. Brief introductions to this technique may be found in [TG 70, Sok 56].

Mode III

The mode III problem differs from the two previous modes in that it is not a true plane elasticity problem, as shear forces perpendicular to the plane of the plate (x, y) exist (Fig. I.5-3c). It is sometimes called an antiplane deformation problem, and it is related to torsion problems in elasticity theory, in areas far removed from the boundary of the cylinder [AC 88]. In the mode III problem, only two stresses $\tau_{xz}(x, y)$, $\tau_{yz}(x, y)$ and one displacement $u_z = w(x, y)$ are present.

The equilibrium equation is obtained from (I.1-3) by setting $\sigma_{z,z}$ equal to zero, i.e.,

$$\tau_{xz, x} + \tau_{yz, y} = 0. \tag{I.5-33}$$

We now introduce a stress function $\phi(x, y)$, (similar to the Prandtl stress function in elastic torsion theory [TG 70, p. 295]),

$$\tau_{xz} = \phi_{,y}, \qquad \tau_{yz} = -\phi_{,x}, \tag{I.5-34}$$

such that stresses derived from it automatically satisfy equilibrium (I.5-33).

Strains follow immediately from Hooke's law (I.2-8):

$$\gamma_{xz} = 2\epsilon_{xz} = (1/G)\tau_{xz}, \qquad \gamma_{yz} = 2\epsilon_{yz} = (1/G)\tau_{yz}. \tag{I.5-35}$$

The nontrivial compatibility equations are from (I.1-14) and (I.1-15), respectively:

$$\epsilon_{xz, xy} - \epsilon_{yz, xx} = 0 \rightarrow (\epsilon_{xz, y} - \epsilon_{yz, x})_{,x} = 0 \tag{I.5-36}$$

$$\epsilon_{yz, xy} - \epsilon_{xz, yy} = 0 \rightarrow (\epsilon_{yz, x} - \epsilon_{xz, y})_{,y} = 0. \tag{I.5-37}$$

These two equations are satisfied provided that

$$\tau_{xz, y} - \tau_{yz, x} = 0 \rightarrow \phi_{,xx} + \phi_{,yy} = 0. \tag{I.5-38}$$

Using the Laplacian operator symbol (I.4-8), we may rewrite the second equation in (I.5-38) as

$$\nabla^2 \phi = 0. \tag{I.5-39}$$

This equation is known as Laplace's equation and its solutions $\phi(x, y)$ are referred to as harmonic functions.

Under transformation from Cartesian coordinates to complex variables (I.4-62), the Laplacian operator and equation become, respectively,

$$\nabla^2 \phi = 4\phi_{,z\bar{z}}, \qquad \nabla^2 \phi = 0 \rightarrow \phi_{,z\bar{z}} = 0. \tag{I.5-40}$$

By integrating the last equation in (I.5-40), we find

$$\phi(z, \bar{z}) = F(z) + G(\bar{z}), \tag{I.5-41}$$

where $F(z)$ and $G(\bar{z})$ are arbitrary functions of z and $\bar{z}$, respectively. By limiting our solution $\phi(z, \bar{z})$ to real functions, we must restrict $G(\bar{z})$ [or $F(z)$] such that

$$\phi(z, \bar{z}) = F(z) + \overline{F(\bar{z})}, \tag{I.5-42}$$

where $\overline{F(\bar{z})}$ is defined in terms $F(z)$ in an analogous fashion to $\overline{\Phi(\bar{z})}$ and $\Phi(z)$ as in (I.4-60).

Equation (I.5-42) may also be interpreted as

$$\phi = 2 \operatorname{Re} F(z), \tag{I.5-43}$$

where Re is the real part of $F(z)$ and Im is the imaginary part of $F(z)$, i.e.,

$$F(z) = \operatorname{Re} F + i \operatorname{Im} F. \tag{I.5-44}$$

Both the real and imaginary parts of any analytical complex function will individually satisfy Laplace's equation [Chu 60].

The displacement $w(x, y)$ is related to the engineering shear strains by (I.1-10), (I.1-11)

$$\gamma_{xz} = w_{,x}, \qquad \gamma_{yz} = w_{,y}. \tag{I.5-45}$$

Therefore, from (I.5-35), we find

$$\tau_{xz} = Gw_{,x}, \qquad \tau_{yz} = Gw_{,y}. \tag{I.5-46}$$

By substituting (I.5-46) into the equilibrium equation (I.5-33), we see that the displacement $w(x, y)$ also satisfies Laplace's equation

$$\nabla^2 w(x, y) = 0, \tag{I.5-47}$$

in addition to the stress function $\phi(x, y)$.

The relationship between $-\phi(x, y)$ and $Gw(x, y)$ is similar to the functions $u(x, y)$ and $v(x, y)$ appearing in the Cauchy–Riemann equations

$$u_{,x} = v_{,y}, \qquad v_{,y} = -u_{,x}, \tag{I.5-48}$$

where $u(x, y)$ and $v(x, y)$ are arbitrary functions. Functions that satisfy (I.5-48) also satisfy Laplace's equation (provided second partial derivatives exist), i.e.,

$$\nabla^2 u = 0, \qquad \nabla^2 v = 0. \tag{I.5-49}$$

The functions u and v are known as conjugate harmonic functions [Chu 60], and lines of u and v intersect orthogonally when plotted in Cartesian coordinates (Figs. I.5-4a and I.5-4b)—except at singularities.

A conformal mapping of the Cartesian plane involving u and v can be obtained in the following fashion [Chu 60, p. 177]:

$$f(z) = u + iv, \qquad (\text{I.5-50})$$

where $f(z)$ is an arbitrary analytical function of the complex variable z (I.4-59). In a conformal mapping, angles in the Cartesian plane (x, y) are preserved when mapped onto the (u, v) plane, where u and v form a new rectangular Cartesian coordinate system. The coordinates (u, v), as defined by (I.5-50), will satisfy both (I.5-48) and (I.5-49). As a consequence of the inverse mapping of (I.5-50), lines of constant u and v will also intersect perpendicularly in the original Cartesian plane (x, y), where they form an orthogonal curvilinear coordinate system. These properties are indicated in Figs. I.5-4a and I.5-4b, where the symbols $\mathbf{e}_u$ and $\mathbf{e}_v$ designate unit vectors in the u and v directions, respectively.

The first derivatives of $f(z)$ with respect to z are related to partial derivatives of u and v as follows [Chu 60, p. 35]:

$$f'(z) = u_{,x} + iv_{,x} \qquad (\text{I.5-51})$$

$$= v_{,y} - iu_{,y}. \qquad (\text{I.5-52})$$

Now that several fundamental properties of analytical function theory have been discussed, let us formulate the mode III problem in terms of a Westergaard function $Z_{\text{III}}(z)$, which is analogous to the two Westergaard functions defined previously for the two other modes of fracture.

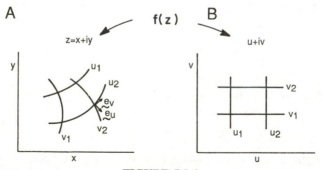

FIGURE I.5-4

Conformal mapping. Reprinted from [UA 83] by permission of Springer-Verlag.

Let us first associate the function $f(z)$ of (I.5-50) with the first integral of the Westergaard function $Z_{III}^*(z)$ with respect to z:

$$f(z) = Z_{III}^*(z) = \text{Re } Z_{III}^* + i \text{ Im } Z_{III}^*. \tag{I.5-53}$$

Let us now assign the stress function $\phi(x, y)$ and displacement $w(x, y)$ as follows:

$$\text{Re } Z_{III}^* = -\phi(x, y), \qquad \text{Im } Z_{III}^* = Gw(x, y). \tag{I.5-54}$$

Because they are related to the real and imaginary parts of an analytical function of z (I.5-52), both the stress function and displacement will satisfy Laplace's equation. However, it remains to be seen if the additional relationships involving ϕ and w are properly satisfied.

These additional relationships can be verified by identifying $u(x, y)$ and $v(x, y)$ of (I.5-50) with $\phi(x, y)$ and $w(x, y)$ as follows:

$$u(x, y) = -\phi(x, y), \qquad v(x, y) = Gw(x, y). \tag{I.5-55}$$

By (I.5-51)–(I.5-54) we see that (I.5-34) and (I.5-46) are satisfied, after equating real and imaginary parts of $f'(z)$; i.e.,

$$f'(z) = \text{Re } Z_{III} + i \text{ Im } Z_{III} = [\text{Re } Z_{III}^*(z)]_{,x} + i[\text{Im } Z_{III}^*(z)]_{,x} \tag{I.5-56}$$

$$= -\phi_{,x} \qquad + iGw_{,x} \tag{I.5-57}$$

$$= [\text{Im } Z_{III}^*(z)]_{,y} - i[\text{Re } Z_{III}^*(z)]_{,y} \tag{I.5-58}$$

$$= Gw_{,y} \qquad + i\phi_{,y} \tag{I.5-59}$$

$$= \tau_{yz} \qquad + i\tau_{xz}. \tag{I.5-60}$$

Thus from (I.5-60), the stresses of the mode III fracture problem are expressible in terms of the Westergaard function by the relations

$$\tau_{xz} = \text{Im } Z_{III}, \qquad \tau_{yz} = \text{Re } Z_{III}, \tag{I.5-61}$$

where $Z_{III}(z)$ is the function given by (4.1-60). Equation (4.1-60) satisfies the boundary conditions of an infinite plate with an internal crack of length $2a$ with tractionless surfaces ∂C:

$$\partial C: \quad -a \le x \le a, \qquad y = 0, \tag{I.5-62}$$

$$t_z = 0 \rightarrow \tau_{yz} = 0, \tag{I.5-63}$$

and a remotely applied traction τ_∞ at infinity ∂N as shown in Fig. I.5-3c:

$$\partial N: \begin{cases} x \rightarrow \pm\infty, & t_x = t_y = t_z = 0 & \rightarrow \tau_{xz} = 0 \tag{I.5-64} \\ y \rightarrow \pm\infty, & t_x = 0, \quad t_y = 0, \quad t_z = \tau_\infty & \rightarrow \tau_{yz} = \tau_\infty. \tag{I.5-65} \end{cases}$$

The exact linear elastic solution for the stresses and the displacements that meet the boundary conditions at infinity are given in Sections 4.1 and 4.3. Around the crack tip $x = a$, $y = 0$ the function Z_{III} assumes the simplified form (4.1-64). The functions Z'_{III} and Z^*_{III} follow analogously from (4.1-29) and (4.1-32) by replacing σ_∞ with τ_∞.

The asymptotic solution for stress around the crack tip is, from (I.5-61),

$$\tau_{xz} = -\left[K_{III}/(2\pi r)^{1/2}\right]\sin(\theta/2) \qquad (I.5\text{-}66)$$

$$\tau_{yz} = \left[K_{III}/(2\pi r)^{1/2}\right]\cos(\theta/2), \qquad (I.5\text{-}67)$$

where the stress intensity factor for the infinite plate with an internal crack of length $2a$ subject to a remotely applied shear traction τ_∞, as shown in Fig. I.5-3c, is

$$K_{III} = \tau_\infty(\pi a)^{1/2}. \qquad (I.5\text{-}68)$$

Similarly from (I.5-54), the asymptotic displacement around the crack tip for mode III is

$$w = (K_{III}/G)(2r/\pi)^{1/2}\sin(\theta/2). \qquad (I.5\text{-}69)$$

The exact displacement for the infinite plate is given as (4.1-66).

I.6 STRIP MODELS OF CRACK TIP PLASTICITY

As we mentioned in the previous section, all stresses predicted by linear elastic fracture mechanics possess an $r^{-1/2}$ singularity at the crack tip. However, in real metals a plastic enclave forms around the crack tip to relieve the stresses from their predicted elastic state. Efforts to find analytical solutions to elastic–plastic fracture problems for plastic zones of finite dimensions have proved successful only for mode III problems. In this section, we explore alternatives to fully developed plastic zones in the form of infinitesimally thin plastic lamina ahead of the crack tip. These plastic strips serve mathematically as boundary conditions in otherwise purely elastic problems.

The prototype plastic strip model is the Dugdale model [Dug 60] for the mode I fracture mechanics problem of an infinite plate with a far-field biaxial traction of magnitude σ_∞. The Dugdale model has a constant traction $t_y = \sigma_0$ applied ahead of the crack tip (Fig. I.6-1) from $x = \pm a$ to $x = \pm c$, $y = 0$. The crack is treated mathematically as if it spanned from $-c \le x \le c$, whereas it is treated physically as if it spanned only from

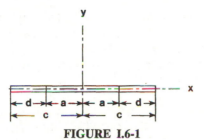

FIGURE I.6-1

Coordinate system and crack regions of plastic strip model.

$-a \leq x \leq a$. By *mathematically*, we mean that there is a discontinuity in the continuum that would allow the single line $-c \leq x \leq c$ to separate into two different curves upon loading. Thus crack tip plasticity is treated merely as a boundary condition for a linear elastic crack problem having a distributed load over a portion of the crack.

The rationale behind the Dugdale model is that the infinite stress of the purely elastic solution is physically unrealistic. The stress must be limited to a finite value. Since stresses generated at the crack tips by the remote traction σ_∞ are infinite, the only way to counter them is to generate opposing stresses with the same order of singularity and magnitude.

To this end, we note the added contribution to the Westergaard potential $Z_I^+(z)$ for two pairs of opposed concentrated forces (see Fig. I.6-2) of magnitude σ_0 (force/plate thickness) applied along the crack surfaces of an internal crack of length $2c$ at $x = \pm b$ [Irw 58, BS 66],

$$Z_I^+ = 2\sigma_0 z (c^2 - b^2)^{1/2} / \left[\pi (z^2 - c^2)^{1/2} (b^2 - z^2) \right]. \qquad (I.6\text{-}1)$$

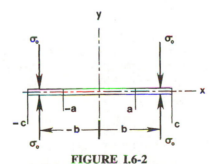

FIGURE I.6-2

Applied forces on near-crack tip regions.

This additional contribution to the Westergaard function (I.6-1) would by itself add $1/r$ stress singularities at the points of application of the concentrated forces, i.e., $x = \pm b$. However, if we integrate Z_I^+ over the lengths of the plastic zones, these particular singularities disappear and we obtain

$$Z_0 = 2\sigma_0 z \int_a^c (c^2 - b^2)^{1/2} / \left[\pi(z^2 - c^2)^{1/2}(b^2 - z^2)\right] db, \quad (I.6\text{-}2)$$

$$= 2(\sigma_0/\pi)\left\{\cot^{-1}\left[(a/z)[(z^2 - c^2)/(c^2 - a^2)]^{1/2}\right]\right.$$

$$\left. - \left[z/[(z^2 - c^2)]^{1/2}\right]\cos^{-1}(a/c)\right\}, \quad (I.6\text{-}3)$$

which is a Westergaard function Z_0 of distributed load σ_0 (units are now those of stress as we have absorbed the division of length of the plastic zone into the original σ_0) which has $r^{-1/2}$ stress singularities at the two crack tips (Fig. I.6-3).

It is the second term of (I.6-3) that produces these $r^{-1/2}$ singular stresses at the crack tips, not the first. We now need to adjust the length of the plastic zone so that the magnitude of the stress caused by the load at infinity is equal to opposing stress induced by the distributed load. From (4.1-6) we see that the form of the Westergaard function for the purely elastic problem Z_I differs from the second term of (I.6-3) only by a constant multiplier.

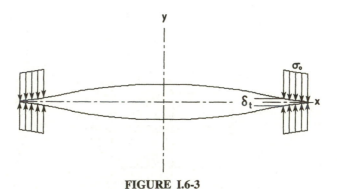

FIGURE I.6-3
Dugdale strip model of crack tip plasticity.

The addition of (4.1-6) to (I.6-3) produces the Westergaard function Z_{IDug} for the combined loads as

$$Z_{IDug} = Z_I + Z_0 = 2(\sigma_0/\pi)\cot^{-1}\left[(a/z)[(z^2 - c^2)/(c^2 - a^2)]^{1/2}\right]$$
$$+\{\sigma_\infty - 2(\sigma_0/\pi)\cos^{-1}(a/c)\}\left[z/[(z^2 - c^2)]^{1/2}\right],$$
$$(I.6-4)$$

where in deriving (I.6-4) we substituted c for a in equation (4.1-6).

In order for the second term of Z_0 to cancel Z_I, we need

$$\sigma_\infty/\sigma_0 = (2/\pi)\cos^{-1}(a/c). \qquad (I.6-5)$$

Thus from (I.6-4) and (I.6-5), the Westergaard potential for Dugdale model Z_{IDug} is [BS 66]

$$Z_{IDug} = 2(\sigma_0/\pi)\cot^{-1}\left[(a/z)[(z^2 - c^2)/(c^2 - a^2)]^{1/2}\right]. \quad (I.6-6)$$

Let us now call the length of one of the two plastic zones d (Fig. I.6-1); i.e.,

$$d \equiv c - a. \qquad (I.6-7)$$

Then by simple algebra we find from (I.6-5) and (I.6-7) that

$$d/a = \sec[(\pi/2)(\sigma_\infty/\sigma_0)] - 1. \qquad (I.6-8)$$

For small values of σ_∞/σ_0, we can expand (I.6-8) in a Maclaurin series to obtain

$$d/a = (1/8)(\pi\sigma_\infty/\sigma_0)^2, \qquad \sigma_\infty/\sigma_0 \ll 1, \qquad (I.6-9)$$

$$d = (\pi/8)(K_I/\sigma_0)^2, \qquad \sigma_\infty/\sigma_0 \ll 1, \qquad (I.6-10)$$

where K_I is the stress intensity factor for an infinite plate with a crack of length $2a$.

Note that the length d could not be expressed in terms of K_I alone for large-scale yielding (I.6-8), as in the case of small-scale yielding (I.6-10).

To obtain the displacements, we need the integral of Z_{IDug} with respect to z, i.e.,

$$Z^*_{IDug} = \int Z_{IDug}\, dz. \qquad (I.6-11)$$

Burdekin and Stone [BS 66] give the result as

$$Z^*_{IDug} = (2\sigma_0/\pi)[z\theta_1 - a\theta_2] \qquad (I.6-12)$$

where

$$\cot \theta_1 = \left\{ \left[1 - (c/z)^2 \right] / \left[(c/a)^2 - 1 \right] \right\}^{1/2} \tag{I.6-13}$$

$$\cot \theta_2 = \left[(z^2 - c^2)/(c^2 - a^2) \right]^{1/2}. \tag{I.6-14}$$

The imaginary part Z^*_{IDug} is given by [BS 66] as

$$\text{Im } Z^*_{\text{IDug}} = (2\sigma_0/\pi) \left\{ a \coth^{-1} \left[\left[(c^2 - z^2)/(c^2 - a^2) \right]^{1/2} \right] \right.$$

$$\left. - z \coth^{-1} \left[(a/z)[(c^2 - z^2)/(c^2 - a^2)]^{1/2} \right] \right\}, \qquad |z| \le a \tag{I.6-15}$$

From (I.5-9), we find the displacement in the y direction as

$$2Gu_y(x, y) = \tfrac{1}{2}(\kappa + 1)\text{Im } Z^*_{\text{IDug}} - y \text{ Re } Z_{\text{IDug}}. \tag{I.6-16}$$

Along the x-axis, $y = 0$, so (I.6-16) assumes the form

$$2Gu_y(x, 0) = \tfrac{1}{2}(\kappa + 1)\text{Im } Z^*_{\text{IDug}}. \tag{I.6-17}$$

At the physical crack tip, $x \to a$. From (I.6-15) and (I.6-17), we find [BS 66]

$$2Gu_y(a, 0) = \tfrac{1}{2}(\kappa + 1)\text{Im } Z^*_{\text{IDug}}\big|_{|z| \to a} \tag{I.6-18}$$

$$= (\kappa + 1)(a\sigma_0/\pi)\ln(c/a). \tag{I.6-19}$$

The crack tip opening displacement δ_t is defined as the relative distance between the crack surfaces at the crack tip (Fig. I.6-3), i.e.,

$$\delta_t = 2u_y(a, 0) = (\kappa + 1)(a\sigma_0/G\pi)\ln(c/a). \tag{I.6-20}$$

By (I.6-5), δ_t can also be written as

$$\delta_t = (\kappa + 1)(a\sigma_0/G\pi)\ln \sec[(\pi\sigma_\infty)/(2\sigma_0)]. \tag{I.6-21}$$

For plane stress, we obtain from (I.2-7), (I.4-61), and (I.6-21)

$$\delta_t = [8a\sigma_0/(\pi E)]\ln \sec[(\pi\sigma_\infty)/(2\sigma_0)]. \tag{I.6-22}$$

For small-scale yielding, we can expand (I.6-22) in a Maclaurin series to obtain

plane stress: $$\delta_t = K_I^2/(E\sigma_0). \tag{I.6-23}$$

A. A. Wells [Wel 63] proposed the use of the crack tip opening displacement as a criterion of ductile fracture. See also [BS 66].

Mode I Small-Scale Yielding Strip Model

Cherepanov presented in [Cher 79], the small-scale yielding solution to the Dugdale model. The function $\Phi(z)$ of equation (4-97) in [Cher 79] may be interpreted as one-half of the mode I Westergaard potential for the Dugdale model under conditions of small-scale yielding Z_{ssy}. From this reference, we obtain

$$Z_{\mathrm{ssy}} = \sigma_0\left\{1 - (\pi i)^{-1}\ln\left[[id^{1/2} - (z - d)^{1/2}]/[id^{1/2} + (z - d)^{1/2}]\right]\right\},$$
$$(\mathrm{I.6\text{-}24})$$

where the coordinate z has been moved (see Fig. I.6-4), so that the origin of the complex plane now coincides with the crack tip of Fig. I.6-1 on the right. The parameter d is again the length of the plastic zone.

Using the complex identity,

$$2i \tan^{-1}z = \ln|(1 + iz)/(1 - iz)|, \qquad (\mathrm{I.6\text{-}25})$$

one may rewrite (I.6-24) is an equivalent form as

$$Z_{\mathrm{ssy}} = \sigma_0\left[1 - (2/\pi)\tan^{-1}\left\{[(z/d) - 1]^{1/2}\right\}\right]. \qquad (\mathrm{I.6\text{-}26})$$

From (I.6-26), we discover through simple mathematical manipulations that

$$z/d = 1 + \tan^2\left[(\pi/2)(1 - Z_{\mathrm{ssy}}/\sigma_0)\right], \qquad (\mathrm{I.6\text{-}27})$$

which then becomes, through the use of elementary trigonometric identities,

$$\sin\left[\pi Z_{\mathrm{ssy}}/(2\sigma_0)\right] = (d/z)^{1/2}. \qquad (\mathrm{I.6\text{-}28})$$

Because

$$\sin^{-1}z^{-1/2}\big|_{|z|\to\infty} \sim z^{-1/2}, \qquad (\mathrm{I.6\text{-}29})$$

it follows that, at a sufficiently large distance from the crack tip, (I.6-28) becomes asymptotically

$$\pi Z_{\mathrm{ssy}}\big|_{|z|\to\infty} \sim 2\sigma_0(d/z)^{1/2}. \qquad (\mathrm{I.6\text{-}30})$$

Notice that (I.6-30) has a similar form to the mode I small-scale yielding Westergaard potential (4.1-25), which differs only by a multiplicative constant (if ζ is identified as z). This provides a means to relate the constants as follows:

$$d = (a/8)(\pi\sigma_\infty/\sigma_0)^2 = (\pi/8)(K_{\mathrm{I}}/\sigma_0)^2. \qquad (\mathrm{I.6\text{-}31})$$

Equations (I.6-31) prove to be identical to the previous relationships (I.6-9) and (I.6-10), which were obtained directly from the exact Dugdale solution under the assumption of small-scale yielding.

Now, through the Euler relationship,

$$r \exp(i\theta) = r \cos \theta + ir \sin \theta, \qquad (I.6-32)$$

and the definitions of the real and imaginary parts of a complex function, we find that (I.6-28) is equal to

$$\sin\left[\pi(\mathrm{Re}\, Z_{ssy} + i\, \mathrm{Im}\, Z_{ssy})/(2\sigma_0)\right] = d^{1/2}r^{-1/2}[\cos(\theta/2) - i\sin(\theta/2)]. \qquad (I.6-33)$$

Expanding the argument of sin( ) in (I.6-33), we deduce that

$$\sin\left[\pi\, \mathrm{Re}\, Z_{ssy}/(2\sigma_0)\right]\cos\left[i\pi\, \mathrm{Im}\, Z_{ssy}/(2\sigma_0)\right]$$
$$- \cos\left[\pi\, \mathrm{Re}\, Z_{ssy}/(2\sigma_0)\right]\sin\left[i\pi\, \mathrm{Im}\, Z_{ssy}/(2\sigma_0)\right]$$
$$= d^{1/2}r^{-1/2}[\cos(\theta/2) - i\sin(\theta/2)]. \qquad (I.6-34)$$

Through the complex relationships,

$$\cos iz = \cosh z, \qquad \sin iz = i\sinh z, \qquad (I.6-35)$$

and by equating the real the imaginary parts of equation (I.6-34), we find

$$\sin\left[\pi\, \mathrm{Re}\, Z_{ssy}/(2\sigma_0)\right]\cosh\left[\pi\, \mathrm{Im}\, Z_{ssy}/(2\sigma_0)\right] = d^{1/2}r^{-1/2}\cos(\theta/2) \qquad (I.6-36)$$

$$\cos\left[\pi\, \mathrm{Re}\, Z_{ssy}/(2\sigma_0)\right]\sinh\left[\pi\, \mathrm{Im}\, Z_{ssy}/(2\sigma_0)\right] = d^{1/2}r^{-1/2}\sin(\theta/2). \qquad (I.6-37)$$

Eliminating the terms containing $\mathrm{Im}\, Z_{ssy}$ in (I.6-37) through the use of the hyperbolic trigonometric relationship

$$\cosh^2(\ ) - \sinh^2(\ ) = 1, \qquad (I.6-38)$$

we obtain

$$r/d = \cos^2(\theta/2)/\sin^2\left[\pi\, \mathrm{Re}\, Z_{ssy}/(2\sigma_0)\right]$$
$$- \sin^2(\theta/2)/\cos^2\left[\pi\, \mathrm{Re}\, Z_{ssy}/(2\sigma_0)\right]. \qquad (I.6-39)$$

Using trigonometric identities, we may rewrite (I.6-39) in the equivalent form

$$\cos^2(\pi \, \text{Re} \, Z_{ssy}/\sigma_0) + (2d/r)\cos(\pi \, \text{Re} \, Z_{ssy}/\sigma_0) + (2d/r)\cos \theta - 1 = 0.$$
(I.6-40)

Solving for the quadratic term in (I.6-40), we find

$$\cos(\pi \, \text{Re} \, Z_{ssy}/\sigma_0) = -(d/r) \pm \left[(d/r)^2 - (2d/r)\cos \theta + 1\right]^{1/2}.$$
(I.6-41)

Along the x-axis, the stresses are, via (4.1-1) and (4.1-2), $y = 0$:

$$\sigma_x = \sigma_y = \text{Re} \, Z_{ssy}, \qquad \tau_{xy} = 0.$$
(I.6-42)

Substituting σ_y from (I.6-42) for the Re Z_{ssy} in (I.6-41), we get

$$\cos(\pi\sigma_y/\sigma_0) = -(d/r) \pm \left[(d/r)^2 - (2d/r)\cos \theta + 1\right]^{1/2}.$$
(I.6-43)

For $\theta = 0$, (I.6-43) becomes

$$\cos(\pi\sigma_y/\sigma_0)|_{\theta=0} = -(d/r) \pm |(d/r) - 1|, \qquad 0 < r \leq \infty$$
(I.6-44)

$$= -1, \qquad 0 < x \leq d \rightarrow \sigma_y = \sigma_x = \sigma_0,$$
(I.6-45)

$$= 1 - 2d/x, \qquad d \leq x \leq \infty \rightarrow \sigma_y|_{x \to \infty} = \sigma_x|_{x \to \infty} = 0.$$
(I.6-46)

For $\theta = \pi$, (I.6-43) becomes

$$\cos(\pi\sigma_y/\sigma_0)|_{\theta=\pi} = -(d/r) \pm |(d/r) + 1|, \qquad 0 < r \leq \infty$$
(I.6-47a)

$$= 1, \qquad -\infty \leq x < 0 \rightarrow \sigma_y = \sigma_x = 0.$$
(I.6-47b)

Thus by (I.6-42), (I.6-45), and (I.6-47b), we find that the boundary conditions along the crack axis, $-\infty \leq x \leq d$, are satisfied. By (I.6-46), we see that the stresses approach the small-scale yielding solution (I.5-10)–(I.5-11) along the crack axis as $x \to \infty$.

Mode III Small-Scale Yielding Strip Model

One can observe the similarity of the Westergaard function for the three principal modes of fracture (4.1-6), (4.1-44), and (4.1-60). One need only replace the traction at infinity to obtain one particular Westergaard function from another. An analogous relationship exists among the Westergaard functions for the Dugdale model and the plastic strip models proposed by Bilby, Cottrell, and Swinden [BSC 63] for modes II and III.

In the case of small-scale yielding, the plastic strip model for mode III has a Westergaard function analogous to the mode I function given by Cherepanov (I.6-24) or its equivalent (I.6-26). The Bilby–Cottrell–Swinden (BCS) plastic strip model for small-scale yielding will therefore follow from (I.6-26) as

$$Z_{\text{BCSssy}} = k\left[1 - (2/\pi)\tan^{-1}\left\{[(z/d) - 1]^{1/2}\right\}\right]. \qquad \text{(I.6-48)}$$

$$d = (\pi/8)(K_{\text{III}}/k)^2, \qquad \text{(I.6-49)}$$

where k is the yield in pure shear, d is the length of the plastic zone, and K_{III} is the mode III stress intensity factor. Opposing shear tractions $t_z = \tau_{yz} = \pm k$ act along the plastic zone d in analogy to the Dugdale model's tensile tractions $t_y = \pm \sigma_0$.

Equation (I.6-48) may also be expressed in a fashion similar to (I.6-28), i.e.,

$$\sin\left[\pi Z_{\text{BCSssy}}/(2k)\right] = (d/z)^{1/2}. \qquad \text{(I.6-50)}$$

We further note from the mode III Westergaard relationship (I.5-61) that

$$Z_{\text{BCSssy}} = \tau_{yz} + i\tau_{xz}. \qquad \text{(I.6-51)}$$

Thus the shear stresses follow from (I.6-50) and (I.6-51) as

$$\sin\left[\pi(\tau_{yz} + i\tau_{xz})/(2k)\right] = (d/z)^{1/2}. \qquad \text{(I.6-52)}$$

Upon solving (I.6-52) for z/d, we find

$$z/d = \csc^2\left[\pi(\tau_{yz} + i\tau_{xz})/(2k)\right] \qquad \text{(I.6-53)}$$

$$= \sec^2\left[\pi(\tau_{yz} + i\tau_{xz} - k)/(2k)\right]. \qquad \text{(I.6-54)}$$

Aside from a phase shift of $\pi/2$ inside the argument of the sec( ), this relationship between z and the shear stresses (I.6-54) represents a conformal mapping of the form 10.7 of Kober's *Dictionary of Conformal Representations* [Kob 52, p. 101]. A depiction of this particular mapping is shown in Figs I.6-4 and I.6-5.

From Figs I.6-4 and I.6-5 we see that τ_{yz} has a constant magnitude k along the plastic zone *ABD* in analogy to the Dugdale model's $\sigma_y = \sigma_0$. However, we also note an infinite stress τ_{xz} at the crack tip, which does not appear in the Dugdale model. This infinite stress in τ_{xz} is also present in

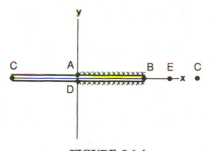

FIGURE I.6-4

Small-scale yielding coordinate system for strip models.

the exact Bilby–Cottrell–Swinden solution (2.4-9), and is therefore not indicative of small-scale yielding. (Note that in Section 2.4 the symbols c and a are interchanged from their use in the Introduction.) Consequently, this infinite stress must cast some doubt on the validity of the Bilby–Cottrell–Swinden model as a physically meaningful solution (see Section 2.4). This singularity is not found in the Dugdale model because the imaginary part of the Westergaard function is not used.

Nonetheless, the Bilby–Cottrell–Swinden solution does predict a crack tip opening displacement for mode III that is completely analogous to the plane stress Dugdale model [BS 66]. To calculate the crack tip opening

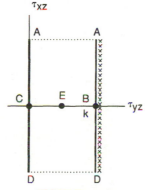

FIGURE I.6-5

Conformal map of a mode III plastic strip model.

displacement, we need the integral of Z_{BCSssy} (I.6-48), i.e.,

$$Z^*_{\text{BCSssy}} \equiv \int Z_{\text{BCSssy}} \, dz = k \int \left[1 - (2/\pi)\tan^{-1}\{[(z/d) - 1]^{1/2}\} \right] dz$$

$$\text{(I.6-55)}$$

$$= kz - (2k/\pi)\left\{ z \tan^{-1}\left[[(z/d) - 1]^{1/2}\right] - d[(z/d) - 1]^{1/2} \right\}$$

$$\text{(I.6-56)}$$

$$= zZ_{\text{BCSssy}} + (2kd/\pi)[(z/d) - 1]^{1/2}. \tag{I.6-57}$$

From (I.6-51), (I.6-54), and (I.6-57), we may express Z^*_{BSCssy} as a function of the stresses, i.e.,

$$Z^*_{\text{BCSssy}}(\tau_{yz}, \tau_{xz}) = d(\tau_{yz} + i\tau_{xz})\sec^2\{\pi(\tau_{yz} + i\tau_{xz} - k)/(2k)\}$$
$$+ (2kd/\pi)\tan\{\pi(\tau_{yz} + i\tau_{xz} - k)/(2k)\}. \quad \text{(I.6-58)}$$

From Figs I.6-4 and I.6-5, we see that evaluating (I.6-58) at the crack tip requires $\tau_{yz} = k$; i.e.,

$$Z^*_{\text{BCSssy}}(k, \tau_{xz}) = d(k + i\tau_{xz})\sec^2\{i\pi\tau_{xz}/(2k)\}$$
$$+ (2kd/\pi)\tan\{\pi i\tau_{xz}/(2k)\} \tag{I.6-59}$$

$$= d(k + i\tau_{xz})\text{sech}^2\{\pi\tau_{xz}/(2k)\}$$
$$+ (2kd/\pi)i \tanh\{\pi\tau_{xz}/(2k)\}. \tag{I.6-60}$$

To find the crack tip opening displacement, we need to evaluate Z^*_{BCSssy} at points A and D, i.e., to find the relative displacement of the crack surfaces at the crack tip. It follows from Figs I.6-4 and I.6-5, that we need the limit of the function $Z^*_{\text{BCSssy}}(k, \tau_{xz})$ as $\tau_{xz} \to \pm\infty$, i.e.,

$$\lim \tau_{xz} \to \pm\infty \, Z^*_{\text{BCSssy}}(k, \tau_{xz}) = \pm i(2kd/\pi). \tag{I.6-61}$$

The crack tip opening displacement δ_{BCS} is therefore, from (I.5-54) and (I.6-61),

$$\delta_{\text{BCSssy}} = w|_{x=0, \, y=0^+} - w|_{x=0, \, y=0^-} \tag{I.6-62}$$

$$= (1/G)\left[\text{Im} \, Z^*_{\text{BCSssy}}(k, \infty) - \text{Im} \, Z^*_{\text{BCSssy}}(k, -\infty) \right] \tag{I.6-63}$$

$$= 4kd/(\pi G) \tag{I.6-64}$$

$$= K^2_{\text{III}}/(2Gk). \tag{I.6-65}$$

This result (I.6-65) is the mode III counterpart to the mode I small-scale yielding crack trip opening displacement for plane stress (I.6-23). An alternative mode III plastic strip model by Cherepanov [Cher 79] is discussed in Chapter 2.

Barenblatt [Bar 59] and Panasyuk [Pan 60] also introduced models that are mathematically similar to the Dugdale model. An interesting discussion of the history of process zones and plastic strip models of crack tips may be found in [NA 87a].

I.7 EXACT ELASTOPLASTIC SOLUTIONS FOR MODE III

In this section we present true elastoplastic solutions involving linear elastic and perfectly plastic materials or linear elastic and isotropic strain hardening materials for mode III fracture mechanics problems. Unlike those in Section I.6, the plastic zones in this section have finite dimensions.

Mode III is the only mode of fracture for which complete analytical elastoplastic solutions have been found. In the case of small-scale yielding, the solution for elastic–perfectly plastic materials is particularly simple. We will begin our discussion with this case, which is referred to subsequently as the small-scale yielding Hult–McClintock solution [HM 56].

The elastoplastic boundary for this problem can be found by substituting the small-scale yielding, linear elastic solution for stresses (I.5-66) and (I.5-67) into the Mises yield condition

$$\tau_{xz}^2 + \tau_{yz}^2 = k^2, \tag{I.7-1}$$

which is obtained from (I.3-1) and (I.3-2) under the assumption that these are the only two stresses that exist from mode III problems. In general, one cannot guarantee that substituting an elastic solution into a yield condition will generate an elastoplastic boundary that will allow a corresponding statically admissible plastic solution. In many cases it will not.

We will find that the prescribed elastic–plastic boundary $\partial\Omega$ is circular, as shown in Fig. 1.1-1. The origin of the polar coordinate system (r, θ) is located at the center of this circle. The crack for the purely elastic solution would extend to the origin of this coordinate system. This is counterindicated by Fig. 1.1-1, which is for the elastic–perfectly plastic case. We will find that solving the initial value problem (Cauchy problem) for the plastic region produces stresses that do not fulfill the boundary condition of a traction-free surface along OS of Fig. 1.1-1. They are, instead, continuous and represent part of the plastic continuum. The ramifications of this shift of elastic stress, relative to the crack tip in terms of the failure criterion for ductile materials, is discussed in Chapter 2.

The elastic–plastic boundary R is from (I.5-66), (I.5-67), and (I.7-1):

$$R \equiv r|_{\partial\Omega} = K_{III}^2/(2\pi k^2). \tag{I.7-2}$$

The elastic stress function $\phi^E(r, \theta)$ of (I.5-34) for the mode III problem is given by (1.1-1) and its partial derivatives with respect to x and y by (1.1-2) and (1.1-3).

In terms of the plastic stress function $\phi(x, y)$,

$$\phi_{,x}^2 + \phi_{,y}^2 = k^2 \quad \text{or} \quad p^2 + q^2 = k^2, \tag{I.7-3}$$

where p and q are the first partial derivatives of ϕ with respect to x and y (I.7-5). Equation (I.7-3) is referred to as the *eiconal* equation in mathematical physics literature.

The method of solution will be by characteristic strip equations [Zwi 89, Sne 57, CH 62]. This solution technique converts the partial differential equation and its initial data into a system of ordinary differential equations. In this theory, a first-order partial differential equation

$$F(x, y, \phi, p, q) = 0, \tag{I.7-4}$$

is to be solved, where

$$p \equiv \phi_{,x}, \quad q \equiv \phi_{,y}. \tag{I.7-5}$$

The strip equations (or Charpit's equations) are

$$x_{,s} = F_{,p} \tag{I.7-6}$$

$$y_{,s} = F_{,q} \tag{I.7-7}$$

$$p_{,s} = -F_{,x} - pF_{,\phi} \tag{I.7-8}$$

$$q_{,s} = -F_{,y} - qF_{,\phi} \tag{I.7-9}$$

$$\phi_{,s} = pF_{,p} + qF_{,q} \tag{I.7-10}$$

where all of the variables are assumed to be functions of two parameters, s and t.

In our case,

$$F(x, y, \phi, p, q) = p^2 + q^2 - k^2. \tag{I.7-11}$$

Therefore from (I.7-6)–(I.7-11) it follows that

$$x_{,s} = F_{,p} = 2p \tag{I.7-12}$$

$$y_{,s} = F_{,q} = 2q \tag{I.7-13}$$

$$p_{,s} = -F_{,x} - pF_{,\phi} = 0 \tag{I.7-14}$$

$$q_{,s} = -F_{,y} - qF_{,\phi} = 0 \tag{I.7-15}$$

$$\phi_{,s} = pF_{,p} + qF_{,q} = 2(p^2 + q^2). \tag{I.7-16}$$

The initial data ($s = 0$) are found from the elastic stress function ϕ^E, whose derivatives are evaluated on the boundary, and the Cartesian coordinates of R. One particular parametrization is provided by (1.1-9)–(1.1-11). In the notation of the Introduction, we simply replace the parameter a by t in (1.1-9)–(1.1-11). The parameter t represents the $\sin(\theta/2)$ on the boundary.

We find

$$\hat{x} = R(1 - 2t^2) \tag{I.7-17}$$

$$\hat{y} = 2Rt(1 - t^2)^{1/2} \tag{I.7-18}$$

$$\hat{p} = -k(1 - t^2)^{1/2} \tag{I.7-19}$$

$$\hat{q} = -kt \tag{I.7-20}$$

$$\hat{\phi} = -2kR(1 - t^2)^{1/2}, \tag{I.7-21}$$

where the caret above a variable indicates evaluation on $\partial\Omega$. We now integrate (I.7-12)–(I.7-16) with respect to s to obtain

$$x = 2ps + c_1 \tag{I.7-22}$$

$$y = 2qs + c_2 \tag{I.7-23}$$

$$p = c_3 \tag{I.7-24}$$

$$q = c_4 \tag{I.7-25}$$

$$\phi = 2(p^2 + q^2)s + c_5 \tag{I.7-26}$$

where the constants of integration c_i ($i = 1-5$) are evaluated from data on the boundary (I.7-17)–(I.7-21) with $s = 0$ in (I.7-22)–(I.7-26); i.e.,

$$c_1 = R(1 - 2t^2) \qquad\qquad\qquad (I.7-27)$$

$$c_2 = 2Rt(1 - t^2)^{1/2} \qquad\qquad (I.7-28)$$

$$c_3 = -k(1 - t^2)^{1/2} \qquad\qquad (I.7-29)$$

$$c_4 = -kt \qquad\qquad\qquad\qquad (I.7-30)$$

$$c_5 = -2kR(1 - t^2)^{1/2}. \qquad\quad (I.7-31)$$

By substituting (I.7-27)–(I.7-31) into (I.7-22)–(I.7-26), we find a parametrized solution (I.7-36) of the initial value problem; i.e.,

$$x = 2ps + R(1 - 2t^2) = 2c_3 s + R(1 - 2t^2)$$

$$= -2k(1 - t^2)^{1/2}s + R(1 - 2t^2) \qquad\qquad (I.7-32)$$

$$y = 2qs + 2Rt(1 - t^2)^{1/2} = 2c_4 s + 2Rt(1 - t^2)^{1/2}$$

$$= -2kts + 2Rt(1 - t^2)^{1/2} \qquad\qquad (I.7-33)$$

$$p = -k(1 - t^2)^{1/2} \qquad\qquad (I.7-34)$$

$$q = -kt \qquad\qquad (I.7-35)$$

$$\phi = 2(p^2 + q^2)s - 2kR(1 - t^2)^{1/2} = 2k^2 s - 2kR(1 - t^2)^{1/2}. \quad (I.7-36)$$

In our problem, it is possible to solve for the parameters s and t from the Cartesian coordinate equations (I.7-32) and (I.7-33):

$$s = [R^2 - (x^2 + y^2)]/\left((2k)\left[(x + R)^2 + y^2\right]^{1/2}\right) \qquad (I.7-37)$$

$$t = y/\left[(x + R)^2 + y^2\right]^{1/2}. \qquad (I.7-38)$$

This allows us to give the following explicit solution (expressed entirely in coordinates) rather than an implicit one (expressed in terms of parameters):

$$\phi(x, y) = -k\left[(x + R)^2 + y^2\right]^{1/2}. \qquad (I.7-39)$$

The stresses follow immediately by partial differentiation of (I.7-39) with respect to the coordinates or by the substitution of t from (I.7-38)

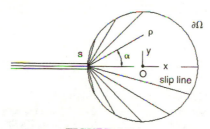

FIGURE I.7-1

Coordinates for the mode III elastoplastic problem.

into (I.7-34) and (I.7-35), i.e.,

$$\tau_{xz} = \phi_{,y} = -ky/\left[(x+R)^2 + y^2\right]^{1/2} \qquad (I.7-40)$$

$$\tau_{yz} = -\phi_{,x} = k(x+R)/\left[(x+R)^2 + y^2\right]^{1/2}. \qquad (I.7-41)$$

Equations (I.7-39)–(I.7-41) may be expressed more compactly in the polar coordinate system (ρ, α) (Fig. I.7-1.):

$$\rho \equiv \left[(x+R)^2 + y^2\right]^{1/2}, \qquad \alpha \equiv \tan^{-1}[y/(x+R)]. \qquad (I.7-42)$$

The coordinate ρ is the radius from the crack tip S in the elastoplastic problem, and α is the angle a slip line makes relative to the x-axis (Fig. I.7-2). A slip line represents a plane of maximum shear stress $\tau_{max} = k$. In Fig. I.7-1 several slip lines emanating from the polar origin S are shown. A slip line is also a characteristic of the partial differential equation (I.7-3).

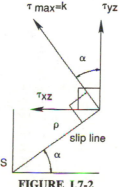

FIGURE I.7-2

Slip line and shear stresses for the mode III plastic region.

In this system, we find

$$\phi = -k\rho \tag{I.7-43}$$

$$\tau_{xz} = -k \sin \alpha, \qquad \tau_{yz} = k \cos \alpha. \tag{I.7-44}$$

Having found a statically admissible solution for stresses, we will now find the associated strains and displacements. The compatibility equation for mode III is by (I.1-10)–(I.1-11) and (I.5-36)–(I.5-37):

$$\gamma_{xz,y} = \gamma_{yz,x}, \tag{I.7-45}$$

where γ_{ij} is total strain.

The elastic strains are, from (I.2-8),

$$\gamma_{xz}^E = (1/G)\tau_{xz}, \qquad \gamma_{yz}^E = (1/G)\tau_{yz}. \tag{I.7-46}$$

The plastic strains, as determined from Hencky's deformation theory of plasticity (I.3-38)–(I.3-39), are

$$\gamma_{xz}^P = 6\Lambda\tau_{xz}, \qquad \gamma_{yz}^P = 6\Lambda\tau_{yz}, \tag{I.7-47}$$

where $\Lambda = \Lambda(x, y)$.

Thus from (I.3-8), (I.7-46), and (I.7-47), the total strains are

$$\gamma_{xz} = \lambda(x, y)\tau_{xz}, \qquad \gamma_{yz} = \lambda(x, y)\tau_{yz} \tag{I.7-48}$$

where

$$\lambda(x, y) \equiv (1/G) + 6\Lambda(x, y). \tag{I.7-49}$$

Now by (I.7-44) and (I.7-48), we have

$$\gamma_{xz} = -k\lambda(x, y)\sin \alpha, \qquad \gamma_{yz} = k\lambda(x, y)\cos \alpha. \tag{I.7-50}$$

Thus the compatibility equation (I.7-45) becomes

$$(\lambda \cos \alpha)_{,x} + (\lambda \sin \alpha)_{,y} = 0 \tag{I.7-51}$$

or in expanded form

$$\lambda_{,x}\cos \alpha - \lambda \sin \alpha \alpha_{,x} + \lambda_{,y}\sin \alpha + \lambda \cos \alpha \alpha_{,y} = 0. \tag{I.7-52}$$

Now by (I.7-42)

$$\rho_{,x} = \cos \alpha \qquad \rho_{,y} = \sin \alpha, \tag{I.7-53}$$

$$\alpha_{,x} = -\sin \alpha/\rho \qquad \alpha_{,y} = \cos \alpha/\rho, \tag{I.7-54}$$

so that (I.7-52) becomes

$$\rho\lambda_{,\rho} + \lambda = 0, \qquad (I.7\text{-}55)$$

i.e., independent of α.

Separating variables and integrating (I.7-55) with respect to ρ, we find that the compatibility equation of strain is satisfied provided

$$\lambda = F(\alpha)/\rho, \qquad (I.7\text{-}56)$$

where $F(\alpha)$ is an arbitrary function of α. The determination of $F(\alpha)$ follows from the continuity of displacement at the elastic–plastic boundary $\partial\Omega$.

The strain–displacement relationships (I.5-45) are valid for both elastic and plastic regions for mode III, i.e.,

$$w_{,x} = \gamma_{xz}, \qquad w_{,y} = \gamma_{yz}. \qquad (I.7\text{-}57)$$

From (I.7-50), (I.7-56), and (I.7-57) it follows that

$$w_{,x} = -kF(\alpha)\sin\alpha/\rho, \qquad w_{,y} = kF(\alpha)\cos\alpha/\rho. \qquad (I.7\text{-}58)$$

Converting (I.7-58) to polar coordinates, we find

$$w_{,\rho}\cos\alpha - w_{,\alpha}\sin\alpha/\rho = -k\sin\alpha\cos\alpha F(\alpha)/\rho \qquad (I.7\text{-}59)$$

$$w_{,\rho}\sin\alpha + w_{,\alpha}\cos\alpha/\rho = k\sin\alpha\cos\alpha F(\alpha)/\rho. \qquad (I.7\text{-}60)$$

Solving for $w_{,\rho}$ from the simultaneous equations (I.7-59) and (I.7-60), we obtain

$$w_{,\rho} = 0 \rightarrow w = f(\alpha). \qquad (I.7\text{-}61)$$

By substituting (I.7-61) into (I.7-59) and (I.7-60), we deduce that

$$f_{,\alpha} = kF(\alpha) \rightarrow f = k\int F(\alpha)\,d\alpha + \text{const.} \qquad (I.7\text{-}62)$$

The displacement w at the elastic–plastic interface is, by (I.5-69),

$$\partial\Omega: \qquad w = (K_{III}/G)(2R/\pi)^{1/2}\sin(\theta/2). \qquad (I.7\text{-}63)$$

By plane geometry (Fig I.7-3), the relationship between θ of a point on $\partial\Omega$ and α is

$$\alpha = \tfrac{1}{2}\theta|_{\partial\Omega}. \qquad (I.7\text{-}64)$$

Thus (I.7-63) becomes

$$\partial\Omega: \qquad w = f(\alpha) = (K_{III}/G)(2R/\pi)^{1/2}\sin\alpha, \qquad (I.7\text{-}65)$$

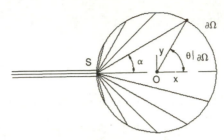

FIGURE I.7-3

Relationship between coordinate angles for points on the elastoplastic boundary.

which by (I.7-2) is also equal to

$$w^P = w|_{\partial\Omega} = f(\alpha) = \left[K_{III}^2/(\pi kG) \right] \sin \alpha. \qquad (I.7-66)$$

Equation (I.7-66) may be continued into the plastic zone to provide the displacements w^P in this region, which are a function only of α.
   By (I.7-62) and (I.7-66),

$$F(\alpha) = \left[K_{III}^2/(\pi k^2 G) \right] \cos \alpha. \qquad (I.7-67)$$

The total strains in the plastic region follow from (I.7-50), (I.7-56), and (I.7-67) as

$$\gamma_{xz} = -K_{III}^2 \cos \alpha \sin \alpha/(\pi kG\rho), \qquad \gamma_{yz} = K_{III}^2 \cos^2\alpha/(\pi kG\rho). \quad (I.7-68)$$

   Thus, the strains remain singular at the crack tip ($\rho = 0$) for the elastoplastic solution, although the order of singularity changes from the purely elastic solution ($1/r^{1/2}$).

Isotropic Hardening
   We now introduce strain hardening into the mode III elastoplastic problem. We assume an isotropic, power law hardening material in the plastic region. This problem was first solved by Rice in 1967 [Ric 67]. Additional discussions of it may be found in [Ric 68a, Hut 79, Cher 79, KP 85], and other sources.
   The plastic stress field is again composed of two shear stresses, τ_{xz} and τ_{yz}, which can solve equilibrium equation (I.5-33), provided they are derived from the stress function (I.5-34). Although equations (I.5-33) and (I.5-34) are introduced in the section dedicated to linear elastic fracture mechanics, the same equilibrium equation applies regardless of the material's constitutive equations.

For our present problem, a linear elastic response is assumed for materials that have not reached yield. A deformation theory of plasticity which relates plastic strains to stresses by a power law (Fig. I.7-4) is assumed for the plastic region:

Elastic for $T \le k$: $\Gamma/\gamma_0 = T/k$,   or $\Gamma G = T$.   (I.7-69)

Plastic for $T > k$: $\Gamma/\gamma_0 = (T/k)^n$, $1 \le n < \infty$,   (I.7-70)

$$\gamma_0 = k/G,$$ (I.7-71)

$$T \equiv \left(\tau_{xz}^2 + \tau_{yz}^2\right)^{1/2},$$ (I.7-72)

$$\Gamma \equiv \left(\gamma_{xz}^2 + \gamma_{yz}^2\right)^{1/2},$$ (I.7-73)

where n is the material hardening exponent, γ_0 is the engineering yield strain in pure shear, k is the corresponding yield stress in pure shear, T is the stress intensity—also called the equivalent stress—and Γ is the strain intensity or equivalent strain. The empirical exponent n may be determined experimentally from torsion tests which provide data in the form of T versus Γ (Fig. I.7-4), for which a power law regression analysis may be performed.

Components of the stress and strain tensors are related as follows:

$$\gamma_{xz}/\gamma_0 = (T/k)^{n-1}(\tau_{xz}/k),$$ (I.7-74)

$$\gamma_{yz}/\gamma_0 = (T/k)^{n-1}(\tau_{yz}/k).$$ (I.7-75)

For $n = 1$, (I.7-74) and (I.7-75) reduce to Hooke's law.

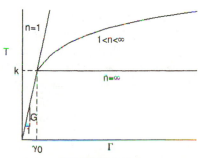

FIGURE I.7-4

Power law strain hardening behavior in shear.

The prescribed elastic–plastic boundary is found as in the previous problem. The material first yields when $T = k$, which is identical to (I.7-1). So, by substituting the small-scale yielding mode III elastic stresses (I.5-66)–(I.5-67) into (I.7-1), we find the same radius R as in the case of the elastic–perfectly plastic material (I.7-2).

By substituting (I.7-74) and (I.7-75) into the compatibility equation for mode III (I.7-45), we find for the isotropic, strain hardening material

$$(n - 1)T_{,y}\tau_{xz} + T\tau_{xz,y} = (n - 1)T_{,x}\tau_{yz} + T\tau_{yz,x}. \qquad \text{(I.7-76)}$$

By further substituting (I.7-72) for T into (I.7-76), followed by the substitution of the stresses τ_{xz} and τ_{yz} in terms of the stress function ϕ from (I.5-34), we obtain

$$\left(n\phi_{,x}^2 + \phi_{,y}^2\right)\phi_{,xx} + 2(n - 1)\phi_{,x}\phi_{,y}\phi_{,xy} + \left(n\phi_{,y}^2 + \phi_{,x}^2\right)\phi_{,yy} = 0.$$
$$\text{(I.7-77)}$$

Equation (I.7-77) is a nonlinear, second-order partial differential equation. It may also be referred to as a quasilinear equation, where *quasilinear* refers to linearity in the highest order of partial derivatives. For $n = 1$, it reduces to Laplace's equation—a linear equation. The material in this case behaves as a linear elastic solid. As $n \to \infty$, the material response approaches that of a perfectly plastic material.

Lieberstein [Lie 72] presents an analysis for classifying the general quasilinear partial differential equations of the second order,

$$a(x, y, \phi, p, q)\phi_{,xx} + 2b(x, y, \phi, p, q)\phi_{,xy} + c(x, y, \phi, p, q)\phi_{,yy}$$

$$= d(x, y, \phi, p, q), \qquad \text{(I.7-78)}$$

where coefficients a, b, c, and d are at most functions of the two independent variables (x, y), the dependent variable $\phi(x, y)$, and its first partial derivatives $p(x, y)$, $q(x, y)$ with respect to x and y as in (I.7-5).

The three classes of quasilinear, second-order equations follow:

hyperbolic type: $b^2 - ac > 0$ (I.7-79)

parabolic type: $b^2 - ac = 0$ (I.7-80)

elliptic type: $b^2 - ac < 0$.   (I.7-81)

Dividing (I.7-77) through by $n\phi_{,x}^2 + \phi_{,y}^2$ and substituting the notation p and q for the partial derivatives of ϕ, we obtain

$$\phi_{,xx} + [2(n-1)pq/(np^2+q^2)]\phi_{,xy} + [(nq^2+p^2)/(np^2+q^2)]\phi_{,yy} = 0.$$

(I.7-82)

For equation (I.7-82), we determine

$$b^2 - ac = -n(p+q)^2/[np^2+q^2]^2, \qquad \text{where } n \geq 1. \quad \text{(I.7-83)}$$

Thus by (I.7-81) and (I.7-83), equation (I.7-77) is elliptic for all finite values of $n \geq 1$.

However, in the limit as $n \to \infty$, equation (I.7-83) becomes

$$b^2 - ac = 0, \tag{I.7-84}$$

which indicates that, as the material approaches the perfectly plastic state, the partial differential equation tends toward the parabolic.

Characteristic curves can be viewed as carriers of data which are initialized on the boundary of a given problem (initial value problem). For hyperbolic equations, there are two families of characteristic curves. For parabolic equations, there is only one family of characteristics. For elliptic equations, there are no real characteristic curves, and as such initial value problems are ill-posed for them. For elliptic partial differential equations, boundary value problems are formulated in their place. A well-posed problem, in the classical sense of J. Hadamard [Lie 72, TA 77], is one for which a solution exists such that the solution is unique and has continuous dependence on the data on its boundary. By the last statement, we mean that a small change in the boundary data does not cause an enormous change in its solution. This is not to say that all ill-posed problem are unimportant. Ill-posed problems may result when modeling certain physical phenomena, particularly those exhibiting unstable behavior.

The slip lines (mentioned in the previous subsection on the elastic–perfectly plastic problem) physically represent traces of planes of maximum shear force. They are also characteristic lines (curves) of the governing quasilinear, first-order partial differential equation, the eiconal equation.

In the limit as $n \to \infty$, (I.7-77) becomes the parabolic equation

$$\phi_{,x}^2 \phi_{,xx} + 2\phi_{,x}\phi_{,y}\phi_{,xy} + \phi_{,y}^2 \phi_{,yy} = 0. \tag{I.7-85}$$

What connection, if any, does this equation have with eiconal equation? It is not immediately obvious. However, we may rewrite (I.7-85) as

$$\left(\phi_{,x}^2 + \phi_{,y}^2\right)_{,x}\phi_{,x} + \left(\phi_{,x}^2 + \phi_{,y}^2\right)_{,y}\phi_{,y} = 0 \qquad (I.7\text{-}86)$$

or

$$\nabla\phi \cdot \nabla(\nabla\phi \cdot \nabla\phi) = 0, \qquad (I.7\text{-}87)$$

where ∇ is the gradient operator and $\cdot$ represents the inner product of two vectors. But (I.7-86) may be further represented by

$$\left(\phi_{,x}^2 + \phi_{,y}^2 - k^2\right)_{,x}\phi_{,x} + \left(\phi_{,x}^2 + \phi_{,y}^2 - k^2\right)_{,y}\phi_{,y} = 0. \qquad (I.7\text{-}88)$$

Thus an eiconal kernal is embedded in (I.7-85).

Returning to elliptic equations, the Laplace equation is the prototype, i.e.,

Laplace equation: $\quad \phi_{,xx} + \phi_{,yy} = 0 \quad$ or $\quad \nabla^2\phi = 0.$ $\qquad (I.7\text{-}89)$

There are two fundamental classes of boundary value problems for Laplace's equation: the *Dirichlet problem* and the *Neumann problem*:

Dirichlet problem: On a boundary $\partial\Omega$, $\phi(x, y)$ is specified.
Neumann problem: On a boundary $\partial\Omega$, $\partial\phi/\partial n$ is specified [see (I.4-69)]. (Solution $\phi(x, y)$ unique to within an arbitrary constant.)

Lacking real-valued characteristics, elliptic equations tend to *average* data on the boundary, in some sense, in the interior, rather than *propagate* it along characteristics as hyperbolic and parabolic equations do. In the case of Laplace's equation, the formalization of this simplistic idea is called the *mean value theorem* [ZT 76, p. 194]. When employing a finite-difference scheme to solutions of Laplace's equation ϕ in the plane, one can arithmetically average the four neighboring values in a square mesh at a position ij, i.e.,

$$\phi^{i,j} = (\phi^{i+1,j} + \phi^{i,j+1} + \phi^{i-1,j} + \phi^{i,j-1})/4. \qquad (I.7\text{-}90)$$

The general equation for isotropic hardening for mode III is the elliptic equation (I.7-77). Owing to its nonlinear, second-order character, it requires a special solution technique that will reduce it to a linear equation. The technique employed will be the Legendre transformation, which is one of the class of transformations [Zwi 89, p. 169] called *contact transformations* [Ste 89].

The Legendre transformation in the plane is as follows [Zwi 89, CH 62]:

$$\omega + \phi = x\xi + y\eta \tag{I.7-91}$$

$$\phi_{,x} = \xi, \qquad \phi_{,y} = \eta \tag{I.7-92}$$

$$\omega_{,\xi} = x, \qquad \omega_{,\eta} = y \tag{I.7-93}$$

$$\phi_{,xx} = \zeta\omega_{,\eta\eta}, \qquad \phi_{,xy} = -\zeta\omega_{,\xi\eta}, \qquad \phi_{,yy} = \zeta\omega_{,\xi\xi} \tag{I.7-94}$$

$$\zeta \equiv \phi_{,xx}\phi_{,yy} - \phi_{,xy}^2 = 1/\left(\omega_{,\xi\xi}\omega_{,\eta\eta} - \omega_{,\xi\eta}^2\right) \neq 0. \tag{I.7-95}$$

Under the Legendre transformation, (I.7-77) becomes

$$(n\eta^2 + \xi^2)\omega_{,\xi\xi} + 2(1 - n)\omega_{,\xi\eta} + (n\xi^2 + \eta^2)\omega_{,\eta\eta} = 0, \tag{I.7-96}$$

which is linear in ω. The form of (I.7-96) may be simplified further by the introduction of polar coordinates (ρ, α) in the ξ, η plane,

$$\xi = -\rho\cos\alpha = -\tau_{yz}, \qquad \eta = -\rho\sin\alpha = \tau_{xz}. \tag{I.7-97}$$

The relationships with the shear stresses in (I.7-97) follow from (I.7-92) and the definitions of the stress function for stresses in the plastic region (I.7-40) and (I.7-41). Note that ρ and α differ from their previous definitions for the perfectly plastic material; however, an analogy exists between k and ρ via α by (I.7-44) and (I.7-97). Inverting (I.7-97), we find

$$\rho = [\xi^2 + \eta^2]^{1/2} = [\tau_{xz}^2 + \tau_{yz}^2]^{1/2} = [\phi_{,x}^2 + \phi_{,y}^2]^{1/2} \tag{I.7-98}$$

$$\alpha = \tan^{-1}(\eta/\xi) = -\tan^{-1}(\tau_{xz}/\tau_{yz}) = \tan^{-1}(\phi_{,y}/\phi_{,x}). \tag{I.7-99}$$

Equation (I.7-96) becomes, in polar coordinates (I.7-97),

$$\rho^2\omega_{,\rho\rho} + n\rho\omega_{,\rho} + n\omega_{,\alpha\alpha} = 0. \tag{I.7-100}$$

Solutions to (I.7-100) (an Euler equation) will be sought in the form

$$\omega(\rho, \alpha) = \rho^m f(\alpha), \tag{I.7-101}$$

where m is a rational constant and $f(\alpha)$ is an arbitrary function.
Upon substituting (I.7-101) into (I.7-100), we obtain

$$nf''(\alpha) + m(m + n - 1)f(\alpha) = 0, \tag{I.7-102}$$

where the double prime on $f(\alpha)$ indicates the second derivative with respect to α.

Solutions to the ordinary differential equation (I.7-102) are of the form

$$f(\alpha) = c_1 \sin(c\alpha) + c_2 \cos(c\alpha), \tag{I.7-103}$$

$$c^2 \equiv m\{1 + [(m-1)/n]\}, \tag{I.7-104}$$

where c_1 and c_2 are arbitrary constants. Therefore, by (I.7-101), solutions to partial differential equation (I.7-100) are

$$\omega(\rho, \alpha) = \rho^m[c_1 \sin(c\alpha) + c_2 \cos(c\alpha)], \tag{I.7-105}$$

where the relationship between c and m, n is given by (I.7-104).

We note that (I.7-100) is an equation of the form (I.7-78), and the standard quasilinear, second-order classifications should apply. The coefficients of (I.7-100) may be interpreted in terms of those of (I.7-78) as follows:

$$a = \rho^2, \qquad b = 0, \qquad c = n, \qquad d = -n\rho\omega_{,\rho}. \tag{I.7-106}$$

Thus

$$b^2 - ac = -n\rho^2 < 0, \qquad \text{as } n \geq 1, \tag{I.7-107}$$

and the transformed equation is elliptic by (I.7-81), as was the original equation. Because it is an elliptic equation, a boundary value problem representing the elastic–plastic interface in the transformed plane (ξ, η) needs to be formulated.

The crack tip in the elastic–perfectly plastic problem shifted a distance R to the left in Fig. I.7-1 from the purely elastic solution. The location of the crack tip for the case of isotropic hardening is unknown beforehand. Let us position the origin O of a Cartesian coordinate system at the tip of the crack, as shown in Fig. I.7-5. The distance from the center of the circular elastoplastic boundary to the crack tip is thus an arbitrary distance

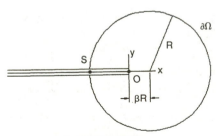

FIGURE I.7-5

Coordinates for isotropic strain hardening for the mode III problem.

βR to the left, where β is to be determined as part of the solution of the problem.

Let us now formulate the analogy of the Dirichlet problem for the transformed equation of the isotropic hardening problem. For $n = 1$, this boundary value problem reduces to the true Dirichlet problem, as the governing equation becomes Laplace's equation.

A parametrization of the circular interface, which was given previously for the perfectly plastic solution, is also applicable for isotropic hardening. One change is needed, however, as the Cartesian coordinate system for the previous problem was at the center of the circular boundary, whereas ours is now at the crack tip. Accounting for this shift in origin, which affects only $\hat{x}$, we have

$$\hat{x} = R(1 - 2t^2) + \beta R, \qquad \hat{y} = 2Rt(1 - t^2)^{1/2} \qquad (I.7\text{-}108)$$

$$\xi|_{\partial\Omega} = \hat{p} = -k(1 - t^2)^{1/2}, \qquad \eta|_{\partial\Omega} = \hat{q} = -kt \qquad (I.7\text{-}109)$$

$$\hat{\phi} = -2kR(1 - t^2)^{1/2}. \qquad (I.7\text{-}110)$$

Further, by the above, we see that

$$t = -\eta|_{\partial\Omega}/k, \qquad (1 - t^2)^{1/2} = -\xi|_{\partial\Omega}/k. \qquad (I.7\text{-}111)$$

We now infer by (I.7-91) and (I.7-108)–(I.7-111) that

$$\omega|_{\partial\Omega} + \hat{\phi} = \hat{x}\xi|_{\partial\Omega} + \hat{y}\eta|_{\partial\Omega} \qquad (I.7\text{-}112)$$

$$\omega|_{\partial\Omega} - 2kR(1 - t^2)^{1/2} = -k[\,\beta R + R(1 - 2t^2)](1 - t^2)^{1/2}$$
$$- 2kRt^2(1 - t^2)^{1/2} \qquad (I.7\text{-}113)$$

$$\omega|_{\partial\Omega} = kR(1 - \beta)(1 - t^2)^{1/2} \qquad (I.7\text{-}114)$$

$$= (\beta - 1)R\xi|_{\partial\Omega}. \qquad (I.7\text{-}115)$$

We note by (I.7-98) that

$$\rho|_{\partial\Omega} = k. \qquad (I.7\text{-}116)$$

In polar coordinates (ρ, α), (I.7-115) assumes the form

$$\omega|_{\partial\Omega} = (1 - \beta)R\rho|_{\partial\Omega}\cos\alpha \qquad (I.7\text{-}117)$$

$$= (1 - \beta)kR\cos\alpha. \qquad (I.7\text{-}118)$$

Solutions (I.7-105) of the governing partial differential equation reduce to (I.7-118), on the boundary, $\rho = k$, provided

$$c_1 = 0, \qquad c_2 = (1 - \beta)Rk^{1+n}, \qquad c = 1 \rightarrow m = -n. \quad \text{(I.7-119)}$$

So a solution to this boundary value problem is of the form

$$\omega(\rho, \alpha) = (1 - \beta)Rk^{1+n}\rho^{-n}\cos \alpha, \qquad \text{(I.7-120)}$$

where β is a constant yet to be determined. Let us now revert to the Cartesian coordinates (ξ, η) in the transformed plane, so that solution (I.7-120) becomes

$$\omega(\xi, \eta) = (\beta - 1)Rk^{1+n}(\xi^2 + \eta^2)^{-1/2(1-n)}\xi. \quad \text{(I.7-121)}$$

By (I.7-93) and (I.7-121), we obtain

$$x = \omega_{,\xi} = (\beta - 1)Rk^{1+n}(\xi^2 + \eta^2)^{-1/2(1+n)}$$

$$\times \left\{1 - \left[(1 + n)\xi^2(\xi^2 + \eta^2)^{-1}\right]\right\} \quad \text{(I.7-122)}$$

$$= (\beta - 1)Rk^{1+n}\rho^{-(1+n)}[\sin^2\alpha - n\cos^2\alpha]. \quad \text{(I.7-123)}$$

$$= (\beta - 1)Rk^{1+n}(\tau_{xz}^2 + \tau_{yz}^2)^{-(n+3)/2}[\tau_{xz}^2 - n\tau_{yz}^2]. \quad \text{(I.7-124)}$$

Similarly, we find from (I.7-121)

$$y = \omega_{,\eta} = (1 - \beta)(1 + n)Rk^{1+n}(\xi^2 + \eta^2)^{-(n+3)/2}\xi\eta \quad \text{(I.7-125)}$$

$$= (1 - \beta)(1 + n)Rk^{1+n}\rho^{-(1+n)}\cos \alpha \sin \alpha \quad \text{(I.7-126)}$$

$$= (\beta - 1)(1 + n)Rk^{1+n}(\tau_{xz}^2 + \tau_{yz}^2)^{-(n+3)/2}\tau_{xz}\tau_{yz}. \quad \text{(I.7-127)}$$

At the leading edge of the plastic zone x_P, whose position relative to the crack tip is shown in Fig. I.7-5, the stresses may be determined from the linear elastic solution as

point P: $\quad x_P = (1 + \beta)R, \qquad y_P = 0; \qquad \tau_{xz} = 0, \qquad \tau_{yz} = k. \quad \text{(I.7-128)}$

Substituting these values into (I.7-124), we may evaluate the constant β as

$$\beta = (n - 1)/(n + 1). \quad \text{(I.7-129)}$$

Expressing x_P in standard polar coordinates (I.4-29), situated at the crack tip, and using relationship (I.7-129), we find the distance r_P to the leading edge of the plastic zone as

$$r_P = 2nR/(n + 1), \qquad 1 \le n < \infty. \quad \text{(I.7-130)}$$

As $n \to \infty$, we see from (I.7-130) that $r_P \to 2R$, which is the same result obtained for the Hult and McClintock small-scale yielding solution.

Although we obtain an elastic–plastic interface, $r_P = R$, from (I.7-130) for $n = 1$, nothing mathematically distinguishes the elastic region from the plastic region for this case. This statement is consistent with the behavior shown in Fig. I.7-4, which shows that the elastic stress–strain line continues into the plastic region.

The relationship between r and the stresses are, in general, obtained from (I.7-124), (I.7-127), and (I.7-130):

$$(r/r_P)^2 = n^{-2}k^{2(n+1)}\left(\tau_{xz}^2 + \tau_{yz}^2\right)^{-(n+2)}\left(\tau_{xz}^2 + n^2\tau_{yz}^2\right). \quad \text{(I.7-131)}$$

By substituting (I.7-97) into (I.7-131) and solving for ρ, we obtain

$$\rho = k(r_P/r)^{1/(1+n)}\left[(1/n)(\sin^2\alpha + n^2\cos^2\alpha)^{1/2}\right]^{1/(1+n)}. \quad \text{(I.7-132)}$$

Substituting ρ from (I.7-132) into (I.7-97), we find that the stresses are

$$\tau_{xz} = -k(r_P/r)^{1/(1+n)}\left[(1/n)(\sin^2\alpha + n^2\cos^2\alpha)^{1/2}\right]^{1/(1+n)}\sin\alpha \quad \text{(I.7-133)}$$

$$\tau_{yz} = k(r_P/r)^{1/(1+n)}\left[(1/n)(\sin^2\alpha + n^2\cos^2\alpha)^{1/2}\right]^{1/(1+n)}\cos\alpha. \quad \text{(I.7-134)}$$

Notice that the singularity in stress varies with the strain hardening exponent n. For $n = 1$, we obtain the elastic $r^{-1/2}$ behavior of linear elastic fracture mechanics.

A relationship between α and θ may obtained by dividing (I.7-126) by (I.7-123) to obtain

$$\sin\theta/\cos\theta = (1 + n)\sin\alpha\cos\alpha/[n\cos^2\alpha - \sin^2\alpha] \quad \text{(I.7-135)}$$

$$= \sin 2\alpha/[\cos 2\alpha + \beta]. \quad \text{(I.7-136)}$$

Thus,

$$\sin\theta(\beta + \cos 2\alpha) = \cos\theta\sin 2\alpha, \quad \text{(I.7-137)}$$

$$\to \beta\sin\theta = \sin 2\alpha\cos\theta - \cos 2\alpha\sin\theta \quad \text{(I.7-138)}$$

$$= \sin(2\alpha - \theta). \quad \text{(I.7-139)}$$

Therefore,

$$2\alpha = \theta + \sin^{-1}(\beta\sin\theta), \quad \text{(I.7-140)}$$

where β is given in terms of n by (I.7-129). Upon substituting α from (I.7-140) into (I.7-133) and (I.7-134), we obtain an explicit solution for the stresses in polar coordinates for the isotropic hardening mode III problem.

We can now see explicitly that the traction-free boundary condition along the crack surfaces in the plastic zone (OS in Fig. I.7-5) is satisfied by substituting $\theta = \pm \pi$ into (I.7-140), followed by substituting the resulting $\alpha = \pm \pi/2$ into (I.7-134), which gives $\tau_{yz} = 0$.

The strains follow by substituting the stresses into (I.7-74) and (I.7-75) to obtain

$$\gamma_{xz}/\gamma_0 = -(r_P/r)^{n/(1+n)}[(1 + n)\sin(2\alpha)/(2n \sin \theta)]^{n/(1+n)}\sin \alpha$$

$$\text{(I.7-141)}$$

$$\gamma_{yz}/\gamma_0 = (r_P/r)^{n/(1+n)}[(1 + n)\sin(2\alpha)/(2n \sin \theta)]^{n/(1+n)}\cos \alpha,$$

$$\text{(I.7-142)}$$

where α is given in terms of θ by (I.7-140). Solutions (I.7-133)–(I.7-134) and (I.7-141)–(I.7-142) for stress and strain agree with those presented in [Hut 79].

A generalization of the Dirichlet problem was formulated and solved for the isotropic hardening mode III elastoplastic problem. Alternatively, a generalized Neumann problem could have been proposed and solved in its place. Let us briefly examine this problem.

For the Neumann problem, we specify $\partial\omega/\partial n$ on the boundary $\partial\Omega$. Since the boundary $\partial\Omega$ is circular in the transformed space (ρ, α), we have:

Neumann problem: $\partial\Omega$ (transformed): $\rho|_{\partial\Omega} = k$. Given $\omega_{,\rho}|_{\partial\Omega}$, find $\omega(\rho, \alpha)$ that satisfies (I.7-96).

Now by the chain rule

$$\omega_{,\rho} = \omega_{,\xi}\xi_{,\rho} + \omega_{,\eta}\eta_{,\rho} = -\omega_{,\xi}\cos \alpha - \omega_{,\eta}\sin \alpha. \quad \text{(I.7-143)}$$

Therefore,

$$\omega_{,\rho}|_{\partial\Omega} = -\omega_{,\xi}|_{\partial\Omega}\cos \alpha - \omega_{,\eta}|_{\partial\Omega}\sin \alpha = -\hat{x} \cos \alpha - \hat{y} \sin \alpha \quad \text{(I.7-144)}$$

$$= -[R(1 - 2t^2) + \beta R]\cos \alpha - 2Rt(1 - t^2)^{1/2}\sin \alpha \quad \text{(I.7-145)}$$

$$= -\left[R\{1 - 2(\eta/k)^2|_{\partial\Omega}\} + \beta R\right]\cos \alpha - 2R(\xi\eta/k^2)|_{\partial\Omega}\sin \alpha$$

$$\text{(I.7-146)}$$

$$= -[R - (2R/k^2)\rho^2|_{\partial\Omega}\sin^2\alpha + \beta R]\cos \alpha$$

$$\quad - (2R/k^2)\rho^2|_{\partial\Omega}\cos \alpha \sin^2\alpha \quad \text{(I.7-147)}$$

$$= -(1 + \beta)R \cos \alpha. \quad \text{(I.7-148)}$$

Using (I.7-105), we calculate

$$\omega_{,\rho} = m\rho^{m-1}[c_1\sin(c\alpha) + c_2\cos(c\alpha)]. \tag{I.7-149}$$

Thus by (I.7-116), (I.7-149) evaluated on the boundary becomes

$$\omega_{,\rho}|_{\partial\Omega} = mk^{m-1}[c_1\sin(c\alpha) + c_2\cos(c\alpha)]. \tag{I.7-150}$$

Setting $c_1 = 0$, $m = -n$ ($c = 1$), we determine from (I.7-148) and (I.7-150) that

$$mk^{m-1}c_2 = -(1 + \beta R) \rightarrow c_2 = (1 + \beta)(R/n)k^{1+n}, \tag{I.7-151}$$

which differs in form from c_2 determined earlier for the generalized Dirichlet problem (I.7-119). However, once we set β equal to its relationship with n (I.7-129) in both expressions for c_2, we get identical results:

$$c_2 = 2Rk^{1+n}/(n + 1). \tag{I.7-152}$$

I.8 PLANE STRAIN PROBLEMS INVOLVING PLASTIC THEORY

As we mentioned in Section I.4, there are two principal types of plane problems of elasticity theory—plane strain and plane stress problems. In addition to these two classifications in plasticity theory, we also consider individually the two most commonly used yield criteria—the Mises and the Tresca yield conditions. As plane strain is the simpler of the two plane problems to describe (because the governing equations for the Mises and Tresca yield conditions are similar and do not vary from one part of the yield surface to another as in plane stress), we begin our discussion there.

Plane Strain

In plane strain, we make the assumption that the displacements $u_x(x, y)$, $u_y(x, y)$, and $u_z(x, y)$ are functions only of the plane of symmetry's Cartesian coordinates x, y [Kac 74]. It follows from the third equation of (I.1-8) that

$$\epsilon_z = 0, \tag{I.8-1}$$

which is, of course, the earmark plane strain condition. We now make the assumption that all elastic strains are negligible. Therefore, (I.8-1) represents not only the plastic strain, but the total strain. From Hencky deformation theory (I.3-36), equation (I.8-1) implies

$$\sigma_z = \tfrac{1}{2}(\sigma_x + \sigma_y). \tag{I.8-2}$$

Furthermore, the stresses τ_{xz} and τ_{yz} are zero from Hencky theory, because no corresponding shear strains exist by (I.3-38)–(I.3-39), due to equations (I.8-1) and (I.1-18)–(I.1-19), with the added assumption that the displacements are functions only of x and y. Thus the stress tensor reduces to the form

$$\begin{bmatrix} \sigma_x & \tau_{xy} & 0 \\ \tau_{xy} & \sigma_y & 0 \\ 0 & 0 & \sigma_z \end{bmatrix}. \tag{I.8-3}$$

If we set τ_{xz} and τ_{yz} equal to zero in the Mises yield condition (I.3-1) and then substitute (I.8-2) for σ_z and (I.-13) for σ_0, we find the plane strain yield criterion as

$$(\sigma_x - \sigma_y)^2 + 4\tau_{xy}^2 = 4k^2. \tag{I.8-4}$$

The Cayley–Hamilton theory [SC 92] allows the determination of the principal stresses σ_i of the general stress tensor by evaluating the following determinant and setting the result equal to zero:

$$\begin{vmatrix} \sigma_x - \sigma_i & \tau_{xy} & \tau_{xz} \\ \tau_{xy} & \sigma_y - \sigma_i & \tau_{yz} \\ \tau_{xz} & \tau_{yz} & \sigma_z - \sigma_i \end{vmatrix} = 0. \tag{I.8-5}$$

In our particular case (I.8-3), we have

$$\begin{vmatrix} \sigma_x - \sigma_i & \tau_{xy} & 0 \\ \tau_{xy} & \sigma_y - \sigma_i & 0 \\ 0 & 0 & \sigma_z - \sigma_i \end{vmatrix} = 0 \tag{I.8-6}$$

$$\rightarrow (\sigma_x - \sigma_i)(\sigma_y - \sigma_i)(\sigma_z - \sigma_i) - \tau_{xy}^2(\sigma_z - \sigma_i) = 0 \tag{I.8-7}$$

$$\rightarrow (\sigma_i - \sigma_z)\left[\sigma_i^2 - (\sigma_x + \sigma_y)\sigma_i + \sigma_x\sigma_y - \tau_{xy}^2\right] = 0. \tag{I.8-8}$$

The three roots σ_i $(i = 1, 2, 3)$ of the cubic equation (I.8-8) follow as

$$\sigma_i = \begin{cases} \sigma_z = \tfrac{1}{2}(\sigma_x + \sigma_y) \quad \text{via (I.8-2)}, & \text{(I.8-9)} \\ \tfrac{1}{2}(\sigma_x + \sigma_y) \pm \tfrac{1}{2}\left[(\sigma_x - \sigma_y)^2 + 4\tau_{xy}^2\right]^{1/2}. & \text{(I.8-10)} \end{cases}$$

Thus σ_z is a principal stress by (I.8-9). By further substituting (I.8-9) into (I.8-10), we show it to be the intermediate principal stress.

Since the maximum shear stress is always one-half of the greatest difference in principal stresses, it follows from (I.8-9)–(I.8-10) that

$$\tau_{max} = \tfrac{1}{2}\left[(\sigma_x - \sigma_y)^2 + 4\tau_{xy}^2\right]^{1/2}. \qquad \text{(I.8-11)}$$

Setting $\tau_{max} = k$ in (I.8-11) and squaring the result, we find the same form for the Tresca yield condition in plane strain as in the Mises condition (I.8-4). Do note, however, that they will not assume identical forms if σ_0 is used rather than k in expressing the plane strain yield criteria, as the relationships between k and σ_0 differ, i.e., (I.3-2) versus (I.3-4).

Note further that Hencky deformation relationships were used in deriving (I.8-4), and therefore the result should hold true only for the Mises yield condition. Nevertheless, if we start with (I.8-4) and derive the plane strain flow rule for the Tresca yield condition, we obtain similar plane strain flow equations, and subsequently a deformation theory similar to that of the plane strain Mises yield condition.

For example, from (I.8-10) we deduce that

$$h(\sigma_i) = \tfrac{1}{2}(\sigma_2 - \sigma_3). \qquad \text{(I.8-12)}$$

Now in general

$$\begin{aligned}
d\epsilon_x = d\Lambda\{ &[\partial h(\sigma_i)/\partial\sigma_1][\partial\sigma_1/\partial\sigma_x] \\
&+ [\partial h(\sigma_i)/\partial\sigma_2][\partial\sigma_2/\partial\sigma_x] \\
&+ [\partial h(\sigma_i)/\partial\sigma_3][\partial\sigma_3/\partial\sigma_x]\},
\end{aligned} \qquad \text{(I.8-13)}$$

and by (I.8-12) for the Tresca yield condition we have

$$\partial h(\sigma_i)/\partial\sigma_1 = 0, \qquad \partial h(\sigma_i)/\partial\sigma_2 = \tfrac{1}{2}, \qquad \partial h(\sigma_i)/\partial\sigma_3 = -\tfrac{1}{2}. \qquad \text{(I.8-14)}$$

From (I.8-10), we determine for plane strain that

$$\partial\sigma_2/\partial\sigma_x = \tfrac{1}{2} + \tfrac{1}{2}(\sigma_x - \sigma_y)/\left[(\sigma_x - \sigma_y)^2 + 4\tau_{xy}^2\right]^{1/2} \qquad \text{(I.8-15)}$$

$$\partial\sigma_3/\partial\sigma_x = \tfrac{1}{2} - \tfrac{1}{2}(\sigma_x - \sigma_y)/\left[(\sigma_x - \sigma_y)^2 + 4\tau_{xy}^2\right]^{1/2}. \qquad \text{(I.8-16)}$$

By further substituting (I.8-11) and (I.8-14)–(I.8-16) into (I.8-13), we obtain the plane strain Tresca flow rule in the x direction as

$$d\epsilon_x = d\Lambda \tfrac{1}{2}(\sigma_x - \sigma_y)/\left[(\sigma_x - \sigma_y)^2 + 4\tau_{xy}^2\right]^{1/2} \qquad \text{(I.817)}$$

$$= d\Lambda(\sigma_x - \sigma_y)/4k. \qquad \text{(I.8-18)}$$

This has the same form as the Prandtl–Reuss (Mises) flow rule (I.3-28), once (I.8-2) is substituted for σ_z. One can show that $d\epsilon_y$ and $d\gamma_{xy}$ have similar relationships with stress for the two different yield criteria (Mises, Tresca) under plane strain loading conditions.

From (I.8-9)–(I.8-10), we found one principal direction, which was in the z direction. Let us now find the other two principal directions that correspond to the principal stresses (I.8-10). These directions will be in the x, y plane, as principal directions are mutually orthogonal.

In general, the principal directions **n** of a stress tensor can be found through the matrix equation

$$
\begin{bmatrix}
\sigma_x - \sigma_i & \tau_{xy} & \tau_{xz} \\
\tau_{xy} & \sigma_y - \sigma_i & \tau_{yz} \\
\tau_{xz} & \tau_{yz} & \sigma_z - \sigma_i
\end{bmatrix}
\begin{Bmatrix}
n_x \\
n_y \\
n_z
\end{Bmatrix}
=
\begin{Bmatrix}
0 \\
0 \\
0
\end{Bmatrix},
\qquad (\text{I.8-19})
$$

where the components (n_x, etc.) of the principal directions (direction cosines) fulfill the condition of a unit vector:

$$
n_x^2 + n_y^2 + n_z^2 = 1. \qquad (\text{I.8-20})
$$

By setting

$$
n_x = \cos \omega, \qquad n_y = \sin \omega, \qquad n_z = 0 \qquad (\text{I.8-21})
$$

in (I.8-19), we fulfill the unit vector condition (I.8-20) for an in-plane principal stress direction in terms of a local cylindrical coordinate ω. Equation (I.8-19) reduces to the following when (I.8-21) and $\tau_{xz} = \tau_{yz} = 0$ are substituted into it:

$$
\sigma_i \cos \omega = \sigma_x \cos \omega + \tau_{xy} \sin \omega \qquad (\text{I.8-22})
$$

$$
\sigma_i \sin \omega = \tau_{xy} \cos \omega + \sigma_y \sin \omega. \qquad (\text{I.8-23})
$$

Eliminating σ_i between equation (I.8-22) and (I.8-23), we find through the use of elementary trigonometric relationships that

$$
\tan 2\omega = 2\tau_{xy}/(\sigma_x - \sigma_y) \qquad (\text{I.8-24})
$$

where ω represents two different angles that correspond to the in-plane principal stresses (I.8-10) measured counterclockwise from the positive x-axis. These principal directions lie 90° apart in the xy plane.

Let us now seek stresses of the form

$$\sigma_x = \sigma - k \sin 2\chi \qquad\qquad (I.8\text{-}25)$$

$$\sigma_y = \sigma + k \sin 2\chi \qquad\qquad (I.8\text{-}26)$$

$$\tau_{xy} = k \cos 2\chi, \qquad\qquad (I.8\text{-}27)$$

so that the yield condition (I.8-4) is automatically satisfied.

The function of σ of (I.8-25)–(I.8-26) is shown to be the hydrostatic stress. The hydrostatic stress is in general one-third of the trace tr( ) of the stress tensor, σ_{ij}, i.e.,

$$\text{hydrostatic stress} \equiv (1/3)\text{tr}\,\sigma_{ij} = (\sigma_x + \sigma_y + \sigma_z)/3. \quad (I.8\text{-}28)$$

In our case, we may further substitute (I.8-1) for σ_z and (I.8-25)–(I.8-26) for σ_x, σ_y to obtain

$$(1/3)\text{tr}\,\sigma_{ij} = \left[\sigma_x + \sigma_y + (\sigma_x + \sigma_y)/2\right]/3 = (\sigma_x + \sigma_y)/2 = \sigma. \quad (I.8\text{-}29)$$

Thus σ in (I.8-25)–(I.8-26) may be interpreted as the hydrostatic stress.

The planes of maximum shear stress k always bisect the orthogonal planes of principal stresses (normal stresses) [SC 92]. We will now show that χ in (I.8-25)–(I.8-27) is related to these shear planes.

By substituting (I.8-25)–(I.8-27) into (I.18-24), we find

$$\tan 2\omega = -\cot 2\chi \qquad\qquad (I.8\text{-}30)$$

$$\rightarrow \cos 2\omega \cos 2\chi + \sin 2\chi \sin 2\omega = 0 \qquad\qquad (I.8\text{-}31)$$

$$\rightarrow \cos 2(\omega - \chi) = 0 \rightarrow 2(\omega - \chi) = \pm\pi/2 \rightarrow \chi = \omega \mp \pi/4. \qquad (I.8\text{-}32)$$

We now arbitrarily assign ω to correspond to the largest principal stress direction and χ to the upper sign of (I.8-32), i.e.,

$$\chi = \omega - \pi/4. \qquad\qquad (I.8\text{-}33)$$

The other maximum shear plane (it is also perpendicular to the xy plane) will be 90° counterclockwise to the χ plane. These planes are shown edge-on in Fig. I.8-1 in connection with the maximum shear stresses k.

The equilibrium equations of plane strain plasticity, in terms of stress, are identical to those for plane strain elasticity (I.4-5) because the corresponding stresses vanish.

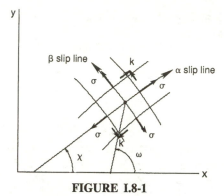

FIGURE I.8-1

Plane strain slip lines, stresses, and associated angles.

Thus, by substituting (I.8-25)–(I.8-27) into the equilibrium equations (I.4-5), we find the simultaneous partial differential equations for σ and χ of a stress field that will satisfy both equilibrium and the yield condition (I.8-4), i.e.,

$$\sigma_{,x} - 2k(\chi_{,x}\cos 2\chi + \chi_{,y}\sin 2\chi) = 0 \qquad (I.8\text{-}34)$$

$$\sigma_{,y} - 2k(\chi_{,x}\sin 2\chi - \chi_{,y}\cos 2\chi) = 0. \qquad (I.8\text{-}35)$$

A natural orthogonal coordinate system exists for (I.8-34) and (I.8-35), which is based on its two families of orthogonal characteristics. (This system of equations can be shown to be hyperbolic.) One of these coordinates is tangent to χ, and the other is 90° counterclockwise. We will designate these plane coordinates as (α, β). Since α and β align themselves with planes of shear stress k, they may also be interpreted physically as slip lines (Fig. I.8-1).

Let us first define the symbol S for simplicity in notation of what is to follow:

$$S \equiv \sigma/(2k). \qquad (I.8\text{-}36)$$

With this definition, the system of partial differential equations (I.8-34)–(I.8-35) can be rewritten as

$$\begin{bmatrix} \chi_{,x} & \chi_{,y} \\ -\chi_{,y} & \chi_{,x} \end{bmatrix} \begin{Bmatrix} \cos 2\chi \\ \sin 2\chi \end{Bmatrix} = \begin{Bmatrix} S_{,x} \\ S_{,y} \end{Bmatrix}. \qquad (I.8\text{-}37)$$

Solving for $\cos 2\chi$ and $\sin 2\chi$, we find

$$\cos 2\chi = (S_{,x}\chi_{,x} - S_{,y}\chi_{,y})/(\chi_{,x}^2 + \chi_{,y}^2) \qquad \text{(I.8-38)}$$

$$\sin 2\chi = (S_{,y}\chi_{,x} - S_{,x}\chi_{,y})/(\chi_{,x}^2 + \chi_{,y}^2). \qquad \text{(I.8-39)}$$

Now using the trigonometric identity

$$\cos^2 2\chi + \sin^2 2\chi = 1 \qquad \text{(I.8-40)}$$

and (I.8-38)–(I.8-39), we obtain

$$S_{,x}^2 + S_{,y}^2 = \chi_{,x}^2 + \chi_{,y}^2. \qquad \text{(I.8-41)}$$

This can also be expressed as

$$\nabla S \cdot \nabla S = \nabla\chi \cdot \nabla\chi. \qquad \text{(I.8-42)}$$

Let us now assume that

$$S = S(\alpha, \beta), \qquad \chi = \chi(\alpha, \beta) \qquad \text{(I.8-43)}$$

with

$$\alpha + i\beta = F(x + iy), \qquad \text{(I.8-44)}$$

where $F(\ )$ is a function amenable to a particular initial value problem. Equation (I.8-44) is similar in form to the conformal mapping transformation (I.5-50). Because α and β are the real and imaginary parts of a complex function of z, i.e., $F(z)$, they form an orthogonal coordinate system and hence a slip line network (α, β).

The Cauchy–Riemann equations associated with (I.8-44) follow as

$$\alpha_{,x} = \beta_{,y} \qquad \alpha_{,y} = -\beta_{,x}. \qquad \text{(I.8-45)}$$

Thus by (I.8-45) α and β are solutions of Laplace's equation

$$\alpha_{,xx} + \alpha_{,yy} = 0, \qquad \beta_{,xx} + \beta_{,yy} = 0 \qquad \text{or} \qquad \nabla^2\alpha = 0, \qquad \nabla^2\beta = 0. \qquad \text{(I.8-46)}$$

We can also establish the following relationships from analytic function theory:

$$\nabla\alpha \cdot \nabla\alpha = \nabla\beta \cdot \nabla\beta \qquad \text{(I.8-47)}$$

$$\nabla\alpha \cdot \nabla\beta = 0 \quad \text{(orthogonality)}. \qquad \text{(I.8-48)}$$

Using the chain rule, we can further prove that

$$\nabla S(\alpha, \beta) = S_{,\alpha}\nabla\alpha + S_{,\beta}\nabla\beta \qquad \text{(I.8-49)}$$

$$\nabla\chi(\alpha, \beta) = \chi_{,\alpha}\nabla\alpha + \chi_{,\beta}\nabla\beta. \qquad \text{(I.8-50)}$$

With the help of (I.8-49) and (I.8-50), we can now express (I.8-42) as

$$\nabla\alpha\cdot\nabla\alpha\left[S_{,\alpha}^2 + S_{,\beta}^2\right] = \nabla\beta\cdot\nabla\beta\left[\chi_{,\alpha}^2 + \chi_{,\beta}^2\right]. \qquad (I.8\text{-}51)$$

Because of (I.8-47), this equation is equivalent to

$$\nabla\alpha\cdot\nabla\alpha\left[S_{,\alpha}^2 + S_{,\beta}^2 - \chi_{,\alpha}^2 - \chi_{,\beta}^2\right] = 0, \qquad (I.8\text{-}52)$$

or provided $\nabla\alpha\cdot\nabla\alpha \neq 0$, then

$$S_{,\alpha}^2 + S_{,\beta}^2 - \chi_{,\alpha}^2 - \chi_{,\beta}^2 = 0. \qquad (I.8\text{-}53)$$

Partial differential equation (I.8-53) can also be put in an alternative form by factoring it, as follows:

$$(S + \chi)_{,\beta}(S - \chi)_{,\beta} + (S - \chi)_{,\alpha}(S + \chi)_{,\alpha} = 0. \qquad (I.8\text{-}54)$$

We see that (I.8-54) will be satisfied if

$$S + \chi = f(\alpha), \qquad S - \chi = g(\beta), \qquad (I.8\text{-}55)$$

where $f(\ )$ and $g(\ )$ are functions that are determined for a given boundary and initial conditions.

Therefore, by (I.8-55) and simple algebra, we obtain a class of solutions (I.8-41) as

$$S = \tfrac{1}{2}[f(\alpha) + g(\beta)], \qquad \chi = \tfrac{1}{2}[f(\alpha) - g(\beta)]. \qquad (I.8\text{-}56)$$

As (I.8-56) stands, we know that it solves (I.8-42) and that it is a necessary condition that it solves the original system of equations (I.8-34)–(I.8-35). We will now check that (I.8-56) is also sufficient to solve the original system of equations. (We may have introduced extraneous solutions by using the trigonometric identity (I.8-40) alone, which employs the squares of the functions $\cos 2\chi$ and $\sin 2\chi$.)

We first express the $\cos 2\chi$ in terms of the functions $f(\alpha)$ and $g(\beta)$. The numerator of (I.8-38) is

$$S_{,x}\chi_{,x} - S_{,y}\chi_{,y}$$

$$= (1/4)\left[f'(\alpha)^2\left(\alpha_{,x}^2 - \alpha_{,y}^2\right) + g'(\beta)^2\left(\beta_{,y}^2 - \beta_{,x}^2\right)\right] \qquad (I.8\text{-}57)$$

$$= (1/4)\left[f'(\alpha)^2 + g'(\beta)^2\right]\left(\alpha_{,x}^2 - \alpha_{,y}^2\right), \qquad (I.8\text{-}58)$$

whereas the denominator of (I.8-38) is

$$\chi_{,x}^2 + \chi_{,y}^2 = (1/4)\Big[f'(\alpha)^2 \big(\alpha_{,x}^2 + \alpha_{,y}^2 \big)$$

$$-2f'(\alpha)g'(\beta)(\alpha_{,x}\beta_{,x} + \alpha_{,y}\beta_{,y})$$

$$+g'(\beta)^2 \big(\beta_{,x}^2 + \beta_{,y}^2 \big) \Big] \tag{I.8-59}$$

$$= (1/4)\Big[f'(\alpha)^2 + g'(\beta)^2 \Big]\big(\alpha_{,x}^2 + \alpha_{,y}^2 \big), \tag{I.8-60}$$

using the Cauchy–Riemann equations. Thus, the primed quantities (derivatives of f and g) cancel when the ratio of (I.8-58) to (I.8-59) is taken to calculate the $\cos 2\chi$ as

$$\cos 2\chi = \big(\alpha_{,x}^2 - \alpha_{,y}^2 \big) / \big(\alpha_{,x}^2 + \alpha_{,y}^2 \big). \tag{I.8-61}$$

Similarly,

$$\sin 2\chi = 2\alpha_{,x}\alpha_{,y} / \big(\alpha_{,x}^2 + \alpha_{,y}^2 \big). \tag{I.8-62}$$

Using the half-angle formulas from trigonometry, we also find that

$$\cos \chi = \alpha_{,x} / \big(\alpha_{,x}^2 + \alpha_{,y}^2 \big)^{1/2} \tag{I.8-63}$$

$$\sin \chi = \alpha_{,y} / \big(\alpha_{,x}^2 + \alpha_{,y}^2 \big)^{1/2}, \tag{I.8-64}$$

which will be used later.

Now by substituting (I.8-56) and (I.8-61)–(I.8-62) into (I.8-34) we derive that

$$f'(\alpha)[0] + 2g'(\beta)\alpha_{,x}[\alpha_{,x}\beta_{,x} + \alpha_{,y}\beta_{,y}] = 0. \tag{I.8-65}$$

By substituting (I.8-45) into (I.8-65), the second bracketed term also becomes zero, and hence (I.8-34) is satisfied. Similarly, (I.8-35) can also be shown to be satisfied.

Having shown that (I.8-56) is sufficient to solve both equilibrium and the yield condition, we come to the conclusion from (I.8-55) that

$$\sigma - 2k\chi = \text{constant}_1 \text{ along an } \alpha \text{ line } (\beta \text{ const}) \tag{I.8-66}$$

$$\sigma + 2k\chi = \text{constant}_2 \text{ along a } \beta \text{ line } (\alpha \text{ const}). \tag{I.8-67}$$

These relationships were obtained independently by H. Hencky [Hen 23] and more general relationships for soils were obtained by F. Kötter [Köt 03].

There are three fundamental statically determinate initial value problems for plane strain (see [Kac 74]):

(1) specifying σ and χ on a noncharacteristic curve,
(2) specifying σ and χ on two intersecting slip lines (characteristics) α and β,
(3) specifying σ and χ on a slip line and the angle χ on a noncharacteristic curve.

Returning to the strain field, we have from the Prandtl–Reuss equations and the plane strain relationship (I.8-2)

$$d\epsilon_x = 2\,d\lambda\big[2\sigma_x - (\sigma_y + \sigma_z)\big] = 3\,d\lambda(\sigma_x - \sigma_y) \qquad \text{(I.8-68)}$$

$$d\epsilon_y = 2\,d\lambda\big[2\sigma_y - (\sigma_x + \sigma_z)\big] = 3\,d\lambda(\sigma_y - \sigma_x) \qquad \text{(I.8-69)}$$

$$d\gamma_{xy} = 12\,d\lambda\,\tau_{xy}. \qquad \text{(I.8-70)}$$

Subtracting (I.8-69) from (I.8-68) and then dividing by (I.8-70), we find

$$(d\epsilon_x - d\epsilon_y)/d\gamma_{xy} = (\sigma_x - \sigma_y)/(2\tau_{xy}). \qquad \text{(I.8-71)}$$

Equation (I.8-71) and the incompressibility equation of plastic strain increments ($d\epsilon_z = 0$),

$$d\epsilon_x + d\epsilon_y = 0, \qquad \text{(I.8-72)}$$

comprise the governing equations of incremental strain for perfectly plastic slip line theory.

We may also divide through by a differential element of time dt to obtain

$$\big(\dot{\epsilon}_x - \dot{\epsilon}_y\big)/\dot{\gamma}_{xy} = (\sigma_x - \sigma_y)/(2\tau_{xy}) \qquad \text{(I.8-73)}$$

$$\dot{\epsilon}_x + \dot{\epsilon}_y = 0, \qquad \text{(I.8-74)}$$

where

$$\dot{\epsilon}_x \equiv d\epsilon_x/dt, \quad \text{etc.} \qquad \text{(I.8-75)}$$

For small deformation theory, these equations may be expressed in terms of velocities v_x, v_y in the x and y directions, respectively, as

$$(v_{x,x} - v_{y,y})/(v_{x,y} + v_{y,x}) = (\sigma_x - \sigma_y)/(2\tau_{xy}) \qquad \text{(I.8-76)}$$

$$v_{x,x} + v_{y,y} = 0, \qquad \text{(I.8-77)}$$

where

$$v_x = du_x/dt, \quad \text{etc.} \tag{I.8-78}$$

There are now five unknowns $(\sigma_x, \sigma_y, \tau_{xy}, v_x, v_y)$ and five equations to solve: (I.8-4), (I.8-34), (I.8-35), (I.8-76), and (I.8-77). The first three together with initial conditions on stress comprise what is called the statically determinate problem. Having solved these, we can then proceed to find a kinematically admissible velocity field for the remaining two equations, together with their initial conditions on velocity.

It is interesting to note that, when problems are solved in this order, the remaining two equations for velocity are linear partial differential equations. However, depending on the initial conditions, it is not always possible to uncouple the five equations.

We can rewrite equation (I.8-76) in the following fashion by substituting the stresses (I.8-25)–(I.8-27) into it:

$$(v_{y,y} - v_{x,x})/(v_{x,y} + v_{y,x}) = \tan 2\chi. \tag{I.8-79}$$

Using the chain rule for partial derivatives and the Cauchy–Riemann equations, we can establish that

$$v_{x,x} = v_{x,\alpha}\alpha_{,x} + v_{x,\beta}\beta_{,x} = v_{x,\alpha}\alpha_{,x} - v_{x,\beta}\alpha_{,y} \tag{I.8-80}$$

$$v_{x,y} = v_{x,\alpha}\alpha_{,y} + v_{x,\beta}\beta_{,y} = v_{x,\alpha}\alpha_{,y} + v_{x,\beta}\alpha_{,x} \tag{I.8-81}$$

$$v_{y,x} = v_{y,\alpha}\alpha_{,x} + v_{y,\beta}\beta_{,x} = v_{y,\alpha}\alpha_{,x} - v_{y,\beta}\alpha_{,y} \tag{I.8-82}$$

$$v_{y,y} = v_{y,\alpha}\alpha_{,y} + v_{y,\beta}\beta_{,y} = v_{y,\alpha}\alpha_{,y} + v_{y,\beta}\alpha_{,x}. \tag{I.8-83}$$

Also, because of (I.8-61) and (I.8-62),

$$\tan 2\chi = 2\alpha_{,x}\alpha_{,y}/\left(\alpha_{,x}^2 - \alpha_{,y}^2\right) \tag{I.8-84}$$

Therefore, by (I.8-80)–(I.8-84), (I.8-79) can be expressed as

$$\left[(v_{x,\alpha} - v_{y,\beta})\alpha_{,x} - (v_{x,\beta} + v_{y,\alpha})\alpha_{,y}\right]\left(\alpha_{,y}^2 - \alpha_{,x}^2\right)$$
$$= 2\alpha_{,x}\alpha_{,y}\left[(v_{x,\beta} + v_{y,\alpha})\alpha_{,x} + (v_{x,\alpha} - v_{y,\beta})\alpha_{,y}\right]. \tag{I.8-85}$$

Several terms in (I.8-85) cancel, leaving

$$v_{x,\alpha}\alpha_x + v_{x,\beta}\alpha_{,y} + v_{y,\alpha}\alpha_{,y} - v_{y,\beta}\alpha_{,x} = 0. \tag{I.8-86}$$

The incompressibility equation (I.8-77) can likewise be expressed with the aid of (I.8-80) and (I.8-83) as

$$v_{x,\alpha}\alpha_{,x} - v_{x,\beta}\alpha_{,y} + v_{y,\alpha}\alpha_{,y} + v_{y,\beta}\alpha_{,x} = 0. \tag{I.8-87}$$

The system of equations (I.8-86) and (I.8-87) can now be added and subtracted to give the algebraically simpler system

$$v_{x,\alpha}\alpha_{,x} + v_{y,\alpha}\alpha_{,y} = 0 \tag{I.8-88}$$

$$v_{x,\beta}\alpha_{,y} - v_{y,\beta}\alpha_{,x} = 0. \tag{I.8-89}$$

Let us now define two velocity components in the slip line mesh.

One, v_α, points in the α direction while the other, v_β, points in the β direction, as shown in Fig. I.8-2. Resolving an arbitrary velocity vector $\mathbf{v}$ into components, we find the following relationships between Cartesian and characteristic coordinates:

$$v_x = v_\alpha \cos \chi - v_\beta \sin \chi \tag{I.8-90}$$

$$v_y = v_\alpha \sin \chi + v_\beta \cos \chi. \tag{I.8-91}$$

Substituting (I.8-90), (I.8-91) into (I.8-88), (I.8-89) and differentiating, we have, respectively,

$$\left[(v_{\alpha,\alpha} - v_\beta \chi_{,\alpha})\cos \chi - (v_{\beta,\alpha} + v_\alpha \chi_{,\alpha})\sin \chi\right]\alpha_{,x}$$
$$+ \left[(v_{\alpha,\alpha} - v_\beta \chi_{,\alpha})\sin \chi + (v_{\beta,\alpha} + v_\alpha \chi_{,\alpha})\cos \chi\right]\alpha_{,y} = 0 \tag{I.8-92}$$

$$\left[(v_{\alpha,\beta} - v_\beta \chi_{,\beta})\cos \chi - (v_{\beta,\beta} + v_\alpha \chi_{,\beta})\sin \chi\right]\alpha_{,y}$$
$$- \left[(v_{\beta,\beta} - v_\alpha \chi_{,\beta})\cos \chi + (v_{\alpha,\beta} - v_\beta \chi_{,\beta})\sin \chi\right]\alpha_{,x} = 0. \tag{I.8-93}$$

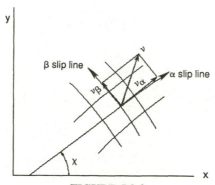

FIGURE I.8-2

Plane strain velocity components along slip lines.

By further expressing cos χ and sin χ into terms of the partial derivatives of α with respect to the Cartesian coordinates (I.8-63) and (I.8-64), we determine

$$v_{\alpha, \alpha} - v_\beta \, \chi_{, \alpha} = 0 \qquad (I.8\text{-}94)$$

$$v_{\beta, \beta} + v_\alpha \, \chi_{, \beta} = 0. \qquad (I.8\text{-}95)$$

We conclude from (I.8-94) and (I.8-95), respectively, that

$$dv_\alpha/d\chi - v_\beta = 0 \quad \text{along an } \alpha \text{ slip line } (\beta \text{ const}) \qquad (I.8\text{-}96)$$

$$dv_\beta/d\chi + v_\alpha = 0 \quad \text{along a } \beta \text{ slip line } (\alpha \text{ const}). \qquad (I.8\text{-}97)$$

These equations are known as Geiringer's equations after [Gei 53].

Prandtl–Hill Solution

L. Prandtl [Pra 21] derived a plane strain slip line network for a lubricated punch pressing against a semi-infinite plate with an otherwise traction-free boundary for an elastic, rigid–perfectly plastic material. A similar slip line net may also be applied to a mode I crack problem [Oro 45]. The original punch problem differs from the mode I crack geometry, shown in Fig. I.8-3, in that the plate is semi-infinite rather than infinite. The two semi-infinite cuts in the plate comprising the mode I problem are separated by the distance $2a$, as shown in Fig. I.8-3. The material is assumed to be rigidly elastic outside the slip lines.

We can solve the plane strain mode I crack problem for a perfectly plastic material, beginning with the tractionless crack surface EQ on the upper left-hand side of Fig. I.8-3. The initial value problem along EQ is essentially type 1, where σ and χ are specified on a noncharacteristic boundary. The functions σ and χ, however, are not given explicitly and must be obtained from equations (I.8-25)–(I.8-27) or these equations in combination with (I.8-4).

This surface is tractionless, so by (I.8-27) we have

along EQ: $\quad \tau_{xy} = 0 \rightarrow \cos 2\chi = 0 \rightarrow \chi = \pi/4 \quad \text{or} \quad 3\pi/4.$ (I.8-98)

We can add π (and integer multiplies of π) to or subtract π from these two possible values of χ to obtain additional values of χ that will also satisfy $\tau_{xy} = 0$. However, there are only two distinct axes (perpendicular to each other) associated with all of these angles. These axes are represented by those in (I.8-98), and as such, only those two values of χ are considered.

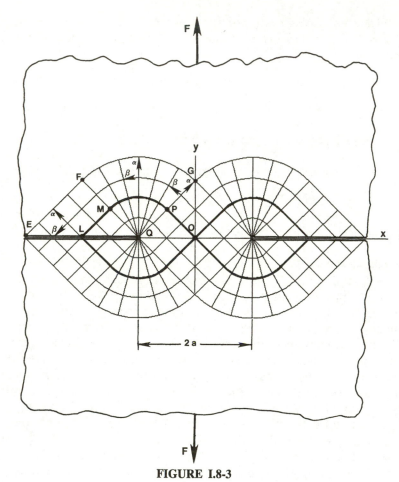

FIGURE I.8-3

Prandtl–Hill slip line mesh for the mode I problem.

A problem arises because traction and the assumption of yield do not allow a unique determination of σ and χ on EQ. We may infer that $\tau_{xy} = \sigma_y = 0$ because the surface is traction-free; however, two possibilities exist for σ_x, i.e., $\pm 2k$, assuming that the material has yielded. The positive value of $2k$ corresponds to $\chi = 3\pi/4$, and the negative value to $\chi = \pi/4$.

Either of these two values for σ_x will satisfy yield (I.8-4) for the known values of σ_y and τ_{xy}. Physical intuition tells us that the correct choice is $2k$, because the tensile forces F at infinity (Fig. I.8-3) will induce tension rather than compression in the slip line network. However, since the assumption of a rigid elastic region is made for the region above EFG (and one cannot determine stress in a rigid region), there is no direct way to prove this choice.

With the assumption that $\sigma_x = 2k$, the hydrostatic stress is calculated as k along EQ by (I.8-29) with the substitution $\sigma_y = 0$. Having determined σ and σ_y on EQ, the angle χ of (I.8-98) is found from (I.8-26) as $3\pi/4$. In summary, we have

along EQ:

$$\sigma_x = 2k, \qquad \sigma_y = 0, \qquad \tau_{xy} = 0, \qquad \chi = 3\pi/4, \qquad \sigma = k.$$

$$(I.8-99)$$

The choice of the χ is always arbitrarily to the extent that it can be associated with either of two opposing directions that lie along the same axis. For example, if we chose χ to be $3\pi/4$ along EQ, then the β direction is 90° counterclockwise to it ($5\pi/4$). Alternatively, we could choose χ as $-\pi/4$, in which case the β direction makes an angle of $\pi/4$ with the x-axis. The substitution of either $\chi = 3\pi/4$ or $\chi = -\pi/4$ in (I.8-25)–(I.8-27) naturally gives the same numerical results for the stresses, as each trigonometric function gives identical values for the two different choices of χ.

The Hencky equations (I.8-66)–(I.8-67) may now be employed to determine the stresses interior to the boundary EQ.

Since the angle χ does not change in region EFQ, the state of stress does not change from the surface EQ by Hencky's equations. In general, any region composed of two families of straight slip lines has a uniform state of stress; see slip line properties due to Hencky in [Kac 74].

Along FQ the slip line network changes from a rectangular grid to a fan of slip lines and arcs of concentric circles. We thus establish a local polar coordinate system (r, θ) with the origin at the crack tip Q (Fig. I.8-4). A side note is needed, however, to justify the use of the polar coordinate system.

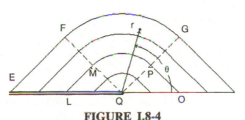

FIGURE I.8-4

Polar coordinates for the slip line fan.

In deriving the Hencky equations, the assumption was made that α and β are the real and imaginary parts of the complex function of z, i.e., (I.8-44). This assumption was just a convenient way to introduce an arbitrary orthogonal coordinate system into the derivation. Many of the common orthogonal coordinates in the plane do satisfy this requirement: Cartesian, elliptic, parabolic, and bipolar are examples. However, polar coordinates do not satisfy this restriction as r does not satisfy the two-dimensional Laplace equation, i.e., the operator (I.4-52) set equal to zero.

However, this restriction is easy to overcome by using circular cylindrical coordinates in the plane (α, β) [MS 71] rather than polar coordinates (r, θ). We define the coordinate system (α, β) for use in FGQ as

$$\alpha + i\beta = \ln z = \ln(r \exp i\theta) \qquad \text{(I.8-100)}$$

$$\to \alpha = \ln r, \qquad \beta = \theta. \qquad \text{(I.8-101)}$$

The function $\ln r$ satisfies Laplace's equation in the plane, unlike the coordinate r by itself. Therefore, along a particular β slip line in the fan, $\alpha = c_1 \to r = c^{c_1}$. Along a given α slip line in the fan the coordinate β is constant and equal to the local polar coordinate angle, $\beta = c_2 = \theta$. Thus the slip line network FGQ shown in Fig. I.8-3 is justified.

Along FQ, the constant$_3$ of (I.8-67) equals $k + 3\pi k/2$ by its initialization along EQ. Therefore, we have in

fan FGQ: $\qquad\qquad \sigma + 2k\theta = k[1 + (3\pi/2)]. \qquad \text{(I.8-102)}$

The stresses in the fan follow immediately by substituting σ from (I.8-102) and $\chi = \theta$ into (I.8-25)–(I.8-27).

At line GQ, $\theta = \pi/4$; therefore, from (I.8-102), $\sigma = (1 + \pi)k$. In GOQ, we again have a uniform state of stress, which is determined by the state of stress along GQ. Using equations, (I.8-25)–(I.8-27), we find in

region GOQ: $\qquad \sigma_x = \pi k, \qquad \sigma_y = (2 + \pi)k, \qquad \tau_{xy} = 0$

$$\text{as } \chi = \pi/4 \text{ and } \sigma = (1 + \pi)k. \quad \text{(I.8-103)}$$

A different solution to the punch problem was given later by R. Hill [Hil 50]. Hill's solution differs from the Prandtl solution, as far as stress is concerned, only where the rigid elastic–perfectly plastic boundary is located. In Hill's solution, the location of the elastic–plastic boundary is along $LMPO$ rather than Prandtl's EFG of Fig. I.8-3. The Hill elastic–plastic boundary is shown in all four quadrants of this figure as a heavy line. Inside $LMPO$, Hill's stress field is identical to Prandtl's.

The forces F at infinity must be carried by the plastic material between the two crack tips—a distance $2a$ in both Prandtl and Hill solutions.

Between the crack tips the plastic stresses are constant in both solutions. This allows us to calculate easily the magnitude of the force F in terms of the yield stress in shear.

In the Prandtl and Hill solutions, $\sigma_y = k(2 + \pi)$ along the crack axis between the two crack tips. Therefore the force F per unit plate thickness required for equilibrium is

$$F = 2ka(2 + \pi). \tag{I.8-104}$$

Although the Prandtl and Hill solutions have a common stress field, there are differences between velocities. We will begin our discussion of velocity with the Prandtl solution.

First of all, the boundary conditions on velocity must be discussed. The normal component of velocity across the elastic–plastic boundary must always be continuous; otherwise, we would have cracks appearing along the interface [Kac 74]. The tangential component of velocity, nevertheless, may be discontinuous.

For the Prandtl mode I problem, let us assume that the upper and lower elastic regions are moving in opposite directions (up and down, respectively) with a speed V, as rigid bodies in translation (Fig. I.8-5).

In the region containing GOQ, we have two orthogonal families of straight slip lines. In any region having this property, the stresses are uniform and the velocities are related to rigid body motion. This is easily verified using the Hencky and Geiringer equations, taking χ constant.

Through symmetry arguments, the diamond-shaped region surrounded by the broken lines must remain motionless.

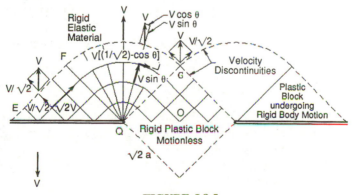

FIGURE I.8-5

Prandtl solution—mode I velocities.

In the fan FGQ, the normal component of velocity must be continuous across the elastic–plastic boundary FG, which is $V \sin \theta$ in the α direction (see Fig. I.8-3 for (α, β) directions), i.e.,

fan FGQ: $$v_\alpha = V \sin \theta. \tag{I.8-105}$$

By Geiringer's equation (I.8-96), the velocity v_α does not change with the radius r in the fan (Fig. I.8-4) because, in this particular case, $\chi = \beta = \theta$; therefore $d\chi = d\beta = d\theta = 0$ along an α line (in general $\beta = \text{constant}$ along any α line).

Therefore, there is a velocity discontinuity separating the fan from the diamond-shaped region. (Velocity discontinuities are designated by broken lines in Fig. I.8-5.)

In general, velocity discontinuities occur tangentially either across slip lines or envelopes of slip lines [Kac 74].

The velocity normal to slip line GQ must be continuous, and it is therefore zero as it borders the motionless plastic block. The component of velocity in the β direction of the fan FGQ is determined by (I.8-105) and Geiringer's equation (I.8-97) where χ is the polar coordinate θ (Fig. I.8-4):

$$dv_\beta + v_\alpha \, d\theta = 0 \rightarrow dv_\beta = -V \sin \theta \, d\theta \tag{I.8-106}$$

$$\rightarrow v_\beta = -V \int \sin \theta \, d\theta \rightarrow v_\beta = V \cos \theta + c_1. \tag{I.8-107}$$

The boundary condition across GQ ($\theta = \pi/4$) is $v_\beta = 0$. Therefore, the constant of integration c_1 of (I.8-107) is evaluated and v_β is obtained as follows:

fan FGQ: $$V \cos \pi/4 + c_1 = 0 \rightarrow v_\beta = V[\cos \theta - (1/2^{1/2})]. \tag{I.8-108}$$

In EFQ the component of velocity across the elastic–plastic boundary EF is continuous; therefore,

region EFQ: $$v_\alpha = V/2^{1/2}. \tag{I.8-109}$$

This velocity is constant in EFQ because of the mutually perpendicular straight slip lines in this region. The velocity in the β direction in EFQ is obtained from (I.8-108) with $\theta = 3\pi/4$. This initializes v_β in Geiringer's equation (I.8-97) along FG for use in region EFQ. As χ does not change in EFQ ($\chi = 3\pi/4$), we have

region EFQ: $$v_\beta = -2^{1/2}V. \tag{I.8-110}$$

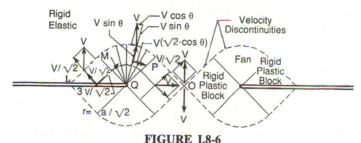

FIGURE I.8-6

Hill solution—mode I velocities.

The Hill velocity field differs from the Prandtl in that there is no diamond-shaped motionless block separating crack tips (Fig. I.8-6). Symmetry arguments again rule out a velocity v_y in the two connecting plastic regions—one of which is designated OPQ. However, these two plastic blocks, touching the origin O of the Cartesian system, can now move incrementally toward each other, as the rigid plastic material above OP has been replaced with rigid elastic material which is moving in the vertical direction.

Across OP the velocity is continuous so that

region OPQ:
$$v_\alpha = V/2^{1/2}. \qquad (I.8\text{-}111)$$

From the lower side perpendicular to OP a similar argument yields

region OPQ:
$$v_\beta = -V/2^{1/2}. \qquad (I.8\text{-}112)$$

These two components of the velocity in region OPQ add as vectors to give (see Fig. I.8-6)

region OPQ:
$$v_x = V, \qquad v_y = 0. \qquad (I.8\text{-}113)$$

Note also that, unlike the Prandtl solution, there is no velocity discontinuity tangential to PQ in the Hill solution.

Along PQ the normal velocity is given by (I.8-112). The Hill velocity in the fan is obtained in a fashion similar to the Prandtl velocity to give

fan MPQ:
$$v_\beta = V(\cos\theta - 2^{1/2}). \qquad (I.8\text{-}114)$$

The α component in the Hill fan is obtained as in the Prandtl fan:

fan MPQ:
$$v_\alpha = V\sin\theta. \qquad (I.8\text{-}115)$$

Using $\theta = 3\pi/4$ in (I.8-114)–(I.8-115), we find that along MQ

line MQ: $v_\alpha = V/2^{1/2}$, $v_\beta = -3V/2^{1/2}$.   (I.8-116)

Continuing the velocity component v_α across LM and the second equation of (I.8-116) allows us to determine that in

region LMQ: $v_\alpha = V/2^{1/2}$, $v_\beta = -3V/2^{1/2}$.   (I.8-117)

The Hill mode I stress and velocity fields may also be found in [Kac 74, pp. 189–190]. Note that Kachanov takes his α and β lines in the opposite sense to ours. This shows their arbitrary nature with respect to signs.

Failure Criteria

The Griffith criterion [Gri 20] of brittle fracture relates the release of stored elastic energy (linear elastic theory) to the breaking of bonds between atoms and the creation of a new surface. Orowan [Oro 50] extended this idea to include ductile materials. The rate of release of stored elastic energy $\mathscr{G}$, which can also be used as a critical parameter for crack growth with limited plasticity [Irw 49], can be related to the stress intensity factor by the formulas (see [Her 76])

Plane strain: $K_\mathrm{I} = [\mathscr{G}E/(1 - \nu^2)]^{1/2}$ (I.8-118)

Plane stress: $K_\mathrm{I} = (\mathscr{G}E)^{1/2}$,   (I.8-119)

where E and ν are Young's modulus and Poisson's ratio, respectively. Because of the relationships between $\mathscr{G}$ and K_I, the concept of a critical $\mathscr{G}_\mathrm{Ic}$ is equivalent to a critical stress intensity factor K_Ic. In experiments, K_Ic in plane strain (thick plates) is conservative relative to the critical stress intensity factor for plane stress (thin plates) for identical values of stress intensity factor—an exception being extremely thin plates (e.g., foils) [Kno 73, AM 88]. The stress intensity factor K_Ic is a material parameter called the *fracture toughness*. A critical stress intensity factor can likewise be defined for modes II and III.

If the fracture toughness is not constant, but instead varies with the change in crack length Δa, the question of stability arises. This problem is addressed by use of the resistance curve or R curve (see [Hut 79, p. 19; Her 76, p. 288].

The concept of $\mathscr{G}$ can be extended to potential energy involving nonlinear elastic materials (e.g., deformation theories of plasticity) through use of the J integral [Ric 68b, Cher 67]:

$$J_\Gamma = \int_\Gamma W\, dy - \mathbf{t} \cdot \mathbf{u}_{,x}\, ds$$ (I.8-120)

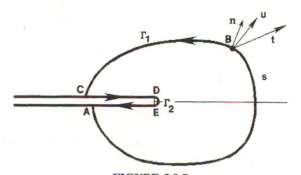

FIGURE I.8-7

Path-independent J integral.

where Γ is a closed path $ABCDEA$ surrounding the crack tip (Fig. I.8-7), s is an arc length along Γ (having an outward normal $\mathbf{n}$) upon which a traction $\mathbf{t}$ acts and displacements $\mathbf{u}$ are evaluated. The symbol W in (I.8-120) is the strain energy density,

$$W \equiv \int \sigma_x \, d\epsilon_x + \int \sigma_y \, d\epsilon_y + \int \sigma_z \, d\epsilon_z$$

$$+ \int \tau_{xy} \, d\gamma_{xy} + \int \tau_{xz} \, d\gamma_{xz} + \int \tau_{yz} \, d\gamma_{yz}, \qquad \text{(I.8-121)}$$

where each integral is evaluated from zero strain to the maximum strain. The J integral may be applied to all three modes of fracture.

It can be shown that [Ric 68b]

$$J_\Gamma = 0, \qquad \text{(I.8-122)}$$

for any closed path (counterclockwise) involving an elastic material (linear or nonlinear) that does not encompass a singularity. There are no contributions to J_Γ along the flat surfaces AE and CD because $dy = 0$ and $\mathbf{t} = 0$. Therefore,

$$J_{\Gamma_1} + J_{\Gamma_2} = 0, \qquad \text{(I.8-123)}$$

where Γ_1 is the path ABC and Γ_2 is the path DE, i.e., along the blunted notch. Along the rounded crack tip $\mathbf{t} = 0$; thus J_{Γ_2} reduces to

$$J_{\Gamma_2} = \int_{DE} W \, dy. \qquad \text{(I.8-124)}$$

We define the J integral as

$$J \equiv J_{\Gamma_2} = -J_{\Gamma_1}. \tag{I.8-125}$$

Since the choice of Γ_1 is arbitrary, the evaluation of J is related to a path-independent integral. For a true crack rather than rounded notch, Γ_2 needs to be approached in the limit as the curve DE degenerates to a point.

If the mode I small-scale yielding solution for plane strain is substituted into (I.8-125), we obtain

$$J = (1 - \nu^2) K_1^2 / E = \mathscr{G}. \tag{I.8-126}$$

Taking into account all three modes of failure simultaneously, we find that for small-scale yielding under plane strain loading conditions

$$J = (1 - \nu^2)[K_{\text{I}}^2 + K_{\text{II}}^2] / E + K_{\text{III}}^2 / (2G). \tag{I.8-127}$$

If the potential energy per unit volume is defined as Π, then J may be interpreted as

$$J = -\partial \Pi / \partial a, \tag{I.8-128}$$

that is, the energy release rate for crack growth, where a is the crack length. (See [Her 76, Hut 79] for a discussion of the experimental determination of J.)

Equation (I.8-127) assumes that the elastic strain energy released goes toward the creation of new crack surfaces. This ignores another possibility of failure in the form of plastic collapse. This type of failure, applied to crack problems, is quite distinct from the J-integral or $\mathscr{G}$ approach. An attempt to combine these two failure criteria—the fracture assessment diagram—is discussed in Section 2.4.

There are two theorems of plasticity theory that are useful in establishing bounds of loads regarding failure by plastic collapse [Cal 85, Men 68]. They are

LOWER BOUND THEOREM: *A body in equilibrium with its external forces such that all stresses are at or below yield is either safe from plastic collapse or, at worst, has collapse impending.*

UPPER BOUND THEOREM: *A body for which the rate of external forces do work equals or exceeds the rate at which energy is being dissipated internally must experience plastic collapse, provided a kinematically admissible velocity field is possible.*

Let us now examine some simple cases of the upper and lower bound theorems. Our first example will be the lower bound theorem applied to the same geometry used for the plane strain Prandtl–Hill mode I crack problem involving an elastically rigid–perfectly plastic material.

The stress distribution chosen is shown in Fig. I.8-8. This has an extremely simple stress distribution. Between the crack tips B and C, plastic material exists. Two stress discontinuities pass through the crack tips and extend to infinity. Normally, stresses in a rigidly elastic region cannot be determined; however, in this special case, it is possible. Across the elastic–plastic boundaries no force is transferred. Thus we may take the normal and shear stresses across the interface to be zero. Because the crack surfaces are also tractionless, we may assume further, that the elastic stresses are zero everywhere.

The resultant forces F per unit plate thickness at infinity, as shown in Fig. I.8-3, would have, in this case, the magnitude

$$F_{LB_1} = 4ka. \tag{I.8-129}$$

The subscript LB_1 on F in (I.8-129) designates it as lower bound (number one). The conditions of the lower bound theorem are met because we have found a stress distribution that is everywhere at or below yield and in a state of equilibrium.

We may apply an arbitrarily pressure to the plastic stresses shown in Fig. I.8-8 without changing the yield status. Let us apply a pressure $p = -2k$ to the previous plastic stresses to obtain the new state shown in

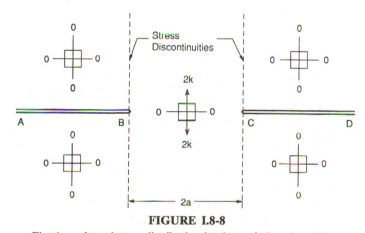

FIGURE I.8-8

First lower bound stress distribution for the mode I crack problem.

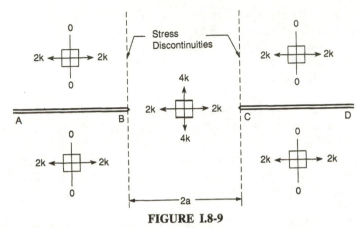

FIGURE I.8-9

Second lower bound stress distribution for the mode I crack problem.

Fig. I.8-9. To reestablish equilibrium, we must now change the yield status of the previously elastic region to that of a plastic state. A uniaxial tension $2k$ will maintain equilibrium across the elastic–plastic boundary, while meeting the tractionless boundary condition across the crack surfaces. This will give us a new lower bound of

$$F_{LB_2} = 8ka, \tag{I.8-130}$$

which is higher than the previous value.

A more complicated geometry involving several stress discontinuities for the punch problem by Shield and Drucker [SD 53] gives, in the analogous mode I crack problem (Fig. I.8-10), a still higher lower bound of

$$F_{LB_3} = 10ka. \tag{I.8-131}$$

The first two lower bound values represent applied forces F on infinite plates that would be safe from plastic collapse, as they both have values lower than the third. The third lower bound force, however, might correspond to the limit load, which is defined as the load at which plastic collapse occurs.

Let us now turn to problems related to the upper bound theorem. We use the Prandtl and Hill velocity fields to calculate the rate of dissipation of energy for the mode I problem. Neither of these two solutions could have been used earlier for the lower bound theorem, because we cannot guarantee that the rigid elastic material did not violate yield, as the stresses are indeterminate in the elastic regions.

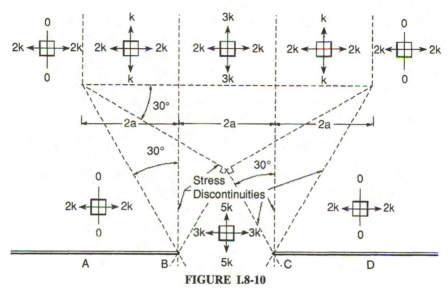

FIGURE I.8-10

Third lower bound stress distribution for the mode I crack problem.

There are two distinct ways that energy is dissipated: One is through the plastic deformation itself, and the other is through friction generated between adjacent surfaces having relative motion.

Mathematically, the upper bound theorem may be written as

$$\int_S \mathbf{t} \cdot \mathbf{v} \, dS + \int_V \mathbf{f} \cdot \mathbf{v} \, dV \geq \int_V \dot{U} \, dV + \int_{S_D} \mathbf{t}_D \cdot \Delta\mathbf{v} \, dS \quad (I.8\text{-}132)$$

where

$$\dot{U} \equiv \sigma_x \dot{\epsilon}_x + \sigma_y \dot{\epsilon}_y + \sigma_z \dot{\epsilon}_z + \tau_{xy} \dot{\gamma}_{xy} + \tau_{xz} \dot{\gamma}_{xz} + \tau_{yz} \dot{\gamma}_{yz}, \quad (I.8\text{-}133)$$

and where $\mathbf{t}$ is a traction acting on a surface S of the body, $\mathbf{f}$ is a body force, V is volume, $\Delta\mathbf{v}$ is the relative velocity between surfaces S_D which dissipate energy through a traction $\mathbf{t}_D$.

For the mode I upper bound analyses, we will assume that body forces (such as weight) are negligible, i.e., $\mathbf{f} = 0$.

The first integral on the left-hand side of equation (I.8-132) will be designated P for external power supplied. The first integral of the right-hand side will be designated $\dot{D}_1$, and the second integral $\dot{D}_2$.

We begin our analysis with the Prandtl velocity field. Because of symmetry we consider only one quadrant of the plate. For the rigid plastic blocks, the integral $\dot{D}_1$ is zero. This leaves only the fans for the determination of $\dot{D}_1$. It is convenient to use polar coordinates in the fan FGQ. The polar strain rates $\dot{\epsilon}_r$, $\dot{\epsilon}_\theta$, and $\dot{\epsilon}_{r\theta}$ are analogous to the polar strains (I.4-53)–(I.4-55), after we make the substitution v_r for u_r and v_θ for u_θ. The transformations between the slip line velocities and polar velocities in the fan FGQ are $v_r = v_\alpha$ and $v_\theta = v_\beta$. The evaluation of $\dot{\gamma}_{r\theta}$ follows from analogy to (I.4-55) as

$$\dot{\gamma}_{r\theta} = 2\dot{\epsilon}_{r\theta} = V/(2^{1/2}r). \qquad (I.8\text{-}134)$$

All other strain rates are zero. The integral $\dot{D}_1$ reduces to the contributions of the four fans, where for one fan FGQ we have

$$\dot{D}_{FGQ_1} = \int_{\pi/4}^{3\pi/4} \int_0^{2^{1/2}a} \tau_{r\theta}\dot{\gamma}_{r\theta}r\,dr\,d\theta. \qquad (I.8\text{-}135)$$

With the substitutions (I.8-134) and the following stress into (I.8-135),

$$\tau_{r\theta} = k \qquad (I.8\text{-}136)$$

we find for fan FGQ

$$\dot{D}_{FGQ_1} = \pi akV/2. \qquad (I.8\text{-}137)$$

The calculation of $\dot{D}_2$ is related to three different surfaces for each quadrant. For the upper left quadrant we have the boundaries between the elastic and plastic regions (EF, FG) and the boundary between the plastic fan and the motionless plastic block (GQ). These are, respectively,

$$\dot{D}_{EF_2} = \int_{EF} \mathbf{t} \cdot \Delta\mathbf{v}\,dS = kV(2^{1/2} - 2^{-1/2})(2^{1/2}a)$$

$$= kVa \qquad (I.8\text{-}138)$$

$$\dot{D}_{FG_2} = \int_{FG} \mathbf{t} \cdot \Delta\mathbf{v}\,dS = k\int_{\pi/4}^{3\pi/4} V(\cos\theta + 2^{-1/2} - \cos\theta)(2^{1/2}a)\,d\theta$$

$$= \pi kVa/2 \qquad (I.8\text{-}139)$$

$$\dot{D}_{GQ_2} = \int_{GQ} \mathbf{t} \cdot \Delta\mathbf{v}\,dS = k(V2^{-1/2})(2^{1/2}a) = kVa. \qquad (I.8\text{-}140)$$

The total rate of work done P by the two external forces F is, by (I.8-104),

$$P = 2FV = 4ka(2 + \pi)V. \qquad (I.8\text{-}141)$$

In order for the upper bound theorem to be satisfied, we need to prove that (considering only one-fourth of the total power because of the previous symmetry considerations)

$$P/4 \geq \dot{D}_{FGQ_2} + \dot{D}_{EF_2} + \dot{D}_{FG_2} + \dot{D}_{GQ_2} \qquad \text{(I.8-142)}$$

$$\rightarrow ka(2 + \pi)V \geq \pi kVa/2 + kVa + \pi kVa/2 + kVa \quad \text{(I.8-143)}$$

$$\rightarrow 0 \geq 0. \qquad \text{QED} \qquad \text{(I.8-144)}$$

Thus the load F of the Prandtl stress and velocity fields (I.8-104) provides an upper bound for the limit load F_{UB}.

We now examine the Hill mode I problem and compare its upper bound with Prandtl's.

The greatest difference between the Hill and Prandtl problems is the elimination of friction between the two plastic regions. This would reduce the dissipation rate were it not for the addition of new friction at the boundary OP between the rigid elastic material and plastic region OPQ.

The contributions to $\dot{D}_1$ are again related to the fan. In MPQ, we have

$$\dot{D}_{MPQ_1} = \int_{\pi/4}^{3\pi/4} \int_0^{a/2^{1/2}} \tau_{r\theta} \dot{\gamma}_{r\theta} r \, dr \, d\theta. \qquad \text{(I.8-145)}$$

With the substitution of (I.8-136) for $\tau_{r\theta}$ and

$$\dot{\gamma}_{r\theta} = 2^{1/2} V/r \qquad \text{(I.8-146)}$$

for $\dot{\gamma}_{r\theta}$, we find

$$\dot{D}_{MPQ_1} = \pi kVa/2. \qquad \text{(I.8-147)}$$

The losses due to friction $\dot{D}_2$ are along OP, MP, and LM. They are, respectively,

$$\dot{D}_{OP_2} = \int_{OP} \mathbf{t} \cdot \Delta\mathbf{v} \, dS = kV(2^{-1/2} + 2^{-1/2})(a2^{-1/2}) = kVa \quad \text{(I.8-148)}$$

$$\dot{D}_{MP_2} = \int_{MP} \mathbf{t} \cdot \Delta\mathbf{v} \, dS = \int_{\pi/4}^{3\pi/4} kV[2^{1/2} - \cos\theta + \cos\theta](a2^{-1/2}) \, d\theta$$

$$= kV(2^{1/2})(a2^{-1/2})(\pi/2) = \pi kVa/2 \qquad \text{(I.8-149)}$$

$$\dot{D}_{LM_2} = \int_{LM} \mathbf{t} \cdot \Delta\mathbf{v} \, dS = kV[(3/2^{1/2}) - (1/2^{1/2})](a2^{-1/2}) = kVa.$$

$$\text{(I.8-150)}$$

The external power term for Hill's solution will be the same as that for Prandtl's solution. Thus, in order for the lower bound to be satisfied for the Hill solution, we must have

$$P/4 \geq \dot{D}_{MPQ_1} + \dot{D}_{OP_2} + \dot{D}_{MP_2} + \dot{D}_{LM_2} \tag{I.8-151}$$

$$\rightarrow ka(2 + \pi)V \geq \pi kVa/2 + kVa + \pi kVa/2 + kVa \tag{I.8-152}$$

$$\rightarrow 0 \geq 0. \quad \text{QED} \tag{I.8-153}$$

Therefore, by (I.8-153), the Hill solution also satisfies the upper bound theorem.

Because the external forces F are the same for the Prandtl and Hill solutions, they provide the same upper bound F_{UB}.

Through the use of the Shield–Drucker stress field for a lower bound F_{LB_3} and the Prandtl–Hill slip line fields for an upper bound F_{UB}, we have now bracketed the actual limit load F^* to a narrow margin,

$$F_{\text{LB}_3} \leq F^* \leq F_{\text{UB}} \tag{I.8-154}$$

$$10ka \leq F^* \leq 2ka(2 + \pi) \tag{I.8-155}$$

$$10ka \leq F^* \leq 10.2832ka, \tag{I.8-156}$$

for this particular crack geometry.

As a final comment on the dissipation rates, one must discard analyses if they contain a negative rate of dissipation. Under such circumstances, energy would have been created by plastic deformation. This is unacceptable physically because energy is lost through heat during plastic flow.

The author is indebted to Professor R. T. Shield for bringing to his attention the analogous Prandtl–Hill punch limit load analysis.

Power Law Hardening Materials under Plane Strain

Several investigators have obtained power law hardening solutions of the mode I crack problems involving plastic deformation theory [Hut 68a, RR 68, Cher 67]. This type of solution, together with its associated stress and strain fields, has acquired the abbreviation HRR in the literature.

This problem has the same homogeneous boundary conditions along the semi-infinite crack seen in the small-scale yielding mode I solution for linear elasticity. At large distances from the crack tip, the stress and strain decay to zero in a manner that resembles the small-scale yielding linear elastic solution; they do so, however, at different rates, which are determined by the power exponent n of the hardening law.

The material response, which is determined from uniaxial tensile test data, is assumed to be nonlinear elastic. Alternatively, it may be viewed as a plastic material obeying a deformation theory satisfying the Mises yield condition (J_2 deformation theory) with isotropic hardening of the form (Ramberg–Osgood model without a linear elastic contribution)

$$\epsilon/\epsilon_0 = \alpha(\sigma/\sigma_0)^n, \qquad 1 \le n \le \infty \qquad \text{(I.8-157)}$$

where α, n are material constants; ϵ, σ are the strain and stress in the direction of the uniaxial load; ϵ_0, σ_0 are the yield strain and yield stress, respectively; and $\sigma_0 = E\epsilon_0$, where E is Young's modulus.

Following the procedure described in [Hut 68a, Hut 68b, Hut 79], an equivalent stress is defined as follows:

$$\sigma_e^2 = 3J_2 = \tfrac{3}{4}\left[(\sigma_r - \sigma_\theta)^2 + 4\tau_{r\theta}^2\right] \qquad \text{plane strain (polar)}, \quad \text{(I.8-158)}$$

where J_2 is the second invariant of the deviatoric stress (see, e.g., [Men 68]). For our purposes, it is sufficient to note that the second invariant of the deviatoric stress is equal to

$$J_2 = (1/6)H(\sigma_{ij}), \qquad \text{(I.8-159)}$$

where $H(\sigma_{ij})$ is given explicitly by (I.3-26) in Cartesian coordinates.

The stress–strain relationships used for plane strain are

$$\epsilon_r/\epsilon_0 = (3/4)\alpha\sigma_e^{n-1}(\sigma_r - \sigma_\theta)/\sigma_0^n \qquad \text{(I.8-160)}$$

$$\epsilon_\theta/\epsilon_0 = (3/4)\alpha\sigma_e^{n-1}(\sigma_\theta - \sigma_r)/\sigma_0^n \qquad \text{(I.8-161)}$$

$$\epsilon_{r\theta}/\epsilon_0 = (3/2)\alpha\sigma_e^{n-1}\tau_{r\theta}/\sigma_0^n, \qquad \text{(I.8-162)}$$

which represent an incompressible material.

A semi-analytical solution to the mode I crack problem is possible. The solution in polar coordinates has the form

$$\sigma_r = K\sigma_0 r^{-1/(n+1)}\tilde{\sigma}_r(\theta, n) \qquad \text{(I.8-163)}$$

$$\sigma_\theta = K\sigma_0 r^{-1/(n+1)}\tilde{\sigma}_\theta(\theta, n) \qquad \text{(I.8-164)}$$

$$\tau_{r\theta} = K\sigma_0 r^{-1/(n+1)}\tilde{\sigma}_{r\theta}(\theta, n) \qquad \text{(I.8-165)}$$

$$\sigma_e = K\sigma_0 r^{-1/(n+1)}\tilde{\sigma}_e(\theta, n) \qquad \text{(I.8-166)}$$

$$\epsilon_r = \alpha\epsilon_0 K^n r^{-n/(n+1)}\tilde{\epsilon}_r(\theta, n) \qquad \text{(I.8-167)}$$

$$\epsilon_\theta = \alpha\epsilon_0 K^n r^{-n/(n-1)}\tilde{\epsilon}_\theta(\theta, n) \qquad \text{(I.8-168)}$$

$$\epsilon_{r\theta} = \alpha\epsilon_0 K^n r^{-n/(n+1)}\tilde{\epsilon}_{r\theta}(\theta, n) \qquad \text{(I.8-169)}$$

where r and θ are measured relative to the crack tip in a manner analogous to the mode I small-scale yielding solution, and K is a constant called the plasticity intensity factor, which is to be determined. The functions $\tilde{\sigma}_i(\theta, n)$ and $\tilde{\epsilon}_i(\theta, n)$ need to be evaluated numerically such that equilibrium, stress–strain relationships, compatibility of strains, the yield condition, and tractionless boundary conditions (homogeneous) along the crack faces are satisfied. In [Hut 68a], a stress function approach was used.

Now the J integral can be expressed in the form [Ric 68b]

$$J = \int_{-\pi}^{\pi} (Wn_x - \mathbf{t} \cdot \mathbf{u}_{,x}) r \, d\theta, \qquad (\text{I.8-170})$$

where the path of integration is any radius r. If the J integral is to be nonzero and path-independent, the term inside parentheses in (I.8-167) needs to be of the form

$$Wn_x - \mathbf{t} \cdot \mathbf{u}_{,x} = f(\theta)/r, \qquad (\text{I.8-171})$$

where $n_x = \cos\theta$. This is necessary because the choice of r is arbitrary, and we can take the limit as $r \to 0$; this makes the integrand of (I.8-170) zero, which in turn makes J zero.

This type of reasoning was used to determine the power law structure for stress, strain, and displacement fields in the HRR solution such that (I.8-171) is satisfied.

We note that the units of (I.8-171) are those of stress times strain. If we multiply the stress σ_r (I.8-163) by the strain ϵ_r (I.8-167), we find

$$\sigma_r \epsilon_r = \alpha \sigma_0 \epsilon_0 K^{n+1} \tilde{\sigma}_r(\theta, n) \tilde{\epsilon}_r(\theta, n) r^{-1}; \qquad (\text{I.8-172})$$

i.e., it is a function of $1/r$ regardless of the exponent n. Similarly, the $\sigma_\theta \epsilon_\theta$ and $\tau_{r\theta} \epsilon_{r\theta}$ products are of the form $1/r$.

We also know that, in the small-scale yielding linear elastic solution, the individual stresses and strains are separable into the form $1/r^{1/2}$ times a function of θ. Thus their product is likewise proportional to $1/r$ and resembles the behavior of (I.8-172).

In fact, for $n = 1$, the HRR solution becomes an incompressible linear elastic material. At the other extreme, as $n \to \infty$, the behavior of the HRR solution approaches the Prandtl perfectly plastic solution. This behavior is analogous to that of the mode III strain hardening material. However, in the HRR field, there is no counterpart to the linear elastic region and hence no elastic–plastic boundary as in the mode III problem.

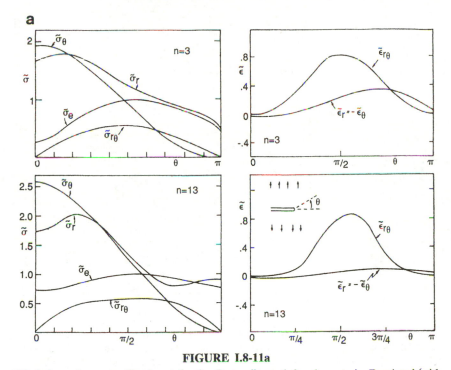

FIGURE I.8-11a

θ-Variations of stress and strains at the tip of a tensile crack for plane strain. Reprinted (with correction—hardening exponent mislabeled on lower strain distribution) from *J. Mech. Phys. Solids*, **16**, J. W. Hutchinson, Singular behavior at the end of a tensile crack in a hardening material, 13–31 (1968), and *J. Mech. Phys. Solids*, **16**, J. W. Hutchinson, Plane stress and strain fields at the crack tip, 337–347 (1968), with kind permission from Elsevier Science Ltd., The Boulevard, Langford Lane, Kidlington OX5 1GB, UK.

The governing equation for the stress function in the HRR solution is elliptic for finite values of n [Ric 68a, Hut 68b]. As $n \to \infty$, the equation becomes hyperbolic as in plane strain slip line theory.

The plasticity intensity factor K is determined by the assumption that as $r \to \infty$, the J integral approaches $\mathscr{G}$ of small-scale yielding linear elastic theory [Hut 68a]. Thus J is evaluated in the power law region and then equated to $\mathscr{G}$ to determine a relationship between K and σ_∞ (the tensile traction at infinity).

A comparison between the HRR stresses and the Prandtl stresses is given in Figs I.8-11a and I.8-11b. These graphs, taken from [Hut 68b], are also in [Hut 79]. Values for the various functions of (θ, n) of the solution

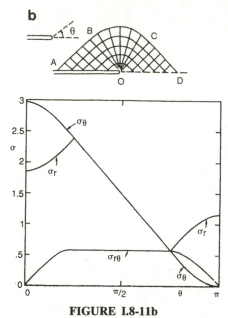

FIGURE I.8-11b

Stress characteristics and stress distribution at the tip of a tensile crack in a perfectly plastic material for plane strain. Reprinted from *J. Mech. Phys. Solids*, **16**, J. W. Hutchinson, Singular behavior at the end of a tensile crack in a hardening material, 13–31 (1968), and *J. Mech. Phys. Solids*, **16**, J. W. Hutchinson, Plane stress and strain fields at the crack tip, 337–347 (1968), with kind permission from Elsevier Science Ltd., The Boulevard, Langford Lane, Kidlington OX5 1GB, UK.

(I.8-63)–(I.8-69) are also plotted in Fig. I.8-11a. Between the values $n = 3$ and $n = 13$, we see a convergence of $\tilde{\sigma}_e$ toward the yield stress (normalized to $\tilde{\sigma} = 1$) in Fig. I.8-11a. We also see how the three polar stresses are converging toward their counterparts in the Prandtl solution between Figs I.8-11a and I.8-11b.

I.9 PLANE STRESS PROBLEMS INVOLVING PLASTIC MATERIAL

Plastic problems involving plane stress loading conditions are more difficult to handle than those involving plane strain, because the governing equations's characteristics change from one portion of the yield surface to another. In our plane stress analysis the plane of symmetry is again the *xy* plane. Plane stress loading conditions require that σ_z, τ_{xz}, and τ_{yz} vanish. Thus the Cayley–Hamilton equation (I.8-5) reduces to

$$\begin{vmatrix} \sigma_x - \sigma_i & \tau_{xy} & 0 \\ \tau_{xy} & \sigma_y - \sigma_i & 0 \\ 0 & 0 & -\sigma_i \end{vmatrix} = 0 \qquad \text{(I.9-1)}$$

$$\rightarrow \sigma_i\left[\tau_{xy}^2 - (\sigma_x - \sigma_i)(\sigma_y - \sigma_i)\right] = 0 \qquad \text{(I.9-2)}$$

$$\rightarrow \sigma_i\left[\sigma_i^2 - (\sigma_x + \sigma_y)\sigma_i + \sigma_x\sigma_y - \tau_{xy}^2\right] = 0. \qquad \text{(I.9-3)}$$

The principal stresses for plane stress are the three roots of the simple cubic equation in σ_i (I.9-3). They are, respectively ($i = 1, 2, 3$),

$$\sigma_1 = (\sigma_x + \sigma_y)/2 + \left[(\sigma_x - \sigma_y)^2 + 4\tau_{xy}^2\right]^{1/2}/2 \qquad \text{(I.9-4)}$$

$$\sigma_2 = (\sigma_x + \sigma_y)/2 - \left[(\sigma_x - \sigma_y)^2 + 4\tau_{xy}^2\right]^{1/2}/2 \qquad \text{(I.9-5)}$$

$$\sigma_3 = \sigma_z = 0. \qquad \text{(I.9-6)}$$

The above stresses are ordered so that $\sigma_1 \geq \sigma_2$. For regions on the yield surface where $\sigma_2 \geq \sigma_1$, the subscripts on σ_1 and σ_2 in equations (I.9-4) and (I.9-5) need to be interchanged.

Tresca Yield Condition

We begin our specific discussion of yield criteria with the Tresca criterion. Under the Tresca yield criterion, stresses reach yield when the maximum shear stress reaches magnitude k, which is the yield stress in pure shear:

Tresca:

$$\tau_{\max} = \max|\sigma_i - \sigma_j|/2 = \sigma_0/2 = k; \qquad i = 1, 2, 3, j = 1, 2, 3.$$
$$\text{(I.9-7)}$$

The Tresca yield surface for plane stress is shown in Fig. I.9-1 as six line segments LM, MN, NP, PQ, QR, and RL.

For region MN, we have the maximum shear stress as

region MN:

$$\sigma_1 > \sigma_2 > 0, \qquad \tau_{\max} = (\sigma_1 - \sigma_3)/2 = \sigma_1/2 = k \qquad \text{(I.9-8)}$$

$$\rightarrow \sigma_x + \sigma_y + \left[(\sigma_x - \sigma_y)^2 + 4\tau_{xy}^2\right]^{1/2} = 4k. \qquad \text{(I.9-9)}$$

At point N, we have a uniaxial state of tension $\sigma_1 = 2k$, $\sigma_2 = 0$.

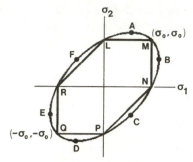

FIGURE I.9-1

Plane stress Tresca and Mises yield surfaces.

For region NP, we have a change in the form of the yield condition because $\sigma_3 = 0$ is now larger than σ_2, i.e.,

region NP: $\sigma_1 > 0 > \sigma_2$, $\tau_{max} = (\sigma_1 - \sigma_2)/2 = k$ (I.9-10)

$$\rightarrow \left[(\sigma_x - \sigma_y)^2 + 4\tau_{xy}^2\right]^{1/2} = 2k.$$ (I.9-11)

At point M, a state of negative pressure $p = -2k$ exists, i.e.,

point M: $\sigma_1 = \sigma_2$, $\tau_{max} = (\sigma_1 - \sigma_3)/2 = \sigma_1/2 = k$ (I.9-12)

$$\rightarrow \left[(\sigma_x - \sigma_y)^2 + 4\tau_{xy}^2\right]^{1/2} = 0,   \qquad \sigma_x + \sigma_y = 4k$$ (I.9-13)

$$\rightarrow \sigma_x = \sigma_y = 2k,   \qquad \tau_{xy} = 0.$$ (I.9-14)

The other regions of the yield surface are analogous to one of the above cases.

We have already studied the governing equations for stress in regions NP and RL, because they are similar in form to those of plane strain. To see this, compare equations (I.9-11) with (I.8-4). One need only square (I.9-11) to obtain (I.8-4). Because of this, the planes of maximum shear stress coincide with those of plane strain, and consequently the slip lines are similar to those of plane strain for regions NP and RL of the plane stress Tresca yield condition. See Fig. I.9-2a for two slip planes for plane strain under a uniaxial load σ.

Strain rates for region NP are also the same as for plane strain. To prove this, let us first reorder the Tresca (or Mises) plane strains (I.8-9)–(I.8-10), so that $\sigma_1 \geq \sigma_2 \geq \sigma_3$. So by (I.8-9)–(I.8-10) and (I.9-4)–(I.9-6), Table I.9-1 is deduced.

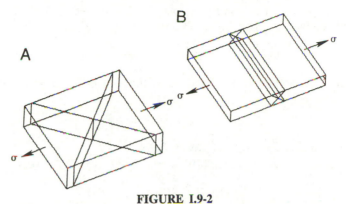

FIGURE I.9-2

Slip planes for (A) plane strain and (B) plane stress.

We see from this table that, if we take $\sigma_z = 0$, then the three principal stress relationships become identical for plane strain and plane stress (region NP). Hence for region NP, under the Tresca yield condition, plane stress appears to be a special case of plane strain where $\sigma_z = 0$.

Furthermore, since the relationship

$$h(\sigma_i) = \max|\sigma_i - \sigma_j|/2 = (\sigma_1 - \sigma_2)/2 \qquad (I.9\text{-}15)$$

is valid for both plane stress (region NP) and plane strain under the Tresca yield condition, we have similar flow rules

$$d\epsilon_1^P = d\Lambda\, \partial h(\sigma_i)/\partial\sigma_1 = d\Lambda/2 \qquad (I.9\text{-}16)$$

$$d\epsilon_2^P = d\Lambda\, \partial h(\sigma_i)/\partial\sigma_2 = -d\Lambda/2 \qquad (I.9\text{-}17)$$

$$d\epsilon_3^P = d\Lambda\, \partial h(\sigma_i)/\partial\sigma_3 = 0. \qquad (I.9\text{-}18)$$

where $d\Lambda$ is an incremental loading function.

TABLE I.9-1
Tresca Plane Stress (region NP) Compared to Plane Strain

Tresca plane stress (region NP)	Plane strain (where $\sigma_1 \geq \sigma_2 \geq \sigma_3$)
$\sigma_1 \geq 0$	$\sigma_1 \geq \sigma_z$
$\sigma_2 \leq 0$	$\sigma_2 \leq \sigma_z$
$\sigma_3 = 0$	$\sigma_3 = \sigma_z$

For the Mises yield condition, we have a different form for h, i.e., I.3-13, which we will distinguish from the Tresca condition by calling it h^*:

$$h^*(\sigma_{ij}) = (\sigma_1 - \sigma_2)^2 + (\sigma_2 - \sigma_3)^2 - (\sigma_3 - \sigma_1)^2. \qquad \text{(I.9-19)}$$

The flow rule for the Mises condition in the first principal stress direction will be

$$d\epsilon_1^P = d\lambda \, \partial h^*(\sigma_{ij})/\partial\sigma_1, \qquad \text{(I.9-20)}$$

where λ is an incremental loading function.

The partial derivative in (I.9-20) is evaluated from (I.9-19) as

$$\partial h^*/\partial\sigma_1 = 2(2\sigma_1 - \sigma_2 - \sigma_3). \qquad \text{(I.9-21)}$$

Now a plane strain relationship for σ_3 is obtained from (I.8-2) and (I.8-10), as

$$\sigma_3 = (\sigma_1 + \sigma_2)/2. \qquad \text{(I.9-22)}$$

Substituting (I.9-22) into (I.9-21), we find the following:

$$\partial h^*(\sigma_{ij})/\partial\sigma_1 = 3(\sigma_1 - \sigma_2). \qquad \text{(I.9-23)}$$

Next, we introduce $\partial h^*(\sigma_{ij})/\partial\sigma_1$ from (I.9-23) into (I.3-22) to obtain

$$d\epsilon_1^P = 3(\sigma_1 - \sigma_2) \, d\lambda. \qquad \text{(I.9-24)}$$

By subtracting (I.9-5) from (I.9-4), we find an alternative expression for (I.9-24) as

$$d\epsilon_1^P = 3\left[(\sigma_x - \sigma_y)^2 + 4\tau_{xy}^2\right]^{1/2} d\lambda. \qquad \text{(I.9-25)}$$

Finally, by replacing the radical in (I.9-25) by (I.9-11), we deduce that

Mises plane strain: $\qquad\qquad d\epsilon_1^P = 6k \, d\lambda. \qquad\qquad\qquad$ (I.9-26)

We observe that flow rule (I.9-26) has the same form as (I.9-16) and differs only by a multiplicative constant. It becomes identical to it, if we set

$$d\Lambda = 12k \, d\lambda. \qquad \text{(I.9-27)}$$

The form of plane strain Prandtl–Reuss equations for $d\epsilon_2^P$ and $d\epsilon_3^P$ may be obtained from (I.9-17) and (I.9-18) by substituting $d\Lambda$ from (I.9-27).

The flow rules between the Tresca and Mises yield criteria for plane strain are also similar in Cartesian coordinates, as they are in the Haigh–Westergaard space. The plane strain Tresca flow rule can be obtained from the Prandtl–Reuss equations (I.8-68)–(I.8-70) through the use of (I.9-27). On can observe this for $d\epsilon_x$ by comparing (I.8-18) to (I.8-68).

The classification of the governing equations for plane strain is hyperbolic for both the Tresca and Mises yield criteria. Therefore, the same must be true of the two plane stress regions NP and RL under the Tresca yield condition, as they have the same governing equations.

Relationship (I.9-18) may seem disturbing to those familiar with linear elasticity's

$$\epsilon_z^E = -(\nu/E)[\sigma_x + \sigma_y],\qquad (I.9\text{-}28)$$

for plane stress, which predicts deformation in the z direction. Nevertheless, for this region of the Tresca yield surface, there is no deformation in the antiplane direction. This is not true, however, of the adjoining regions of the Tresca yield surface MN and PQ where $d\epsilon_z^P$ exists.

Region MN and, by analogy, regions LM, PQ, QR have governing equations of the parabolic class. In this case, the planes of maximum shear stress make 45° angles with the xy plane. The families of slip lines, which coincide with the number of characteristics of the governing equations, reduce from two to one going from MN to NP.

In Fig. I.9-2b, two slip planes are shown which correspond to a plate under a uniaxial load σ and plane stress loading conditions for a specimen subject to the Tresca yield condition. The intersection of the two slip planes leaves one trace in the center plane of the plate, i.e., a single slip line. This region of the Tresca yield condition is discussed in detail in Section 1.1, in connection with the analytic continuation of stress across a mode I elastoplastic boundary, and thus is not repeated here. Strains and displacements for region MN are also discussed later in Sections 1.3 and 1.4, respectively.

For additional information regarding the Tresca yield condition under plane stress loading conditions, see [Kac 74]. There, stress discontinuities, velocity discontinuities, and behavior at the sharp corners of the yield surface are discussed in detail. Kachanov also describes a method of solution different from that presented in Chapter 1.

Mises Yield Condition

The Mises yield condition with no work hardening can be obtained from (I.3-24), (I.3-26), and (I.3-27) as

$$(\sigma_x - \sigma_y)^2 + (\sigma_y - \sigma_z)^2 + (\sigma_z - \sigma_x)^2$$
$$+ 6\left(\tau_{xy}^2 + \tau_{xz}^2 + \tau_{yz}^2\right) = 2\sigma_0^2. \qquad (I.9\text{-}29)$$

For plane stress, the following stresses are zero,

$$\sigma_z = \tau_{xz} = \tau_{yz} = 0, \tag{I.9-30}$$

so that (I.9-29) reduces to the form

$$\sigma_x^2 - \sigma_x \sigma_y + \sigma_y^2 + 3\tau_{xy}^2 = \sigma_0^2. \tag{I.9-31}$$

Similarly, using the principal stress form of the Mises yield condition (4.2-1) by substituting $\sigma_3 = 0$ into it, we obtain

$$\sigma_1^2 - \sigma_1 \sigma_2 + \sigma_2^2 = \sigma_0^2. \tag{I.9-32}$$

V. V. Sokolovsky investigated solutions satisfying (I.9-32) and equilibrium (I.-45) of the form [Kac 74]

$$\sigma_1 = 2k \cos(\gamma - \pi/6), \qquad \sigma_2 = 2k \cos(\gamma + \pi/6), \tag{I.9-33}$$

where γ is a function (x, y) related to the hydrostatic stress σ (I.8-28),

$$\sigma \equiv (\sigma_1 + \sigma_2 + \sigma_3)/3 = (\sigma_1 + \sigma_2)/3 \quad \text{for plane stress,} \tag{I.9-34}$$

by the formula

$$\cos \gamma = 3^{1/2} \sigma/(2k). \tag{I.9-35}$$

Transforming (I.9-33) into Cartesian coordinátes, we find, through the use of the strength of materials formulas

$$2\sigma_x = \sigma_1 + \sigma_2 + (\sigma_1 - \sigma_2)\cos 2\beta \tag{I.9-36}$$

$$2\sigma_y = \sigma_1 + \sigma_2 - (\sigma_1 - \sigma_2)\cos 2\beta \tag{I.9-37}$$

$$2\tau_{xy} = (\sigma_1 - \sigma_2)\sin 2\beta, \tag{I.9-38}$$

that

$$\sigma_x/k = 3^{1/2}\cos \gamma + \sin \gamma \cos 2\beta \tag{I.9-39}$$

$$\sigma_y/k = 3^{1/2}\cos \gamma - \sin \gamma \cos 2\beta \tag{I.9-40}$$

$$\tau_{xy}/k = \sin \gamma \sin 2\beta, \tag{I.9-41}$$

where β is the angle to the direction of the largest principal stress σ_1. Substituting these into the equilibrium equations (I.4-5), we obtain

$$(3^{1/2}\sin \gamma \cos 2\beta - \cos \gamma)\gamma_{,x}$$
$$+ 3^{1/2}\sin \gamma \sin 2\beta \, \gamma_{,y} - 2 \sin \gamma \beta_{,y} = 0 \tag{I.9-42}$$

$$(3^{1/2}\sin \gamma \cos 2\beta + \cos \gamma)\gamma_{,y}$$
$$- 3^{1/2}\sin \gamma \sin 2\beta \, \gamma_{,x} - 2 \sin \gamma \beta_{,x} = 0. \tag{I.9-43}$$

Solution techniques vary for solving (I.9-42) and (I.9-43) because the classification of partial differential equations depends upon where the state of stress falls on the Mises yield surface [Kac 74]. The angle γ starts at point M in Fig. I.9-1 and moves clockwise from 0 to 2π, passing through points $MBNCPDQERFLAM$ at $\pi/6$ intervals. See Table I.9-2 for the regions of hyperbolicity, parabolicity, and ellipticity in terms of γ.

With respect to the characteristics of the partial differential equations (I.9-42) and (I.9-43), there are two families in a hyperbolic region, as there are in plane strain. However, unlike the characteristics of plane strain, they are not orthogonal to each other, nor do they correspond to slip lines. In a parabolic region, there is only one family of characteristics, and in the elliptic regions there are no real characteristics.

Kachanov [Kac 74] considers in detail every region of the yield surface, including stress discontinuities and example problems. We, however, cannot undertake the task of examining every region of the Mises yield surface, as we do not use the material beyond this section. Instead, we limit our discussion to the plane stress equivalent of the Prandtl mode I crack problem, which was solved by Hutchinson [Hut 68b, Hut 79] and used for comparison with a power law hardening material as $n \to \infty$.

Hutchinson's solution is given in terms of the polar coordinate θ. For stresses that are independent of the coordinate r, the equilibrium equations (I.4-50)–(I.4-51) reduce to the following:

$$\tau_{r\theta,\theta} + \sigma_r - \sigma_\theta = 0 \qquad\qquad (I.9\text{-}44)$$

$$\sigma_{\theta,\theta} + 2\tau_{r\theta} = 0. \qquad\qquad (I.9\text{-}45)$$

TABLE I.9-2
Partial Differential Equation Classification for Plane Stress (Mises)

Region	System Eqs. (I.9-42)–(I.9-43)	γ (range)
Arc MB	Elliptic	$0 \to \pi/6$
Point B	Parabolic	$\pi/6$
Arc $BNCPD$	Hyperbolic	$\pi/6 \to 5\pi/6$
Point D	Parabolic	$5\pi/6$
Arc DQE	Elliptic	$5\pi/6 \to 7\pi/6$
Point E	Parabolic	$7\pi/6$
Arc $ERFLA$	Hyperbolic	$7\pi/6 \to 11\pi/6$
Point A	Parabolic	$11\pi/6$
Arc AM	Elliptic	$11\pi/6 \to 2\pi$

In polar coordinates, the yield condition (I.9-31) transforms to, using equations (I.4-44)–(I.4-46),

$$\sigma_r^2 - \sigma_r \sigma_\theta + \sigma_\theta^2 + 3\tau_{r\theta}^2 = \sigma_0^2. \qquad (I.9\text{-}46)$$

Hutchinson normalizes his stresses such that σ_0 in (I.9-46) is 1 and uses the notation $\sigma_{r\theta}$ for $\tau_{r\theta}$.

In Figs I.9-3a and I.9-3b, we see plots of the solution that Hutchinson [Hut 68b, Hut 79] presents for a perfectly plastic material and a power law hardening material. The perfectly plastic solution below corresponds to the regions marked alphabetically in Fig. I.9-3b:

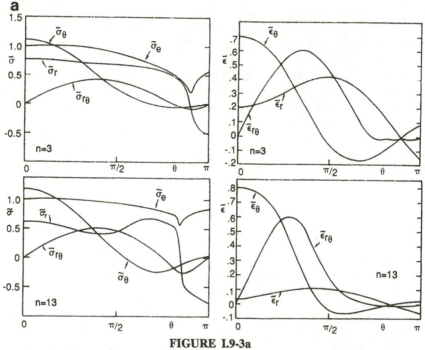

FIGURE I.9-3a

θ-Variations of stress and strains at the tip of a tensile crack for plane stress. Reprinted from *J. Mech. Phys. Solids*, **16**, J. W. Hutchinson, Singular behavior at the end of a tensile crack in a hardening material, 13–31 (1968), and *J. Mech. Phys. Solids*, **16**, J. W. Hutchinson, Plane stress and strain fields at the crack tip, 337–347 (1968), with kind permission from Elsevier Science Ltd., The Boulevard, Langford Lane, Kidlington OX5 1GB, UK.

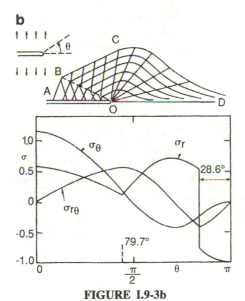

FIGURE I.9-3b

Stress characteristics and stress distribution at the tip of a tensile crack in a perfectly plastic material for plane stress. Reprinted from *J. Mech. Phys. Solids*, **16**, J. W. Hutchinson, Singular behavior at the end of a tensile crack in a hardening material, 13–31 (1968), and *J. Mech. Phys. Solids*, **16**, J. W. Hutchinson, Plane stress and strain fields at the crack tip, 337–347 (1968), with kind permission from Elsevier Science Ltd., The Boulevard, Langford Lane, Kidlington OX5 1GB, UK.

region *ABO*:

$$\sigma_r/\sigma_0 = -\tfrac{1}{2}(1 + \cos 2\theta), \qquad \sigma_\theta/\sigma_0 = -\tfrac{1}{2}(1 - \cos 2\theta),$$

$$\tau_{r\theta}/\sigma_0 = \tfrac{1}{2} \sin 2\theta \tag{I.9-47}$$

region *BCO*:

$$\sigma_r/\sigma_0 = \tfrac{1}{4}(-1 + 3\sin 2\theta_{OB}) + \tfrac{1}{4}(1 + \cos \theta_{OB})\cos 2(\theta - \theta_{OB})$$

$$+ \tfrac{1}{2} \sin 2\theta_{OB}\sin 2(\theta - \theta_{OB})$$

$$\sigma_\theta/\sigma_0 = -\sigma_r/\sigma_0 + \tfrac{1}{2}(-1 + 3\cos 2\theta_{OB}) \tag{I.9-48}$$

$$\tau_{r\theta}/\sigma_0 = -\tfrac{1}{4}(1 + \cos 2\theta_{OB})\sin 2(\theta - \theta_{OB}) + \tfrac{1}{2} \sin 2\theta \cos 2(\theta - \theta_{OB})$$

fan (*CDO*, first derived by [Hil 52]):

$$\sigma_\theta/\sigma_0 = 2\sigma_r/\sigma_0 = (2/3^{1/2})\cos \theta, \qquad \tau_{r\theta}/\sigma_0 = (1/3^{1/2})\sin \theta. \tag{I.9-49}$$

Regions *ABO* and *BCO*, where both families of characteristics are straight lines, have uniform states of stress.

The angles θ_{OB} and θ_{OC} correspond to the lines separating the three distinct regions shown, i.e.,

$$\theta_{OB} = 151.4°, \qquad \theta_{OC} = 79.7°. \tag{I.9-50}$$

These angles were found numerically, subject to the boundary conditions of a continuous state of stress across *OC* and a discontinuous tangential stress σ_r across *OB*. No continuous stress field could be found.

One interesting aspect of this stress discontinuity is that it separates regions of tension and compression. Stresses (I.9-47)–(I.9-48) transform into a Cartesian system as follows:

region *ABO*:

$$\sigma_x/\sigma_0 = -1, \qquad \sigma_y = 0, \qquad \tau_{xy} = 0. \tag{I.9-51}$$

region *BCO*:

$$\sigma_x/\sigma_0 = 0.012, \qquad \sigma_y/\sigma_0 = 0.301, \qquad \tau_{xy}/\sigma_0 = -0.552. \tag{I.9-52}$$

We can see clearly now that there is a uniform state of compression in *ABO* and of tension in *BCO*. Across the stress discontinuity, we find by substituting θ_{OB} from (I.9-50) into (I.9-47) and (I.9-48), respectively,

$$\sigma_r^-/\sigma_0 = -0.771, \qquad \sigma_\theta/\sigma_0 = -0.229, \qquad \tau_{r\theta}/\sigma_0 = -0.420, \tag{I.9-53}$$

$$\sigma_r^+/\sigma_0 = 0.542, \qquad \sigma_\theta/\sigma_0 = -0.229, \qquad \tau_{r\theta}/\sigma_0 = -0.420, \tag{I.9-54}$$

where the superscripts designate the compressive $(-)$ and tensile $(+)$ regions. There is a jump in σ_r, i.e., $\Delta\sigma_r = |\sigma_r^+ - \sigma_r^-|$, of magnitude 1.313 σ_0 across *OB*.

We can find neither a corresponding compressive region in the Prandtl plane strain solution nor a stress discontinuity. Physically, stress discontinuities represent the last remnants of elastic regions in perfectly plastic solutions. This would seem to imply that in an elastoplastic solution of the plane stress problem, under the Mises yield condition, there would be a narrow elastic region separating two plastic regions [Hut 68b].

In the analytic continuation of stresses across a prescribed elastic–plastic boundary for the Tresca yield condition in plane stress (Section 1.1), the presence of a disequilibrated stress discontinuity in this region suggests that an elastic unloading is necessary for equilibrium to be established.

Returning to the plane stress Mises solution, we find that ahead of the crack, i.e., along line *OD*, the two families of characteristics run together to form a single characteristic. This region is parabolic by Table I.9-2, as opposed to the rest of the stress field which is hyperbolic.

To prove this we determine, by substituting $\theta = 0$ into (I.9-49), that

line OD:

$$\sigma_\theta/\sigma_0 = 2/3^{1/2}, \qquad \sigma_r/\sigma_0 = 1/3^{1/2}, \qquad \tau_{r\theta} = 0$$

$$\rightarrow \sigma/\sigma_0 = 1/3^{1/2} \rightarrow \langle \gamma_{OD} = \pi/6 \rightarrow \text{point } B \text{ on yield surface}.$$

$$(I.9\text{-}55)$$

Similarly, we find that regions ABO and BCO are hyperbolic:

region ABO: $\langle \gamma_{ABO} = 2\pi/3 \rightarrow$ point P on yield surface $\qquad$ (I.9-56)

region BCO: $\langle \gamma_{BCO} \approx 2^{1/2} \rightarrow$ point between N and C. $\qquad$ (I.9-57)

Power Law Hardening Materials under Plane Stress

Let us now examine the HRR solution for plane stress. The stress–strain relationships change from (I.8-160)–(I.8-162) to the following:

$$\epsilon_r/\epsilon_0 = \alpha \sigma_e^{n-1}(\sigma_r - \tfrac{1}{2}\sigma_\theta)/\sigma_0^n \qquad (I.9\text{-}58)$$

$$\epsilon_\theta/\epsilon_0 = \alpha \sigma_e^{n-1}(\sigma_\theta - \tfrac{1}{2}\sigma_r)/\sigma_0^n \qquad (I.9\text{-}59)$$

$$\epsilon_{r\theta}/\epsilon_0 = \tfrac{3}{2}\alpha \sigma_e^{n-1}\tau_{r\theta}/\sigma_0^n . \qquad (I.9\text{-}60)$$

The form of the effective stress σ_e is given by (I.9-46), where σ_e replaces σ_0. The functions of θ and n, i.e., $\tilde{\sigma}_r(\theta, n)$, $\tilde{\sigma}_\theta(\theta, n)$, $\tilde{\sigma}_{r\theta}(\theta, n)$, $\tilde{\sigma}_e(\theta, n)$, and $\tilde{\epsilon}_r(\theta, n)$, $\tilde{\epsilon}_\theta(\theta, n)$, $\tilde{\epsilon}_{r\theta}(\theta, n)$, are analogous to their definitions for plane strain, (I.8-163)–(I.8-169).

In Figs. I.9-3a and I.9-3b, we see these functions plotted. The discontinuous stress σ_r, which we observed in the perfectly plastic case at θ_{OB}, appears to be approached by the work hardening material as $n \rightarrow \infty$. This lends strong support for its acceptance in the perfectly plastic state.

I.10 NUMERICAL SOLUTIONS OF THE MODE I ELASTOPLASTIC PROBLEM

In Section I.7 we examined analytical elastoplastic solutions of the mode III problem. No corresponding solutions have been found for the other two principal modes of fracture. In this section, we examine solutions of the mode I problem by numerical methods. Mode I is by far the most important mode of fracture from a practitioner's point of view, and thus we limit our discussion to this case.

First, let us examine the shapes that are predicted for mode I elastic–plastic boundaries by the small-scale yielding, linear elastic solution. In Fig. I.10-1a and I.10-1b, we see curves plotted by Broek [Bro 82] that represent approximate locations of the elastoplastic boundaries of the mode I problem for both plane stress and plane strain under the Mises and Tresca yield criterion, respectively.

The curves in Fig. I.10-1a for the Mises yield condition can be obtained by substituting the small-scale yielding stresses (I.5-10)–(I.5-12) into either (I.8-4) for plane strain or (I.9-31) for plane stress. For plane strain, Poisson's ratio was taken to be $\nu = \frac{1}{3}$. The locations of these curves in polar coordinates (r, θ), with the origin at the crack tip, are given below:

Mises yield condition $(-\pi \le \theta \le \pi)$:
plane stress:

$$r_P = [1/(2\pi)](K_I/\sigma_0)^2 \cos^2(\theta/2)[1 + 3\sin^2(\theta/2)]. \quad \text{(I.10-1)}$$

plane strain:

$$r_P = [1/(2\pi)](K_I/\sigma_0)^2 \cos^2(\theta/2)\left[(1 - 2\nu)^2 + 3\sin^2(\theta/2)\right]. \quad \text{(I.10-2)}$$

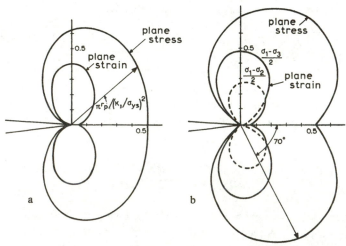

FIGURE I.10-1

Prescribed elastic–plastic boundaries according to Mises and Tresca yield criteria and small-scale yielding linear elastic stress: (a) Mises, (b) Tresca. Reprinted from [Bro 82] by permission of Kluwer Academic Publishers.

In the figures, the radius to the plastic zone r_P has been normalized according to the relationship provided in Fig. I.10-1a ($\sigma_{ys} = \sigma_0$).

For the Tresca yield condition, we substitute (I.5-10)–(I.5-12) into (I.9-9) for plane stress ($\sigma_0 = 2k$). For plane strain (Tresca), we use either

$$(\sigma_1 - \sigma_2)/2 = k, \qquad |\theta| < 2\sin^{-1}(1 - 2\nu) \qquad \text{(I.10-3)}$$

or

$$(\sigma_1 - \sigma_3)/2 = k, \qquad |\theta| \geq 2\sin^{-1}(1 - 2\nu) \qquad \text{(I.10-4)}$$

where σ_1 and σ_3 are defined as in (I.9-4)–(I.9-5), and σ_2 as in the second equation of (I.4-4). Thus for the

Tresca yield condition ($-\pi \leq \theta \leq \pi$):
plane stress:

$$r_P = [1/(2\pi)](K_I/\sigma_0)^2 \cos^2(\theta/2)[1 + |\sin(\theta/2)|]^2. \qquad \text{(I.10-5)}$$

plane strain:

$$r_{P_1} = [1/(2\pi)](K_I/\sigma_0)^2 \cos^2(\theta/2)[1 - 2\nu + |\sin(\theta/2)|]^2, \qquad |\theta| < \theta_I.$$
$$\text{(I.10-6)}$$

$$r_{P_2} = [1/(2\pi)](K_I/\sigma_0)^2 \sin^2\theta, \qquad |\theta| \geq \theta_I. \qquad \text{(I.10-7)}$$

where the magnitude of the angle θ that divides contours r_{P_1} and r_{P_2} is defined as follows (see [CZ 91]):

$$\theta_I \equiv 2\sin^{-1}(1 - 2\nu). \qquad \text{(I.10-8)}$$

The plane strain curve is plotted as a solid line, which is the outermost envelope of its two constituents (I.10-6) and (I.10-7), which are shown extended into the plastic region as broken lines [Bro 82].

We recall that no change of plane on the Tresca yield surface occurs for plane strain slip line theory, as is evident in the plane strain elastic–plastic locus for the mode I elastic solution, (I.10-3) and (I.10-4). Because plastic material is incompressible, the counterpart of Poisson's ratio is $1/2$, as can be seen by comparing (I.8-2) to the second equation of (I.4-4). Upon substituting $\nu = 1/2$ in (I.10-8), we also see that for an incompressible elastic material, the yield locus is restricted to a single region of the Tresca yield surface, i.e., r_{P_2} of (I.10-7) governs the whole field.

For incompressible elastic material, we also see for plane strain that the Mises and Tresca yield loci assume identical forms, after we substitute $\nu = 1/2$ and replace σ_0 by its equivalent in terms of k, i.e., (I.3-2), (I.3-4).

If we plot the plane strain elastic–plastic locus for an incompressible material (Fig. I.10-2), we find that the leading edge of the plastic zone touches the crack tip; i.e., there is no finite plastic region directly ahead of the crack. In [RJ 70], it is mentioned that this may be true as well in elastoplastic solutions solved numerically, as in [LMOR 71] with $\nu = 1/2$. The curve shown in Fig. I.10-2 may be identified as a conchoid [Law 72] of the quadrifolium (four-leaf rose), when rewritten in the form

$$r_P = [1/(16\pi)](K_I/K)^2(1 - \cos 2\theta). \qquad (I.10\text{-}9)$$

For a comparison of boundaries determined from the small-scale yielding solution to an exact linear elastic solution for an infinite plate subject to biaxial tensile tractions at infinity σ_∞ under the Mises yield condition and plane strain loading ($\nu = 0.3$), see Section 4.2.

Numerical Solutions

Let us now compare the prescribed elastic–plastic boundaries with curves determined through solutions of the mode I elastoplastic problem through numerical means.

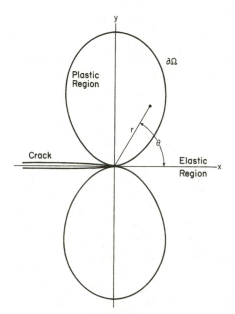

FIGURE I.10-2

Prescribed plane strain elastic–plastic boundary for incompressible materials.

In Fig. I.10-3, we see mode I elastic–plastic boundaries that were found numerically using the finite element method in [KPPC 70a, KPPC 70b], with further discussions in [AC 88, PM 78, Cher 79], for a linear elastic/non–work-hardening plastic material under the Mises yield condition. These curves for both plane strain (Poisson's ratio $\nu = 0.46$) and plane stress (incompressible $\nu = 1/2$) were obtained for a material that used as far-field displacements the small-scale yielding solution. (The use of the small-scale yielding solution as a source for far-field boundary conditions has become known in the literature as the *boundary layer method*.). The finite elements used were constant strain triangles. The outermost boundary was rectangular.

The x^* and y^* coordinates are nondimensionalized with respect to the stress intensity factor K_I and yield stress σ_0, as follows:

$$x^* \equiv (8/\pi)(\sigma_0/K_I)^2 x, \qquad y^* \equiv (8/\pi)(\sigma_0/K_I)^2 y. \quad (\text{I.10-10})$$

These solutions were obtained by minimizing the potential energy in both the exclusively linear elastic region and the yielded region where both linear elastic and perfectly plastic components (a non–work-hardening material) contribute. Yield was determined by calculating strains from the displacement field. When the material's equivalent strain exceeded the yield strain, a plastic contribution to the strain energy was included. As a deformation theory was being applied, no possibility of residual plastic strains resulting from material that had undergone linear elastic relaxation was considered.

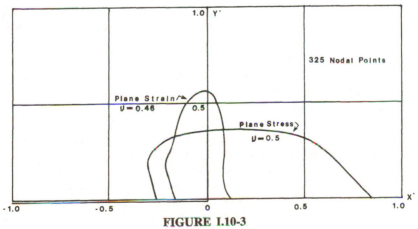

FIGURE I.10-3

Mode I elastic–plastic boundaries determined numerically for the Mises yield condition. After Kudryavtsev, Parton, Peskov, and Cherapanov [KPPC 70a, KPPC 70b].

As the authors noted, the plastic zone of the plane stress solution somewhat resembles the elongated shape of the Dugdale model's plastic zone. The plane stress plastic zone also extends farther ahead of the crack tip than the plane strain plastic zone, in agreement with the behavior we observed for the purely elastic, small-scale yielding approximation. However, the extent of the numerical elastic–plastic boundary perpendicular to the crack is smaller in plane stress than in plane strain, unlike the purely elastic approximation.

Analytical expressions were fitted to the numerical curves in [KPPC 70a, KPPC 70b] of the elastic–plastic boundaries (see also [Cher 79]), which can assume the following forms:

plane stress:

$$r_P^* = 0.25 \, (\pi - \theta) - 0.15 \sin(3\theta/2)], \qquad 0 \le \theta \le \pi, \quad \text{(I.10-11)}$$

plane strain:

$$r_P^* = 0.55(1 + 24 \cos^2\theta)^{-1/2}, \qquad \text{elliptically shaped,} \quad \text{(I.10-12)}$$

where

$$r_P^* = \left[(x^*)^2 + (y^*)^2\right]^{1/2}, \qquad \theta = \tan^{-1}(y^*/x^*). \quad \text{(I.10-13)}$$

It was found that, as the number of nodes in the finite element scheme increased, the elastic–plastic boundaries decreased in size, while the imposed displacements at the outermost boundary were held constant. The curves given here are somewhat smaller than the curves shown in Fig. I.10-3, which were taken from data generated with the same number of nodes, 325. The analytical expressions reflect a refinement of the maximum number of nodes employed in each case. Note that in the case of plane stress, the leading edge of the analytical boundary is rounded by (I.10-1), unlike that shown in Fig. I.10-3. In the case of plane strain, the elliptical boundary given by (I.10-12) is symmetrical with respect to the y^*-axis, unlike that shown in Fig. I.10-3.

Another finite element analysis for a linear elastic/non–work-hardening material under the Mises yield condition and plane strain loading conditions was discussed in [LMOR 71]. There, Poisson's ratio was taken to be 0.3 and flow theory was used rather than a deformation theory of plasticity. The smoothed shape of the elastic–plastic boundary from this study is shown in Fig. I.10-4b for the upper half-plane. The finite elements employed were polar, resembling the geometry shown in Fig. I.4-1. Figure I.10-4a shows the yielded elements as a function of the load increment. A

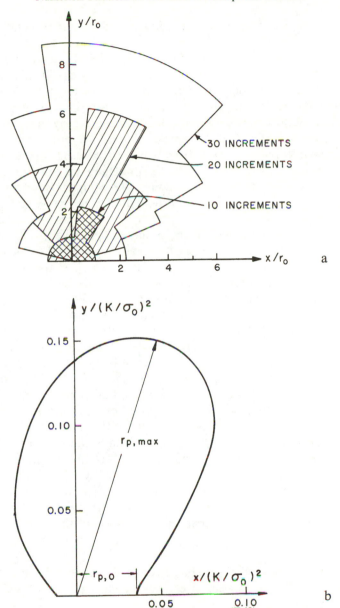

FIGURE I.10-4

Growth of the plastic zone. (a) Outlines of yielded finite element elements after 10, 20, and 30 elastic–plastic load increments with coordinates made dimensionless by radius r_0 of the innermost elements. (b) Smoothed estimates of the elastic–plastic boundary, plotted in terms of similarity parameter $(K/\sigma_0)^2$ for small-scale yielding (K is the stress intensity factor.) Reprinted from [LMOR 71] by permission of Kluwer Academic Publishers.

boundary layer approach was used for far-field boundary conditions on stress.

Perhaps the feature that most distinguishes the plastic zones obtained by finite element analyses from the plastic zones predicted by linear elastic fracture mechanics is that the crack tip is completely engulfed by the plastic zone in the former case. In the latter case, the trailing portion of the plastic zone just touches the crack tip of the purely elastic problem, which seems to imply that the crack surfaces do not extend a finite distance into the plastic region. This was not the case in the mode III analytical solution, where the crack tip predicted by the purely elastic solution (the small-scale yielding solution) was completely surrounded by plastic material for both perfectly plastic material and power law hardening materials.

Another feature prominent in the numerical governed solution of the plane strain problems involving plastic material governed by incremental plasticity (flow theory) is that the *wings* of the *butterfly* shape of the plastic zone lean forward. This forward lean can be measured as the angle to the radius of the plastic zone at its greatest extent from the crack tip. In Fig. I.10-4b this angle to $r_{P,\,max}$ is approximately 70° [LMOR 71], unlike the plastic zones predicted by linear elastic fracture mechanics, i.e., Figs I.10-1a, I.10-2, and 4.2-1. Furthermore, it was observed in a numerical analysis by Tuba [Tub 66] at 69°. This type of behavior was also displayed in a finite element elastoplastic solution obtained in [TF 89] for cracklike flaws having a rounded edge (Mises yield condition/non−work-hardening material). This particular solution is discussed in Section 1.5 in connection with elastic unloading in the trailing portion of the plastic zone.

Following Du and Hancock [DH 91], the lean of the lobes of the plastic zones is a function of the side tractions which are applied parallel to the crack axis in a plate. In terms of the notation of Rice [Ric 74], the related stress is called the T stress, and in the case of linear elastic fracture mechanics, it is tied to the nonsingular second term of a Williams asymptotic expansion [Wil 57] of a linear elastic solution of the form

$$\sigma_x = A(\theta)/r^{1/2} + B(\theta) + C(\theta)r^{1/2} + \cdots. \qquad (I.10\text{-}14)$$

Let us now define the general T stress for linear elastic fracture mechanics as a finite uniaxial stress parallel to the crack axis. This is expressed in matrix form as

$$\begin{bmatrix} \sigma_x & \tau_{xy} \\ \tau_{xy} & \sigma_y \end{bmatrix} = K_I/(2\pi r)^{1/2} \begin{bmatrix} f_{xx}(\theta) & f_{xy}(\theta) \\ f_{xy}(\theta) & f_{yy}(\theta) \end{bmatrix} + \begin{bmatrix} T & 0 \\ 0 & 0 \end{bmatrix}, \qquad (I.10\text{-}15)$$

where f_{ij} are the functions of the angle θ as defined in (I.5-10)−(I.5-12).

For the Griffith crack [Gri 20] of length $2a$ subject to a uniaxial load σ_∞ in the y direction, the Williams expansion along the x-axis ($\theta = 0$) is [Han 92]

$$\sigma_x/\sigma_\infty = 2^{-1/2}\left[(r/a)^{-1/2} - 2^{1/2} + (3/4)(r/a)^{1/2} - (5/32)(r/a)^{3/2}\right.$$

$$\left. +(7/128)(r/a)^{5/2} + O(r/a)^{7/2} \cdots \right. \tag{I.10-16}$$

$$\sigma_y/\sigma_\infty = \sigma_x/\sigma_\infty + 1 \tag{I.10-17}$$

$$\tau_{xy} = 0. \tag{I.10-18}$$

Thus the T stress in the case of a uniaxial load is, by (I.10-15) and (I.10-16),

$$T = -\sigma_\infty. \tag{I.10-19}$$

For the biaxial load, as shown in Fig. I.5-3a, T would be

$$T = 0, \tag{I.10-20}$$

as the tensile traction simply adds a constant stress $\sigma_x^+ = \sigma_\infty$ to the previous stress state.

In [DH 91], the predictions of the effect of the T stress on the shape of the plastic zone determined by an elastoplastic finite element analysis of a non–work-hardening material under the Mises yield condition is shown in Fig. I.10-5. The T stress was incorporated through a boundary layer approach for the far-field displacement using a biaxial loading with differ-

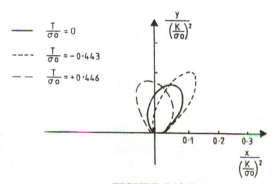

FIGURE I.10-5

The effect T stress on the plastic zone shapes. Reprinted from *J. Mech. Phys. Solids*, **39**, Z.-Z. Du and J. W. Hancock, The effect of non-singular stresses on crack-tip constraint, 555–567 (1991), with kind permission from Elsevier Science Ltd., The Boulevard, Langford Lane, Kidlington OX5 1GB, UK.

ent magnitudes in the x and y directions. The outer boundary itself was circular and the mesh was composed of polar elements, as shown in Fig. I.4-1. The loading conditions were plane strain with Poisson's ratio taken as 0.3 for most computations, although a few runs were performed at 0.49 to investigate incompressibility. The symbol σo in these figures represents the yield stress, and K is the stress intensity factor.

We see in Fig. I.10-5 that if T is compressive, the butterfly wings expand and swing forward of the leading edge of the crack. If T is tensile, the plastic zone shrinks and moves backward. The shapes of these curves agree with the work of [LC 73], which were discussed in this context in [Ric 74].

Let us now observe the effect of these side forces T on the predictions of elastic–plastic boundaries from linear elastic fracture mechanics alone by observing Fig. 4.2-1. The curves composed of broken lines are the plane strain small-scale yielding loci as predicted by the Mises yield criterion for $\nu = 0.3$ at various load levels indicated in the figure. The solid lines represent the elastic–plastic loci as predicted by the exact linear elastic solution for a plate with an internal crack of length $2a$ subject to a biaxial load σ_∞. The solid-line loci reflect a greater T stress than the broken-line loci, as the approximate loci ignore any term beyond $r^{-1/2}$ in the Williams expansion. Thus the exact loci move backward in conformity with one of the predictions of Du and Hancock in their finite element solutions. Du and Hancock also mention that the maximum r_p should decrease with greater T stress, but this is not observed in our purely elastic solution. Both of these analyses, however, indicate that nonsingular stresses do have a pronounced effect on the shape of plastic zones.

The Du and Hancock solutions also show that the T stresses affect the sectors around the crack tip for which the Prandtl stress field applied. We will examine this aspect of their solution in Section 1.5

I.11 MISCELLANEOUS MATHEMATICAL TOPICS

Complete Solutions

A complete solution of a first-order nonlinear partial differential equation [Sne 57] is one that satisfies the governing equation and contains two arbitrary constants (a, b). As an example of a nonlinear first-order equation, let us choose the governing equation of the mode III problem in the plastic region in terms of the stress function $\phi(x, y)$ which has been normalized with respect to yield stress in pure shear k, i.e.,

$$\phi_{,x}^2 + \phi_{,y}^2 = 1. \tag{I.11-1}$$

One complete solution (they are not unique) is

$$\phi = x \cos a + y \sin a + b. \tag{I.11-2}$$

It is easily confirmed that (I.11-2) satisfies (I.11-1) by taking the partial derivatives of ϕ, i.e.,

$$\phi_{,x} = \cos a, \qquad \phi_{,y} = \sin a, \tag{I.11-3}$$

and then substituting them into (I.11-1).

Let us now assume that constant b cannot be chosen independently of constant a, but is instead a function of a; i.e.,

$$\phi = x \cos a + y \sin a + b(a). \tag{I.11-4}$$

Equation (I.11-4) is now called one-parameter subfamily of the complete solution.

Taking a partial derivative of $\phi(x, y)$ with respect to a while holding ϕ, x, and y constant, we obtain the following relationship:

$$0 = -x \sin a + y \cos a + b'(a). \tag{I.11-5}$$

where the prime denotes differentiation with respect to a.

Let us now relax the condition that parameter a be held constant and assume instead that it is a function of x and y; i.e., $a = a(x, y)$. If we then take partial derivatives of (I.11-4) with respect to x and y, we find in place of (I.11-4)

$$\phi_{,x} = \cos a - x \sin a\, a_{,x} + y \cos a\, a_{,x} + b'(a) a_{,x} \tag{I.11-6}$$

$$= \cos a + [-x \sin a + y \cos a + b'(a)] a_{,x} \tag{I.11-7}$$

$$\phi_{,y} = -x \sin a\, a_{,y} + \sin a + + y \cos a\, a_{,y} + b'(a) a_{,y} \tag{I.11-8}$$

$$= \sin a + [-x \sin a + y \cos a + b'(a)] a_{,y}. \tag{I.11-9}$$

Notice that the bracketed terms in both (I.11-7) and (I.11-9) have the same form as relationship (I.11-5). If we impose (I.11-5) on both (I.11-7) and (I.11-9), we find

$$\phi_{,x} = \cos a, \qquad \phi_{,y} = \sin a, \tag{I.11-10}$$

which are the same partial derivatives of ϕ with respect to x and y that are obtained from (I.11-2) with both a and b held constant (I.11-3).

Equation (I.11-5) represents the projection of the characteristics of the surface $\phi(x, y)$ onto the xy plane. They are often called simply the characteristics. For other partial differential equations the characteristics may be a family of curves rather than the straight lines found for the eiconal equation.

Now consider a particular function for $b(a)$, for example,

$$b(a) = -\cos a. \tag{I.11-11}$$

Thus (I.11-5), with (I.11-11) substituted for $b(a)$, becomes, after taking the derivative of $b(a)$ with respect to a,

$$0 = -x \sin a - y \cos a + \sin a, \tag{I.11-12}$$

from which we can solve for parameter $a = a(x, y)$, as

$$a = \tan^{-1}[y/(x-1)]. \tag{I.11-13}$$

The solution of the partial differential equation is therefore obtained by substituting $a(x, y)$ from (I.11-13) into (I.11-11) and from there substituting both of them into (I.11.4); i.e.,

$$\phi = (x-1)\cos\tan^{-1}[y/(x-1)] + y\sin\tan^{-1}[y/(x-1)]. \tag{I.11-14}$$

It is readily verified that (I.11-14) solves the original partial differential equation; however, to simplify calculations and to gain further insight into this solution, we will first express it in an alternative form.

Let us introduce a new Cartesian coordinate system (X, Y) which is a translation of the original Cartesian axes (x, y) along the x-axis a unit distance to the right. The standard polar coordinates (ρ, α) relative to the new Cartesian system (X, Y) are then

$$X = x - 1 = \rho \cos \alpha, \qquad Y = y = \rho \sin \alpha. \tag{I.11-15}$$

Our supposed solution ϕ of (I.11-14) becomes, by applying (I.11-13) and (I.11-15) to it,

$$\phi = \rho \cos^2 a + \rho \sin^2 a = \rho \tag{I.11-16}$$

$$= [X^2 + Y^2]^{1/2} \tag{I.11-17}$$

$$= \left[(x-1)^2 + y^2\right]^{1/2}. \tag{I.11-18}$$

By taking the partial derivatives of (I.11-18) with respect to x and y, it is now simple to prove that the original partial differential equation (I.11-1) is indeed satisfied. It is interesting to note that we obtained (I.11-18) from (I.11-2) despite the fact that it cannot be obtained directly by choosing a and b to be any particular set of constants.

If ϕ of (I.11-2) is interpreted as a surface, where a and b are arbitrary constants, it represents a family of planes that have a slope of magnitude 1 relative to the xy plane. The one-parameter subsystem, on the other hand, is a family of planes with a slope of magnitude 1, each of which touches surface (I.11-18), and may therefore be interpreted geometrically as a cone.

Cones, as well as cylinders and other ruled surfaces, may be generated in space by the motion of a straight line. The individual traces of lines that are left by the moving line are called generators. By choosing a and b, as we have in (I.11-4) and (I.11-11), the planes intersect for different values of a in such a way that the lines of intersection comprise the generators of the cone (I.11-18). The elimination of the parameter a from equations (I.11-4), (I.11-11), and (I.11-12) forms the envelope of the one-parameter family of solutions. The analytical expression for the envelope, in this case, also solves the partial differential equation.

By introducing polar coordinates (I.11-15), we have actually thrown away half of the solution of (I.11-14); i.e., a second cone exists which is a reflection of the first cone relative to the xy plane in the negative ϕ direction. This situation occurs because we assume in (I.11-16) that ρ, being a polar radius, is positive. If we accept instead that ρ can be negative, then ϕ can also be negative an the second cone is generated. This second cone of (I.11-14) can be accounted for by placing a $\pm$ sign before the radical sign in (I.11-18).

In general, there are three categories of solutions [Sne 57] that can be found from a complete solution ϕ of a first-order nonlinear equation of arbitrary form:

$$f(\phi, x, y, a, b) = 0. \tag{I.11-19}$$

These categories are

Case 1: Set a and b equal to particular constant values.

Case 2: Take a partial derivative of a one-parameter subsystem of the complete solution with respect to one of the parameters and set the result equal to zero:

$$f(\phi, x, y, a, b(a)) = 0 \tag{I.11-20}$$

$$\partial f(\phi, x, y, a, b(a))/\partial a = 0. \tag{I.11-21}$$

The function ϕ determined from the elimination of a between (I.11-20) and (I.11-21) constitutes a solution, which represents the envelope of the one-parameter subsystem. It may be impossible in specific cases to eliminate a from the simultaneous equations (I.11-20)–(I.11-21), as we were able to do in the case of (I.11-18), which is termed an explicit solution. Nonetheless, a parametrized solution involving a and the two simultaneous equations may prove very useful in itself. Probably, case 2 is the most common occurrence of the three types for solving initial value problems.

Case 3: Take partial derivatives of the complete solution with respect to both independent parameters (a, b) and set those results equal to zero:

$$f(\phi, x, y, a, b) = 0 \qquad (I.11\text{-}22)$$

$$\partial f(\phi, x, y, a, b)/\partial a = 0 \qquad (I.11\text{-}23)$$

$$\partial f(\phi, x, y, a, b)/\partial b = 0. \qquad (I.11\text{-}24)$$

The function ϕ is obtained from the elimination of a and b from the system of three equations. In the case of the complete solution (I.11-2) to the eiconal equation (I.11-1), such an envelope does not exist.

In addition to these three cases, given one complete solution of a partial differential equation, other complete solutions of the same equation can be derived from it (see [Sne 57]).

The general solution of first-order partial differential equations is an alternative type of solution that contains an arbitrary function $f(\ )$, rather than arbitrary parameters as in a complete solution. The following is an example of a general solution,

$$\phi(x, y) = f(x - y), \qquad (I.11\text{-}25)$$

to partial differential equation

$$\phi_{,x} + \phi_{,y} = 0. \qquad (I.11\text{-}26)$$

General solutions may be found for first-order partial differential equations only if the equations are linear.

Monge–Ampere Family of Partial Differential Equations

A Monge–Ampere equation is a second-order, nonlinear partial differential equation that has special integrability properties [CH 62]. The most general form of Monge–Ampere equation is

$$R\phi_{,xx} + S\phi_{,xy} + T\phi_{,yy} + U\left(\phi_{,xx}\phi_{,yy} - \phi_{,xy}^2\right) = V, \qquad (I.11\text{-}27)$$

where $R, S, T, U,$ and V are functions of variables x, y, ϕ, $\phi_{,x}$, and $\phi_{,y}$. A simple technique for solving a limited version of the Monge–Ampere equation, applicable to plane stress plasticity, where R, S, T, U, V are constants is discussed in this subsection. Techniques for solving more general Monge–Ampere equations can be found in [Ayr 52, Sne 57, For 59].

Let us assume that solutions of the restricted Monge–Ampere equation can be found in the form

$$A\phi_{,x} + B\phi_{,y} + Cx + Dy = F(\alpha\phi_{,x} + \beta\phi_{,y} + \gamma x + \delta y), \qquad (I.11\text{-}28)$$

where A, B, C, D and $\alpha, \beta, \gamma, \delta$ are constants and $F(\ )$ is an arbitrary function. Taking a partial derivative of (I.11-28) with respect to x, we find

$$A\phi_{,xx} + B\phi_{,xy} + C$$

$$= (\alpha\phi_{,xx} + \beta\phi_{,xy} + \gamma)F'(\alpha\phi_{,x} + \beta\phi_{,y} + \gamma x + \delta y). \quad \text{(I.11-29)}$$

Similarly, taking a partial derivative of (I.11-28) with respect to y, we get

$$A\phi_{,xy} + B\phi_{,yy} + D$$

$$= (\alpha\phi_{,xy} + \beta\phi_{,yy} + \delta)F'(\alpha\phi_{,x} + \beta\phi_{,y} + \gamma x + \delta y). \quad \text{(I.11-30)}$$

Now eliminate $F'(\alpha\phi_{,x} + \beta\phi_{,y} + \gamma x + \delta y)$ from the simultaneous equations (I.11-29) and (I.11-30) to find

$$\frac{A\phi_{,xx} + B\phi_{,xy} + C}{\alpha\phi_{,xx} + \beta\phi_{,xy} + \gamma} = \frac{A\phi_{,xy} + B\phi_{,yy} + D}{\alpha\phi_{,xy} + \beta\phi_{,yy} + \delta}. \quad \text{(I.11-31)}$$

Multiplying the means and extremes of (I.11-31) and collecting terms, we find an equation that has the form of the Monge–Ampere equation (I.11-27):

$$(\delta A - \alpha D)\phi_{,xx} + (\alpha C + \delta B - \beta D - \gamma A)\phi_{,xy} + (\beta C - \gamma B)\phi_{,yy}$$

$$+ (\beta A - \alpha B)\left[\phi_{,xx}\phi_{,yy} - \phi_{,xy}^2\right] = \gamma D - C\delta. \quad \text{(I.11-32)}$$

Let us now explore the possibilities of using the intermediate integral (I.11-28) of (I.11-32) for solving the governing equations of plasticity theory, which are second-order, nonlinear equations in terms of a stress function. If we find a governing equation of the form (I.11-32), we can immediately reduce it to a first-order equation by (I.11-28). From there we might be able to apply a standard solution technique for finding complete solutions of first-order equations. Ordinarily, a second-order nonlinear, partial differential equation is insoluble by analytical means.

We find by substituting a stress function of the form (I.4-2) into the plane strain yield condition for a perfectly plastic material (Mises or Tresca) that

$$(\phi_{,xx} - \phi_{,yy})^2 + 4\phi_{,xy}^2 = 4k^2 \quad \text{(I.11-33)}$$

$$\rightarrow \phi_{,xx}^2 - 2\phi_{,xx}\phi_{,yy} + \phi_{,yy}^2 + 4\phi_{,xy}^2 = 4k^2, \quad \text{(I.11-34)}$$

which is obviously not a Monge–Ampere equation. As (I.11-33) also applies to the plane stress regions NP and RL of the Tresca yield surface (Fig. I.9-1), the Monge–Ampere equation does not apply there as well.

For the Mises plane stress equation, by (I.9-31) we have

$$\phi_{,xx}^2 - \phi_{,xx}\phi_{,yy} + \phi_{,yy}^2 + 3\phi_{,xy}^2 = \sigma_0^2, \tag{I.11-35}$$

which is again not of the Monge–Ampere classification.

The only stress function for a perfectly plastic material that has the form of a Monge–Ampere equation for plane problems involving the two most commonly used yield criteria is the plane stress Tresca for regions *LM*, *MN*, *PQ*, and *RQ* of the yield surface (Fig. I.9-1); and even in this case it is not immediately obvious.

From (I.9-9), we infer for region *MN*

$$\phi_{,xx} + \phi_{,yy} + \left[(\phi_{,yy} - \phi_{,xx})^2 + 4\phi_{,xy}^2\right]^{1/2} = 4k. \tag{I.11-36}$$

Squaring this equation to remove the radical, one obtains

$$2k\phi_{,xx} + 2k\phi_{,yy} - \left(\phi_{,xx}\phi_{,yy} - \phi_{,xy}^2\right) = 4k^2, \tag{I.11-37}$$

which is a Monge–Ampere equation, where

$$R = T = 2k, \qquad S = 0, \qquad U = -1, \qquad V = 4k^2. \tag{I.11-38}$$

Perhaps the easiest way to identify a set of coefficients for the intermediate integral (I.11-28) is to note that (I.11-37) is factorable into

$$\frac{\phi_{,xx} - 2k}{\phi_{,xy}} = \frac{\phi_{,xy}}{\phi_{,yy} - 2k}. \tag{I.11-39}$$

By comparing (I.1-39) with (I.11-31), we can choose

$$A = \beta = 1, \qquad B = D = \alpha = \gamma = 0, \qquad C = \delta = -2k. \tag{I.11-40}$$

Thus one intermediate integral of (I.11-37) is

$$\phi_{,x} - 2kx = F(\phi_{,y} - 2ky). \tag{I.11-41}$$

The choice of coefficients (I.11-40) is by no means unique. For example, we can replace all the nonzero coefficients of (I.11-40) by their negatives and have a slightly different form of intermediate integral.

Order Symbols

There are two symbols $O(\ )$ and $o(\ )$ that are commonly used to characterize the order of singularities and of powers in general. The definitions of these as $x \to 0$ are [BH 86]:

function $f(x)$ is of $O(g(x))$ provided $\lim x \to 0 \ |f(x)|/|g(x)| \le$ constant

function $f(x)$ is of $o(g(x))$ provided $\lim x \to 0 \ |f(x)|/|g(x)| = 0$.

1

On the Continuance of an Analytical Solution across the Elastic–Plastic Boundary of a Mode I Fracture Mechanics Problem

Analytical elastoplastic solutions involving linear elastic and finite-dimensional plastic regions have been found only for mode III fracture mechanics problems. Under conditions of small-scale yielding, the elastic–plastic boundary for the mode III problem can be determined by substituting the stresses from linear elastic fracture mechanics into the Mises/Tresca yield condition. In contrast, numerical studies for mode I problems involving the Mises yield condition [Tub 66, LMOR 71, KPPC 70a, KPPC 70b, PM 78, Cher 79] have shown boundaries that differ in shape from loci determined from linear elastic fracture mechanics in general (see Sections I.10 and 4.2). Here, we will analytically investigate a mode I elastoplastic problem for the Tresca yield criterion under plane stress loading conditions.

In this study, the mode I small-scale yielding stresses are substituted into the Tresca yield condition to obtain a prescribed elastoplastic boundary. A plastic stress function for a perfectly plastic material is sought—a function that satisfies both equilibrium and the yield condition across the elastic–plastic interface. An intermediate integral is found for the governing partial differential equation, which is a nonlinear, second-order equation of the Monge–Ampere class. From a complete solution of the intermediate integral, the initial value problem is solved analytically as in [Ung 90a].

The plastic stress field that is determined from this function exhibits a discontinuity in the trailing portion of the plastic zone. Physical implications of this solution together with possible applications are discussed in the Preface and Section 1.5.

In the course of investigating this mode I problem, we develop a method of solving elastoplastic problems based on concepts from differential geometry. The solution technique finds an integral plastic surface that circumscribes a known elastic surface. This method of solution can also be applied to mode III problems, as well as other elastoplastic problems where a complete solution can be found to the governing partial differential equation of the plastic stress function.

We first demonstrate the solution process for a mode III problem that has a simple solution. This problem has been solved previously by other investigators using different techniques. Once insight is gained from working the mode III problem, we can apply a modified version of the solution scheme to the mode I problem, which has a higher-order partial differential equation.

1.1 ELASTOPLASTIC STRESS ANALYSES FOR
MODES I AND III

Mode III

The stress function ϕ^E of small-scale yielding and its relationship to the elastic antiplane shear stresses τ_{xz}^E and τ_{yz}^E for the mode III fracture mechanics problem with a stress intensity factor K_{III} follow:
mode III:

$$
\left.
\begin{aligned}
\phi^E &= -(2r/\pi)^{1/2} K_{III}\cos(\theta/2) \\
\tau_{xz}^E &= \phi_{,y}^E = -(2\pi r)^{-1/2} K_{III}\sin(\theta/2) \\
\tau_{yz}^E &= -\phi_{,x}^E = (2\pi r)^{-1/2} K_{III}\cos(\theta/2)
\end{aligned}
\right\} \quad -\pi \le \theta \le \pi
$$

$$(1.1\text{-}1)$$
$$(1.1\text{-}2)$$
$$(1.1\text{-}3)$$

where the commas in (1.1-2) and (1.1-3) denote partial differentiation. The relationships between the polar coordinates (r,θ) and the rectangular

Cartesian coordinates (x, y) employed in (1.1-1)–(1.1-3) are

$$x = r \cos \theta = r[1 - 2\sin^2(\theta/2)], \qquad y = r \sin \theta = 2r \sin(\theta/2)\cos(\theta/2), \tag{1.1-4}$$

where the trigonometric identities involving $\theta/2$ in (1.1-4) are cited for later use.

The potential ϕ^{E} is a harmonic function and the stresses (1.1-2)–(1.1-3) derived from it satisfy equilibrium equation (2.1-3).

The notation for the first partial derivatives of the plastic stress function $\phi(x, y)$ with respect to x and y is

$$p \equiv \phi_{,x}, \qquad q \equiv \phi_{,y}. \tag{1.1-5}$$

In the mode III problem all stresses are zero except for the antiplane stresses. Consequently, the Tresca or Mises yield condition for a perfectly plastic material takes the following form [Hut 79]:

$$\tau_{xz}^2 + \tau_{yz}^2 = k^2 \qquad \text{or} \qquad p^2 + q^2 = k^2, \tag{1.1-6}$$

where k is the yield stress in pure shear.

If the elastic mode III stresses (1.1-2)–(1.1-3) are substituted into yield condition (1.1-6), the locus of points that satisfy this relationship is a circle of radius R where

$$R = K_{\mathrm{III}}^2/(2\pi k^2). \tag{1.1-7}$$

This circle, which is shown in Fig. 1.1-1, is the assumed elastic–plastic interface $\partial\Omega$.

Let us now parametrize the elastic stress function $(\hat{\phi})$, its first partial derivatives $(\hat{p}, \hat{q})$, and the Cartesian coordinates $(\hat{x}, \hat{y})$ on the elastoplastic interface in terms of the parameter a; i.e.,

$$\partial\Omega: \qquad a = \sin(\theta/2) \rightarrow \cos(\theta/2) = (1 - a^2)^{1/2}. \tag{1.1-8}$$

When (1.1-7) and (1.1-8) are substituted in (1.1-1)–(1.1-4), we obtain

$$
\left.
\begin{aligned}
\hat{\phi} &\equiv -2kR(1 - a^2)^{1/2} \\
\hat{p} &= -k(1 - a^2)^{1/2}, \qquad \hat{q} \equiv -ka \\
\hat{x} &\equiv R(1 - 2a^2), \qquad \hat{y} \equiv 2Ra(1 - a^2)^{1/2}
\end{aligned}
\right\} \quad -1 \le a \le 1.
\quad
\begin{aligned}
&(1.1\text{-}9) \\
&(1.1\text{-}10) \\
&(1.1\text{-}11)
\end{aligned}
$$

Interior to $\partial\Omega$, the definitions of the functions $\hat{\phi}$, $\hat{p}$, $\hat{q}$, $\hat{x}$, and $\hat{y}$ in terms of the parameter a remain the same as in (1.1-9)–(1.1-11), but the relationship between a and the coordinates differs from that in (1.1-8).

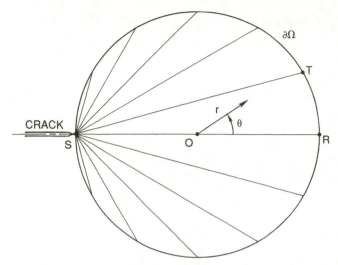

FIGURE 1.1-1

Mode III plastic zone. Reprinted from *Eng. Fract. Mech.* **36**, D. J. Unger, Analytic Continuation of stresses across a mode I elastoplastic interface, 763–776 (1990), with permission from Pergamon Press Ltd., Headington Hill Hall, Oxford OX3 0BW, UK.

Methods for finding complete solutions of nonlinear, first-order equations are detailed in [Sne 57]. It is easily verified that the following relationship for ϕ is a solution to partial differential equation (1.1-6):

$$\phi = -k(1 - a^2)^{1/2}x - kay + b \qquad (1.1-12)$$

provided a and b are constants. Equation (1.1-12) is a complete solution to (1.1-6) as it involves two arbitrary parameters a and b.

Sneddon [Sne 57] describes a method of finding an integral surface of a first-order, nonlinear partial differential equation that circumscribes a given surface. This procedure finds the envelope of a one-parameter subsystem of a complete solution. An imposed condition is

$$\partial\Omega: \qquad \frac{p}{\hat{p}} = \frac{q}{\hat{q}} = 1. \qquad (1.1-13)$$

In our analysis the prescribed surface is related to the elastic stress function ϕ^{E}. The governing equation is (1.1-6), and the surface that circumscribes ϕ^{E} is related to the plastic stress function ϕ. The imposed condition (1.1-13) suits our purpose as it ensures that the antiplane stresses will be continuous across the elastic–plastic boundary. This fulfills an equilibrium requirement.

The technique described in [Sne 57] requires the elimination of the parameters a, b from relationships corresponding to (1.1-9)–(1.1-13). The first step is to reduce the two-parameter complete solution to a one-parameter subsystem such that ϕ equals ϕ^E on the elastic–plastic boundary. This is accomplished by setting $b = b(a)$ where

$$b(a) \equiv \hat{\phi} - \hat{x}\hat{p} - \hat{y}\hat{q}. \qquad (1.1\text{-}14)$$

Thus (1.1-12) assumes form (1.1-15) after the substitution of (1.1-10) and (1.1-14), i.e.,

$$\phi = \hat{\phi} + (x - \hat{x})\hat{p} + (y - \hat{y})\hat{q}. \qquad (1.1\text{-}15)$$

On the elastic–plastic boundary $\phi = \hat{\phi}$ as $x = \hat{x}$ and $y = \hat{y}$.

In (1.1-12) a and b were assumed to be constants; however, in (1.1-15) the parameter a must be a function of (x, y) as it varies with θ on the boundary by (1.1-8). Consequently $\hat{\phi}$, $\hat{p}$, $\hat{q}$, $\hat{x}$, and $\hat{y}$, which are functions of a, must also be functions of the coordinates. This implies that (1.1-15) cannot satisfy (1.1-6) with the parameter a as a function of the coordinates without some additional condition. This restriction may be found by taking the derivative of (1.1-15) with respect to the parameter a while treating x, y, and ϕ as constants; i.e.,

$$\hat{\phi}_{,a} - \hat{x}_{,a}\hat{p} + (x - \hat{x})\hat{p}_{,a} - \hat{y}_{,a}\hat{q} + (y - \hat{y})\hat{q}_{,a} = 0. \qquad (1.1\text{-}16)$$

Equation (1.1-16) may be interpreted as the family of characteristic lines of (1.1-6) and (1.1-15).

We now prove that (1.1-15) is a solution of (1.1-6) provided that (1.1-16) is satisfied. Taking the partial derivative of (1.1-15) with respect to x and using a chain rule for differentiations of $\hat{\phi}$, $\hat{p}$, $\hat{q}$, $\hat{x}$, and $\hat{y}$, which are functions of the parameter a, we find

$$\phi_{,x} = \hat{\phi}_{,a}a_{,x} + (1 - \hat{x}_{,a}a_{,x})\hat{p} + (x - \hat{x})p_{,a}a_{,x} - \hat{y}_{,a}a_{,x}\hat{q} + (y - \hat{y})\hat{q}_{,a}a_{,x}$$

$$= \hat{p} + \left[\hat{\phi}_{,a} - \hat{x}_{,a}\hat{p} + (x - \hat{x})\hat{p}_{,a} - \hat{y}_{,a}\hat{q} + (y - \hat{y})\hat{q}_{,a} \right]a_{,x}. \qquad (1.1\text{-}17)$$

By substituting (1.1-16) into (1.1-17), we obtain

$$\phi_{,x} = \hat{p}. \qquad (1.1\text{-}18)$$

Similarly, we can prove that

$$\phi_{,y} = \hat{q}. \qquad (1.1\text{-}19)$$

Thus any exclusive relationship that exists between partial derivatives of ϕ on the boundary is also satisfied in the region interior to $\partial\Omega$; i.e.,

$$\hat{p} = f(\hat{q}) \rightarrow p = f(q). \qquad (1.1.20)$$

The function f is determined by eliminating a between equations (1.1-10). This procedure yields

$$\hat{p}^2 + \hat{q}^2 = k^2 \rightarrow p^2 + q^2 = k^2, \qquad (1.1-21)$$

which proves our original assertion about (1.1-6), (1.1-15), and (1.1-16).

We now seek the explicit form of our solution $\phi(x, y)$. Substituting the relationships for $\hat{\phi}$, $\hat{p}$, $\hat{q}$, $\hat{x}$, and $\hat{y}$ from (1.1-9)–(1.1-11) into (1.1-16) and taking derivatives with respect to a as indicated, we find

$$y/(x + R) = a/(1 - a^2)^{1/2} \qquad \text{or} \qquad a(x, y) = y \Big/ \big[(x + R)^2 + y^2\big]^{1/2}.$$
$$(1.1-22)$$

Equation (1.1-22) provides the parameter a as a function of (x, y) in the region interior to $\partial\Omega$, i.e., the plastic region. It will naturally reduce to (1.1-8) on the boundary $\partial\Omega$. By substituting $a(x, y)$ from (1.1-22) into (1.1-9)–(1.1-11), we infer from (1.1-15) that

$$\phi(x, y) = -k\big[(x + R)^2 + y^2\big]^{1/2}. \qquad (1.1-23)$$

Solution (1.1-23) is the required envelope of the one-parameter subsystem (1.1-15) of the complete solution (1.1-12). It represents geometrically a surface that circumscribes the elastic surface defined by (1.1-1).

The stresses can be obtained from (1.1-23) by differentiating $\phi(x, y)$ with respect to x and y in a fashion analogous to (1.1-2) and (1.1-3) where $\phi(x, y)$, τ_{xz}^{P}, and τ_{yz}^{P} replace ϕ^{E}, τ_{xz}^{E}, and τ_{yz}^{E}. Alternatively, they can be found by substituting $a(x, y)$ from (1.1-22) into (1.1-10), (1.1-18), and (1.1-19); i.e.,

$$\tau_{xz}^{P} = \phi_{,y} = \hat{q}(a(x, y))$$
$$= -ky \Big/ \big[(x + R)^2 + y^2\big]^{1/2}, \quad r \leq R, \qquad (1.1-24)$$

mode III:

$$\tau_{yz}^{P} = -\phi_{,x} = -\hat{p}(a(x, y))$$
$$= k(x + R) \Big/ \big[(x + R)^2 + y^2\big]^{1/2}. \qquad (1.1-25)$$

Equations (1.1-24) and (1.1-25) are identified as the plastic stress field of the small-scale yielding elastoplastic solution. Typical slip lines such as ST are shown in Fig. 1.1-1. This family of slip lines corresponds to the family of characteristics defined by (1.1-16).

For the statically admissible stress solution, i.e., (1.1-24) and (1.1-25), compatible strains and displacements have been found previously for Hencky deformation theory. See Section I.7 and [Ric 68a, Hut 79].

Mode I

There are fundamental differences between stress functions found in mode III analyses and stress functions found in mode I analyses. First of all there are two types of plane problems: plane stress and plane strain. In addition, the two most commonly used yield criteria, Mises and Tresca, have different governing equations for the plane stress problem. This differs from the antiplane problem where both criteria assume the same form, (1.1-6). Most importantly, the governing equations in the plane problems are nonlinear, second-order equations, rather than the nonlinear, first-order equation of the antiplane problem.

The technique developed in the previous section relied on finding a complete solution of the governing first-order equation from which an integral surface could be found that circumscribed the elastic stress surface. This process cannot be directly applied to plane problems as they require solutions of second-order equations. However, reducing a nonlinear, second-order equation to a first-order equation is sometimes possible. The equation that results from such a reduction is called the intermediate integral. Unfortunately, these kinds of integrations are performable only for special classes of second-order equations. One important class is the Monge–Ampere family of equations [Sne 57].

Of the types of plane problems mentioned earlier, only the plane stress problem for the Tresca yield condition has a governing equation of the Monge–Ampere class. We will find in the subsequent analysis an intermediate integral to this second-order equation. From a complete solution of the intermediate integral, a plastic stress function that circumscribes the Airy stress function for the mode I problem will be determined. We will also discover that the intrinsic geometric requirements for finding a plastic stress function that circumscribes an elastic surface guarantees equilibrium across the elastic–plastic interface.

The Airy stress function ϕ^E [biharmonic $\nabla^4\phi^E \equiv \nabla^2(\nabla^2\phi^E) = 0$] for the mode I fracture problem, under conditions of small-scale yielding, has the following form:

mode I: $\qquad \phi^E = (4/3)cr^{3/2}\cos^3(\theta/2), \qquad -\pi \le \theta \le \pi, \qquad$ (1.1-26)

$$c \equiv K_I/(2\pi)^{1/2}, \qquad\qquad\qquad (1.1\text{-}27)$$

where K_I is the mode I stress intensity factor. Taking the first derivatives of ϕ^E with respect to x and y, we find

$$\phi^E_{,x} = 2cr^{1/2}\cos^3(\theta/2), \qquad\qquad (1.1\text{-}28)$$

$$\phi^E_{,y} = 2cr^{1/2}\cos^2(\theta/2)\sin(\theta/2). \qquad\qquad (1.1\text{-}29)$$

The second derivatives of ϕ^E are related to the elastic stresses as follows: mode I:

$$\sigma_x^E = \phi_{,yy}^E = cr^{-1/2}\cos(\theta/2)[1 - \sin(\theta/2)\sin(3\theta/2)] \quad (1.1\text{-}30)$$
$$\sigma_y^E = \phi_{,xx}^E = cr^{-1/2}\cos(\theta/2)[1 + \sin(\theta/2)\sin(3\theta/2)] \quad (1.1\text{-}31)$$
$$\tau_{xy}^E = -\phi_{,xy}^E = cr^{-1/2}\cos(\theta/2)\sin(\theta/2)\cos(3\theta/2) \quad (1.1\text{-}32)$$

$$-\pi \le \theta \le \pi$$

where σ_x and σ_y are the normal stresses in the x and y directions, respectively, and τ_{xy} is the shear stress in the xy plane. All other stresses have zero magnitudes. The relationships between Cartesian and polar coordinates are identical to those given in (1.1-4).

Yield occurs for the Tresca condition when the maximum shear stress reaches the critical value k, i.e., the yield stress in pure shear. The Tresca yield surface is shown schematically in Fig. 1.1-2 in terms of the principal stresses σ_1 and σ_2 ($\sigma_3 = 0$ for plane stress). The algebraic relationships between stresses for $\sigma_1 \ge \sigma_2$ are

$$2\sigma_1 = \sigma_x + \sigma_y + \left[(\sigma_x - \sigma_y)^2 + 4\tau_{xy}^2\right]^{1/2} \quad (1.1\text{-}33)$$

$$2\sigma_2 = \sigma_x + \sigma_y - \left[(\sigma_x - \sigma_y)^2 + 4\tau_{xy}^2\right]^{1/2} \quad (1.1\text{-}34)$$

$$\sigma_3 = 0. \quad (1.1\text{-}35)$$

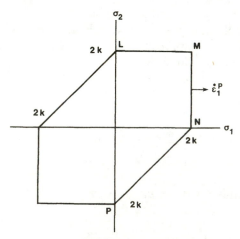

FIGURE 1.1-2

Tresca yield surface. Adapted from *Eng. Fract. Mech.* **36**, D. J. Unger, Analytic continuation of stresses across a mode I elastoplastic interface, 763–776 (1990), with permission from Pergamon Press Ltd., Headington Hill Hall, Oxford OX3 OBW, UK.

From the substitution of the mode I stresses (1.1-30)–(1.1-32) into (1.1-33)–(1.1-34), we find that $\sigma_1 \geq \sigma_2 \geq 0$. Thus the mode I stresses meet the yield condition along side MN (Fig. 1.1-2) of the yield surface where $\sigma_1 = 2k$; i.e.,

Side MN of yield surface:

$$\sigma_1 = 2k, \qquad \sigma_1 \geq \sigma_2 \geq 0. \tag{1.1-36}$$

We may therefore infer from (1.1-33) and (1.1-36) that

$$\left[(\sigma_x - \sigma_y)^2 + 4\tau_{xy}^2\right]^{1/2} = 4k - (\sigma_x + \sigma_y) \quad \text{for} \quad \sigma_1 \geq \sigma_2 \geq 0. \tag{1.1-37}$$

By substituting the stresses (1.1-30)–(1.1-32) in (1.1-37), we obtain the following locus of the assumed elastoplastic boundary $\partial\Omega$:

$$\partial\Omega: \qquad\qquad cr^{-1/2}\cos(\theta/2)[1 + |\sin(\theta/2)|] = 2k. \tag{1.1-38}$$

The shape of this curve $OABCD$ is shown in Fig. 1.1-3 for the half-plane, $y \geq 0$. A similar curve has appeared in [Bro 82].

The relationships between the partial derivatives of the plastic stress function and the plastic stresses are analogous to those for the Airy stress

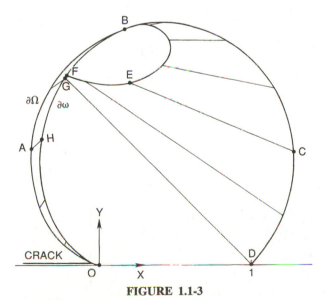

FIGURE 1.1-3

Mode I plastic zone. Adapted from *Eng. Fract. Mech.* **36**, D. J. Unger, Analytic continuation of stresses across a mode I elastoplastic interface, 763–776 (1990), with permission from Pergamon Press Ltd., Headington Hill Hall, Oxford OX3 OBW, UK.

function, i.e., (1.1-30)–(1.1-32). If we substitute these general relationships for stresses from (1.1-30)–(1.1-32) into the yield criteria (1.1-37) and square both sides, we find the following nonlinear, second-order equation of the Monge–Ampere class:

$$\phi_{,xy}^2 - \phi_{,xx}\phi_{,yy} + 2k(\phi_{,xx} + \phi_{,yy}) = 4k^2. \qquad (1.1\text{-}39)$$

A plastic stress function ϕ that is a solution of (1.1-39) produces stresses that satisfy equilibrium and the yield condition $\sigma_1 = 2k$ or equilibrium and the yield condition $\sigma_2 = 2k$. The extraneous solution $(\sigma_2 = 2k)$ comes from squaring yield condition (1.1-37) to eliminate the radical. We shall see, however, that the uniqueness of the initial value problem for the Monge–Ampere equation eliminates this extraneous solution in practice.

Techniques for finding intermediate integrals of the Monge–Ampere class of equations are discussed in [Sne 57, For 59]. One intermediate integral to (1.1-39) is

$$2yk - q = F(2xk - p), \qquad (1.1\text{-}40)$$

where $F(\ )$ is an arbitrary function and p, q are the first partial derivatives of ϕ with respect to x and y, as in (1.1-5). It is readily verified that any solution to (1.1-40) also satisfies (1.1-39). To show this, we take partial derivatives of (1.1-40) with respect to x and y. We obtain

$$-\phi_{,xy} = F'(2xk - p)(2k - \phi_{,xx}) \rightarrow F'(2xk - p)$$

$$= \phi_{,xy}/(\phi_{,xx} - 2k), \qquad (1.1\text{-}41)$$

$$2k - \phi_{,yy} = F'(2xk - p)(-\phi_{,xy}) \rightarrow F'(2xk - p)$$

$$= (\phi_{,yy} - 2k)/\phi_{,xy}. \qquad (1.1\text{-}42)$$

After eliminating the function $F'(2xk - p)$ from (1.1-41) and (1.1-42), we recover equation (1.1-39).

The parametric equations for r, ϕ, p, q, x, and y on the elastoplastic boundary $\partial\Omega$ for $y \geq 0$ are, respectively,

$$\left.\begin{aligned}
\hat{r} &\equiv (c/2k)^2(1 - a)(1 + a)^3 && (1.1\text{-}43)\\
\hat{\phi} &\equiv (1/6)(c^4/k^3)(1 - a)^3(1 + a)^6 && (1.1\text{-}44)\\
\hat{p} &\equiv (c^2/k)(1 + a)(1 - a^2)^2 && (1.1\text{-}45)\\
\hat{q} &\equiv (c^2/k)a(1 + a)(1 - a^2)^{3/2} && (1.1\text{-}46)\\
\hat{x} &\equiv (1/4)(c/k)^2(1 - a)(1 + a)^3(1 - 2a^2) && (1.1\text{-}47)\\
\hat{y} &\equiv (1/2)(c/k)^2a(1 + a)^2(1 - a^2)^{3/2} && (1.1\text{-}48)
\end{aligned}\right\} \quad 0 \leq a \leq 1,$$

where a has the same relationship to θ on $\partial\Omega$ as in (1.1-8). These parametrizations were obtained by substituting a into the relationships (1.1-4), (1.1-26), (1.1-28), (1.1-29), and (1.1-38). Because of the variables that appear in intermediate integral (1.1-40), the following parametrized relationships are also evaluated [from (1.1-45)–(1.1-48)]:

$$2\hat{x}k - \hat{p} = (1/2)(c^2/k)(1 + a)^2(1 - a^2)(2a - 1 - 2a^2), \quad (1.1\text{-}49)$$

$$2\hat{y}k - \hat{q} = (c^2/k)(1 + a)a^2(1 - a^2)^{3/2}. \quad (1.1\text{-}50)$$

The terms $\hat{x}k - \hat{p}$ and $2\hat{y}k - \hat{q}$ on the boundary $\partial\Omega$ determine the function $F(\ )$ of (1.1-40). Through $F(\ )$ the specific form of the governing first-order equation for the mode I problem can be obtained in principle. The function $F(\ )$ of mode I resembles the function $f(\ )$ of mode III.

In order to find an explicit expression for $F(\ )$, we must solve for a from either (1.1-49) or (1.1-50). We subsequently substitute this expression for a into the remainder of the two equations to obtain $F(\ )$. However, the order of algebraic equation that one must solve in order to obtain parameter a exceeds four, which is the maximum order for which a general solution exists (for roots expressed as radicals, proved by Abel and Galois).

To circumvent this, we seek a complete solution of (1.1-40) such that parametric relationships established between variables on the boundary are satisfied interior to $\partial\Omega$; i.e.,

$$2xk - p = 2\hat{x}k - \hat{p}, \qquad 2yk - q = 2\hat{y}k - \hat{q}. \quad (1.1\text{-}51)$$

These relationships (1.1-51) ensure that partial differential equation (1.1-40) is satisfied without the need for an explicit determination of $F(\ )$.

The total derivative of $\phi(x, y)$ is

$$d\phi = p\,dx + q\,dy. \quad (1.1\text{-}52)$$

By substituting (1.1-51) into (1.1-52), we get

$$d\phi = [\hat{p} + 2k(x - \hat{x})]\,dx + [\hat{q} + 2k(y - \hat{y})]\,dy. \quad (1.1\text{-}53)$$

If we treat $\hat{p}$, $\hat{q}$, $\hat{x}$, and $\hat{y}$ as constants and integrate (1.1-53), the result is

$$\phi = k(x^2 + y^2) + (\hat{p} - 2k\hat{x})x + (\hat{q} - 2k\hat{y})y + b, \quad (1.1\text{-}54)$$

where b is a constant of integration. Equation (1.1-54) is a complete solution to the equation (1.1-40), provided a and b are constants and relationships (1.1-44)–(1.1-48) are enforced.

As in the mode III example, we now seek from the complete solution a surface that circumscribes the elastic surface. First, we define b as a function of a such that ϕ equals $\hat\phi$ on the boundary $\partial\Omega$, i.e.,

$$b = b(a) = \hat\phi - \hat x\hat p - \hat y\hat q + k(\hat x^2 + \hat y^2). \tag{1.1-55}$$

By the substitution of (1.1-55) into (1.1-54), the complete solution is reduced to the following one-parameter system:

$$\phi = \hat\phi + (x - \hat x)\hat p + (y - \hat y)\hat q + k(x - \hat x)^2 + k(y - \hat y)^2. \tag{1.1-56}$$

As (1.1-56) stands, the parameter a must be treated as a constant in order for the original partial differential equation to be satisfied. Nevertheless, the parameter a must be a function of (x, y) in order to fulfill the boundary conditions. Equation (1.1-56) will solve (1.1-40) if we relax the condition that a be held constant, provided the following relationship is satisfied:

$$\hat\phi_{,a} - \hat x_{,a}\hat p + (x - \hat x)\hat p_{,a} - \hat y_{,a}\hat q + (y - \hat y)\hat q_{,a}$$
$$+ 2k(\hat x - x)\hat x_{,a} + 2k(\hat y - y)\hat y_{,a} = 0. \tag{1.1-57}$$

Equation (1.1-57) is obtained from (1.1-56) by its differentiation with respect to a while holding x, y, and ϕ constant. It is the family of characteristic lines of (1.1-40) and (1.1-56). Taking a partial derivative of (1.1-56) with respect to x, we find

$$p \equiv \phi_{,x} = \hat\phi_{,a}a_{,x} + (1 - \hat x_{,a}a_{,x})\hat p + (x - \hat x)\hat p_{,a}a_{,x} - \hat y_{,a}a_{,x}\hat q$$
$$+ (y - \hat y)\hat q_{,a}a_{,x} + 2k(x - \hat x)(1 - \hat x_{,a}a_{,x}) + 2k(\hat y - y)\hat y_{,a}a_{,x} \tag{1.1-58}$$

which by factoring $a_{,x}$ becomes

$$p = \hat p + 2k(x - \hat x) + \Big[\hat\phi_{,a} - \hat x_{,a}\hat p + (x - \hat x)\hat p_{,a} - \hat y_{,a}\hat q + (y - \hat y)\hat q_{,a}$$
$$+ 2k(\hat x - x)\hat x_{,a} + 2k(\hat y - y)\hat y_{,a}\Big]a_{,x}. \tag{1.1-59}$$

By applying condition (1.1-57), we reduce equation (1.1-59) to

$$p = \hat p + 2k(x - \hat x). \tag{1.1-60}$$

Similarly, we can show that

$$q \equiv \phi_{,y} = \hat q + 2k(y - \hat y). \tag{1.1-61}$$

Thus by the imposition of (1.1-57), the first derivatives of ϕ with respect to x and y in (1.1-56) behave operationally as if $\hat{\phi}$, $\hat{p}$, $\hat{q}$, $\hat{x}$, and $\hat{y}$ were constants. One should be forewarned, however, that second derivatives of ϕ with respect to x and y do not behave in this operational fashion.

Because (1.1-60) and (1.1-61) have the same form as (1.1-51), we have proved that (1.1-56) is a solution of (1.1-40) with $a = a(x, y)$ provided that condition (1.1-57) is fulfilled.

On the elastic–plastic boundary, we see from (1.1-60) and (1.1-61) that

$$\partial\Omega: \qquad\qquad p = \hat{p} \quad \text{and} \quad q = \hat{q} \qquad\qquad (1.1\text{-}62)$$

as $x = \hat{x}$ and $y = \hat{y}$. Equation (1.1-62) shows that the first partial derivatives of the elastic and plastic stress functions agree on the elastic–plastic boundary. We note that (1.1-62) satisfies an equilibrium requirement that the tractions be continuous across an interface (see the subsection on uniqueness and continuity of stress).

For convenience, let us define the following functions of a:

$$P(a) \equiv \hat{p} - 2k\hat{x} = (1/2)(c^2/k)(1 - a)(1 + a)^3(2a^2 + 1 - 2a), \tag{1.1-63}$$

$$Q(a) \equiv \hat{q} - 2k\hat{y} = -(c^2/k)(1 + a)a^2(1 - a^2)^{3/2}, \tag{1.1-64}$$

$$\psi(a) \equiv \hat{\phi} - k(\hat{x}^2 + \hat{y}^2)$$
$$= (c^4/k^3)(1 - a)^2(1 + a)^6[(1/6)(1 - a) - (1/16)], \tag{1.1-65}$$

$$-\hat{x}P(a) = (1/8)(c^4/k^3)(1 - a)^2(1 + a)^6(1 - 2a^2)(2a - 2a^2 - 1), \tag{1.1-66}$$

$$-\hat{y}Q(a) = (1/2)(c^4/k^3)a^3(1 - a)^3(1 + a)^6, \tag{1.1-67}$$

$$H(a) \equiv \psi(a) - \hat{x}P(a) - \hat{y}Q(a)$$
$$= (1/48)(c^4/k^3)(1 - a)^2(1 + a)^6(4a - 1). \tag{1.1-68}$$

With the substitution of (1.1-63), (1.1-64), and (1.1-68) into solution (1.1-56), we get

$$\phi = xP(a) + yQ(a) + H(a) + k(x^2 + y^2). \tag{1.1-69}$$

Differentiating (1.1-69) with respect to a while treating ϕ, x, y as constants, we obtain an alternative form of characteristic equation (1.1-57) in terms of $P'(a)$, $Q'(a)$, and $H'(a)$ as

$$xP'(a) + yQ'(a) + H'(a) = 0. \tag{1.1-70}$$

By taking derivatives of $P(a)$, $Q(a)$, and $H(a)$ from (1.1-63), (1.1-64), and (1.1-68) with respect to a, we find

$$P'(a) = (c^2/k)a(1 - 2a)(3a - 2)(1 + a)^2, \tag{1.1-71}$$

$$Q'(a) = (c^2/k)a(1 + a)(1 + 2a)(3a - 2)(1 - a^2)^{1/2}, \tag{1.1-72}$$

$$H'(a) = (1/4)(c^4/k^3)a(1 - a)(2 - 3a)(1 + a)^5. \tag{1.1-73}$$

After substitution of (1.1-71), (1.1-72), and (1.1-73) into (1.1-70), we obtain the explicit form of the characteristic equation:

$$(c^2/k)a(1 + a)(2\text{-}3a)\Big[(1 + a)(1 - 2a)x + (1 + 2a)(1 - a^2)^{1/2}y$$

$$-(1/4)(c/k)^2(1 - a)(1 + a)^4\Big] = 0. \tag{1.1-74}$$

Dividing both sides of (1.1-74) by the factor $(c^2/k)a(1 + a)(2 - 3a)$ and rearranging the equation, we derive that, for $y \geq 0$,

$$(1 + a)(1 - 2a)x + (1 - a^2)^{1/2}(1 + 2a)y$$

$$= (1/4)(c/k)^2(1 - a)(1 + a)^4, \quad 0 < a \leq 1, \quad a \neq 2/3. \tag{1.1-75}$$

The singular characteristic $a = 0$ corresponds to slip line DG of Fig. 1.1-3. Along this line the stresses do not vary. Instead a biaxial state of stress $\sigma_x = \sigma_y = 2k$ exists (corner N of the Tresca yield surface of Fig. 1.1-2.). The singular characteristic $a = 2/3$ is tangent to the elastic–plastic boundary (point B of Fig. 1.1-3).

We now express p and q from (1.1-60) and (1.1-61) in terms of $P(a)$ and $Q(a)$ through the use of definitions (1.1-63) and (1.1-64):

$$p = P(a) + 2kx, \tag{1.1-76}$$

$$q = Q(a) + 2ky. \tag{1.1-77}$$

Using (1.1-76), (1.1-77), and the chain rules of differentiation, we conclude that

$$\sigma_x^P = q_{,y} = Q'(a)a_{,y} + 2k, \tag{1.1-78}$$

$$\sigma_y^P = p_{,x} = P'(a)a_{,x} + 2k, \tag{1.1-79}$$

$$\tau_{xy} = -p_{,y} = -P'(a)a_{,y}. \tag{1.1-80}$$

The expressions $a_{,y}$ and $a_{,y}$ in (1.1-78)–(1.1-80) are obtained by the partial differentiation of the characteristic equation (1.1-75) with respect to x and *y*. They are respectively

$$a_{,x} = (1 - 2a)(1 + a)/D, \tag{1.1-81}$$

$$a_{,y} = (1 + 2a)(1 - a^2)^{1/2}/D, \tag{1.1-82}$$

where the denominator D in (1.1-81) and (1.1-82) is defined as

$$D \equiv x(1 + 4a) + y(4a^2 + a - 2)(1 - a^2)^{-1/2}$$
$$+ (1/4)(c/k)^2(3 - 5a)(1 + a)^3. \tag{1.1-83}$$

We now introduce the normalized Cartesian coordinates (X, Y) and the normalized stresses $S_x^P, S_y^P, T_{xy}^P, S_1, S_2$:

$$X \equiv 4k^2x/c^2, \qquad Y \equiv 4k^2y/c^2, \tag{1.1-84}$$

$$S_x^P \equiv \sigma_x^P/k, \qquad S_y^P \equiv \sigma_y^P/k, \qquad T_{xy}^P \equiv \tau_{xy}^P/k, \tag{1.1-85}$$

$$S_1 \equiv \sigma_1/k, \qquad S_2 \equiv \sigma_2/k. \tag{1.1-86}$$

The normalized coordinates are so defined that a unit distance spans the tip of the crack to the end of the plastic zone on the crack axis, i.e., the distance of *DO* of Fig. 1.1-3. The stresses assume the following form in the normalized notation upon substitution of (1.1-84)–(1.1-85) into (1.1-78)–(1.1-83):

Normalized mode I plastic stresses, $Y \geq 0$, with $0 \leq a \leq 1$, $a \neq 2/3$:

$$S_x^P = 2 + \frac{4a(1 + a)(3a - 2)(1 + 2a)^2(1 - a^2)}{X(1 + 4a) + Y(4a^2 + a - 2)(1 - a^2)^{-1/2} + (3 - 5a)(1 + a)^3}, \tag{1.1-87}$$

$$S_y^P = 2 + \frac{4a(3a - 2)(1 - 2a)^2(1 + a)^3}{X(1 + 4a) + Y(4a^2 + a - 2)(1 - a^2)^{-1/2} + (3 - 5a)(1 + a)^3}, \tag{1.1-88}$$

$$T_{xy}^P = \frac{4a(2 - 3a)(1 + a)^2(1 - 4a^2)(1 - a^2)^{1/2}}{X(1 + 4a) + Y(4a^2 + a - 2)(1 - a^2)^{-1/2} + (3 - 5a)(1 + a)^3}. \tag{1.1-89}$$

The characteristic equation (1.1-75) becomes, in normalized coordinates,

$$(1 + a)(1 - 2a)X + (1 - a^2)^{1/2}(1 + 2a)Y = (1 + a)^4(1 - a),$$

$$0 \le a \le 1, \quad a \neq 2/3. \quad (1.1\text{-}90)$$

Several characteristic lines, including AH and CE, are shown in the normalized Cartesian plane (Fig. 1.1-3). The slip planes are oriented at an angle of $\pi/4$ to the xy plane [Kac 74]. The stress σ_1 is perpendicular to the characteristic lines, and the stress σ_2 is parallel to the characteristic lines.

If it were possible to analytically solve (1.1-90) for a, then the parameter a could be eliminated from the stresses (1.1-87)–(1.1-89). We were able to do this in the analogous equations of mode III.

The principal stresses in normalized notation for the upper half-plane for $a \neq 2/3$ are

$$S_1 = 2, \quad (1.1\text{-}91)$$

$$S_2 = 2 + \frac{8a(3a - 2)(1 + a)^2}{X(1 + 4a) + Y(4a^2 + a - 2)(1 - a^2)^{-1/2} + (3 - 5a)(1 + a)^3}.$$

$$(1.1\text{-}92)$$

Parabolic–Hyperbolic Plastic Boundary

The characteristic lines of (1.1-90) terminate when the stresses no longer satisfy yield condition (1.1-37). This locus of points occurs where σ_2 equals zero. At these points, the stresses move from region MN on the yield surface to region NP on the yield surface (Fig. 1.1-2).

We should also mention that the partial differential equations are different in regions MN and NP. In region MN a parabolic equation of the Monge–Ampere class governs. In region NP a nonlinear, second-order hyperbolic equation outside the Monge–Ampere class applies. This change from a parabolic equation to a hyperbolic equation is accompanied by a change in the number of characteristics at each point. In the parabolic case, a single characteristic goes through each point of the domain. In the hyperbolic case, two characteristics pass through each point of the domain. The number of slip lines that correspond to the number of characteristics also changes in a similar fashion.

It is curious that in region NP of the plane stress Tresca condition, the governing equation and the family of characteristics are identical to those found in plane strain Tresca and plane strain Mises criteria [Kac 74].

Let us call the boundary between the parabolic plastic zone and the hyperbolic plastic zone $\partial\omega$. The locus of $\partial\omega$ is found in parametric form by solving for X and Y from the simultaneous equations (1.1-90) and (1.1-92), where in (1.1-92) the stress S_2 is set equal to zero. The result is

$$\partial\omega: \qquad \sigma_1 = 2k, \qquad \sigma_2 = 0, \qquad \sigma_3 = 0, \qquad y \geq 0 \qquad (1.1\text{-}93)$$

$$X = (1 + a)^2(1 - a)[1 + a - (2/3)(1 - a)(1 + 2a)(9a^2 - 4a + 2)]/$$
$$(1 - 2a),$$

$$0 < a \leq 1, \quad a \neq 2/3, \quad a \neq 1/2, \tag{1.1-94}$$

$$X = 15/32, \quad a = 1/2, \tag{1.1-95}$$

$$Y = (2/3)(1 - a)(1 + a)^2(1 - a^2)^{1/2}(9a^2 - 4a + 2),$$

$$0 < a \leq 1, \quad a \neq 2/3. \tag{1.1-96}$$

Note that l'Hospital's rule is required to generate (1.1-95) from (1.1-94). The boundary $\partial\omega$ is shown in Fig. 1.1-3 as curve *OHGFBEF*. A portion of $\partial\omega$ that passes through node F is omitted in the figure for clarity.

Example Let us evaluate the normalized stresses along the characteristic *CE* of Fig. 1.1-3 using the formulas developed here. Characteristic *CE* begins at $\theta = \pi/6$ on the boundary $\partial\Omega$. Therefore, from (1.1-8), $a = \sin(\pi/12)$. By substituting this value for a into (1.1-90), a linear relationship between X and Y is established. Then by choosing arbitrary values of X, we can calculate corresponding values of Y for the fixed parameter a. The limits on X are found by substituting this value for a into (1.1-47) for $\partial\Omega$ and (1.1-94) for $\partial\omega$. Once values of a, X, and Y are set, the normalized stresses are obtained from (1.1-87)–(1.1-89) and (1.1-92). Specific evaluations are given in Table 1.1-1.

Uniqueness and Continuity of Stress

Courant and Hilbert [CH 62] prove that solutions of the initial value problem for the general Monge–Ampere equation are unique. Our particular initial value problem is defined as follows:

> *Find a twice-differentiable function $\phi(x, y)$ that is a solution of equation (1.1-39) which has initial values $\hat{\phi}$, $\hat{p}$, and $\hat{q}$ on boundary $\partial\Omega$ of arc length s which satisfy the strip condition*

$$d\hat{\phi}/ds = \hat{p}\,d\hat{x}/ds + \hat{q}\,d\hat{y}/ds. \tag{1.1-97}$$

If we prove that the strip condition is satisfied for our initial data, then by invoking Courant and Hilbert's theorem we know that solution (1.1-56) is

TABLE 1.1-1

Normalized Mode I Stresses along the Slip Line CE, $a = \sin(\pi / 12)$, $S_1 = 2$

X	Y	S_x^P	S_y^P	T_{xy}^P	S_2
0.203	1.186 $(\partial\omega)$	0.293	1.707	0.707	0
0.3	1.141	0.488	1.741	0.626	0.229
0.4	1.104	0.647	1.768	0.560	0.415
0.5	1.062	0.776	1.790	0.507	0.566
0.6	1.021	0.883	1.808	0.463	0.691
0.7	0.980	0.972	1.824	0.426	0.796
0.8	0.938	1.048	1.837	0.394	0.885
0.9	0.897	1.114	1.848	0.367	0.962
1.0	0.855	1.171	1.858	0.343	1.029
1.1	0.814	1.221	1.866	0.323	1.088
1.2	0.773	1.266	1.874	0.304	1.140
1.280	0.739 $(\partial\Omega)$	1.298	1.880	0.291	1.177

unique. By multiplying (1.1-97) by ds/da, we bring equation (1.1-97) into the form

$$\hat{\phi}' = \hat{p}\hat{x}' + \hat{q}\hat{y}' \tag{1.1-98}$$

where the prime on each variable in (1.1-98) denotes differentiation with respect to a. The quantities $\hat{\phi}'$, $\hat{x}'$, and $\hat{y}'$ are determined from (1.1-44), (1.1-47), and (1.1-48) to be

$$\hat{\phi}' = (1/2)(c^4/k^3)(1 - 3a)(1 - a)^2(1 + a)^5 \tag{1.1-99}$$

$$\hat{x}' = (1/2)(c/k)^2(1 + a)^2(6a^3 - 2a^2 - 4a + 1) \tag{1.1-100}$$

$$\hat{y}' = (1/2)(c/k)^2(1 + a)^2(1 + 2a - 6a^2)(1 - a^2)^{1/2}. \tag{1.1-101}$$

Through the substitution of (1.1-45), (1.1-46), and (1.1-99)–(1.1-101) into (1.1-98), we find that the strip condition is satisfied and hence solution (1.1-56) is unique.

It should come as no surprise that the strip condition is fulfilled, as $\hat{\phi}$, $\hat{p}$, and $\hat{q}$ are derived from the Airy potential ϕ^E.

Let us now investigate the consequences of uniqueness on possible stresses at the elastoplastic boundary. We introduce a procedure similar to the one employed by Courant and Hilbert in their proof of uniqueness of the initial value problem for the general Monge–Ampere equation.

Higher-order differential relationships that exist on $\partial\Omega$ are

$$\hat{\phi}_{,xx}\, d\hat{x}/ds + \hat{\phi}_{,xy}\, d\hat{y}/ds = d\hat{p}/ds \qquad (1.1\text{-}102)$$

$$\hat{\phi}_{,xy}\, d\hat{x}/ds + \hat{\phi}_{,yy}\, d\hat{y}/ds = d\hat{q}/ds \qquad (1.1\text{-}103)$$

where a caret over a second derivative of ϕ signifies that the value on the boundary is function of a. By multiplying by ds/da, these equations become

$$\hat{\phi}_{,xx}\hat{x}' + \hat{\phi}_{,xy}\hat{y}' = \hat{p}', \qquad (1.1\text{-}104)$$

$$\hat{\phi}_{,xy}\hat{x}' + \hat{\phi}_{,yy}\hat{y}' = \hat{q}'. \qquad (1.1\text{-}105)$$

The variables $\hat{p}'$ and $\hat{q}'$ in (1.1-104) and (1.1-105) are found by differentiating (1.1-45) and (1.1-46) with respect to a; i.e.,

$$\hat{p}' = (c^2/k)(1 - a)(1 - 5a)(1 + a)^2 \qquad (1.1\text{-}106)$$

$$\hat{q}' = (c^2/k)(1 + a)(1 - a^2)^{1/2}(1 + a - 5a^2). \qquad (1.1\text{-}107)$$

If we divide (1.1-104) and (1.1-105) by $\hat{x}'$, we find

$$\hat{\phi}_{,xx} = \alpha(a) - \gamma(a)\hat{\phi}_{,xy} \qquad (1.1\text{-}108)$$

$$\hat{\phi}_{,xy} = \beta(a) - \gamma(a)\hat{\phi}_{,yy} \qquad (1.1\text{-}109)$$

where known quantities on the boundary $\alpha(a)$, $\beta(a)$, and $\gamma(a)$ are defined as

$$\alpha(a) \equiv \hat{p}'/\hat{x}', \qquad \beta(a) \equiv \hat{q}'/\hat{x}', \qquad \gamma(a) \equiv \hat{y}'/\hat{x}'. \qquad (1.1\text{-}110)$$

By eliminating $\hat{\phi}_{,xy}$ from (1.1-108) and (1.1-109), we obtain

$$\hat{\phi}_{,xx} = \gamma(a)^2 \hat{\phi}_{,yy} - \beta(a)\gamma(a) + \alpha(a). \qquad (1.1\text{-}111)$$

From (1.1-109) and (1.1-111) and the Monge–Ampere equation (1.1-39), we deduce

$$\hat{\phi}_{,yy} = \left[4k^2 - \beta(a)^2 + 2k\beta(a)\gamma(a) - 2k\alpha(a)\right]\Big/$$
$$\left[2k + 2k\gamma(a)^2 - \beta(a)\gamma(a) - \alpha(a)\right]. \qquad (1.1\text{-}112)$$

Notice that terms containing $\hat{\phi}_{,yy}^2$ (generated by the Monge–Ampere equation) have canceled to produce (1.1-112), which is linear in $\hat{\phi}_{,yy}$. Had quadratic terms in $\hat{\phi}_{,yy}$ remained, there would be a second possible stress distribution on the boundary that would satisfy the initial value problem as $\sigma_x^P = \phi_{,yy}$. Because $\hat{\phi}_{,xy}$ and $\hat{\phi}_{,xx}$ vary linearly with $\hat{\phi}_{,yy}$ via (1.1-109) and (1.1-111), they too have unique values on the boundary $\partial\Omega$. Thus for any particular initial value problem only one possible stress distribution may be associated with it on a given elastic–plastic boundary as $\sigma_y^P = \phi_{,xx}$ and $\tau_{xy}^P = -\phi_{,xy}$.

By the use of relationships (1.1-100), (1.1-101), (1.1-106), (1.1-107), and (1.1-110), equation (1.1-112) becomes

$$\hat{\phi}_{,yy} = 2k(1 - 3a^2 + 4a^4)/(1 + a). \qquad (1.1\text{-}113)$$

Similarly, from (1.1-109), (1.1-110), (1.1-111), and (1.1-113), we find $\hat{\phi}_{,xy}$ and $\hat{\phi}_{,xx}$ to be

$$\hat{\phi}_{,xy} = 2ka(4a^2 - 1)(1 - a^2)^{1/2}/(1 + a), \qquad (1.1\text{-}114)$$

$$\hat{\phi}_{,xx} = 2k(1 - a)(1 + 4a^2). \qquad (1.1\text{-}115)$$

Using the trigonometric identities

$$\sin(3\theta/2) = 3\sin(\theta/2) - 4\sin^3(\theta/2),$$

$$\cos(3\theta/2) = 4\cos^3(\theta/2) - 3\cos(\theta/2) \qquad (1.1\text{-}116)$$

and (1.1-8), (1.1-30)–(1.1-32), (1.1-43), and (1.1-113)–(1.1-116), we find that all stresses are continuous on the elastic–plastic boundary:

$$\sigma_x^P = \hat{\phi}_{,yy} = \sigma_x^E, \qquad (1.1\text{-}117)$$

$$\partial\Omega: \qquad \sigma_y^P = \hat{\phi}_{,xx} = \sigma_y^E, \qquad (1.1\text{-}118)$$

$$\tau_{xy}^P = -\hat{\phi}_{,xy} = \tau_{xy}^E. \qquad (1.1\text{-}119)$$

Therefore the uniqueness theorem rules out the possibility of a second solution, i.e., a solution with a discontinuous stress field across the elasto-plastic interface.

Although we have proved that for a particular initial value problem the stresses are uniquely determined on a given boundary, the converse of this statement is not true. There is an ambiguity in a stress function ϕ, be it elastic [Mal 69] or plastic, that is inherent to having the stresses derived from its second derivatives.

To illustrate this ambiguity, let us define n_x and n_y as components of a unit outward normal vector to the boundary $\partial\Omega$ such that

$$n_x = dy/ds, \qquad n_y = -dx/ds. \qquad (1.1\text{-}120)$$

Now by substituting (1.1-120) into (1.1-102) and (1.1-103) and employing the relationships between partial derivatives of ϕ and the stresses, we find

$$\partial\Omega: \quad \begin{cases} \sigma_x^{\mathrm{P}} n_x + \tau_{xy}^{\mathrm{P}} n_y = d\hat{q}/ds = t_x & (1.1\text{-}121) \\ \tau_{xy}^{\mathrm{P}} n_x + \sigma_y^{\mathrm{P}} n_y = -d\hat{p}/ds = t_y & (1.1\text{-}122) \end{cases}$$

where t_x and t_y are interpreted as the tractions on the boundary in the x and y directions, respectively. Integrating (1.1-121) over the arc length ds, we deduce

$$\hat{p} = -\int t_y\, ds + c_1, \qquad \hat{q} = \int t_x\, ds + c_2, \qquad (1.1\text{-}123)$$

where c_1 and c_2 are constants of integration. Consequently, if t_x and t_y are specified on the boundary $\partial\Omega$, then $\hat{p}$ and $\hat{q}$ are determined to within arbitrary constants.

If we substitute (1.1-123) into the strip condition (1.1-97) and integrate over the arc length, we find that a third arbitrary constant c_3 is introduced into the initial data, i.e.,

$$\hat{\phi} = \int (dx/ds)\hat{p}\, ds + \int (dy/ds)\hat{q}\, ds + c_3. \qquad (1.1\text{-}124)$$

Thus the initial value problem is not unique for prescribed tractions on $\partial\Omega$.

Let us now find the most general solution ϕ^* of our problem for prescribed tractions on $\partial\Omega$.

For the tractions t_x and t_y on $\partial\Omega$, we infer from (1.1-121)–(1.1-122) that

$$t_x = d\hat{q}^*/ds = d\hat{q}/ds, \qquad -t_y = d\hat{p}^*/ds = d\hat{p}/ds, \quad (1.1\text{-}125)$$

where $\hat{p}^*$ and $\hat{q}^*$ are the first partial derivatives of ϕ^* on $\partial\Omega$ and $\hat{p}$ and $\hat{q}$ are given by (1.1-45) and (1.1-46). By integrating equations (1.1-125) over ds, we find

$$\hat{p}^* = \hat{p} + c_1^*, \qquad \hat{q}^* = \hat{q} + c_2^*, \qquad (1.1\text{-}126)$$

where c_1^* and c_2^* are arbitrary constants.

The strip condition for $\hat{\phi}^*$, which is analogous to (1.1-98), is

$$\hat{\phi}^{*\prime} = \hat{p}^* \hat{x}' + \hat{q}^* \hat{y}', \qquad (1.1\text{-}127)$$

where the prime indicates differentiation with respect to a. From (1.1-126) and (1.1-127), we obtain the relationship

$$\hat{\phi}^{*\prime} = (\hat{p} + c_1^*)\hat{x}' + (\hat{q} + c_2^*)\hat{y}'. \tag{1.1-128}$$

By substituting $\hat{\phi}'$ from (1.1-98) into (1.1-128) and integrating over da, we determine the initial condition for the function ϕ^* to be

$$\hat{\phi}^* = \hat{\phi} + c_1^*\hat{x} + c_2^*\hat{y} + c_3^*, \tag{1.1-129}$$

where c_3^* is an arbitrary constant and $\hat{\phi}$, $\hat{x}$, and $\hat{y}$ are given by (1.1-44), (1.1-47), and (1.1-48).

We find the following solution ϕ^* of the initial value problem defined by (1.1-39), (1.1-126), and (1.1-129) by the technique used earlier for (1.1-39) and (1.1-44)–(1.1-46):

$$\phi^* = \phi + c_1^*x + c_2^*y + c_3^*, \tag{1.1-130}$$

where ϕ is the function defined by (1.1-56).

The derived stresses using the generalized solution ϕ^* from (1.1-130) are identical to those derived from the original solution ϕ from (1.1-56).

We conclude that the plastic stress field is unique and continuous across the elastoplastic boundary for prescribed tractions on $\partial\Omega$.

Stress Discontinuities

If two families of parabolic characteristics meet at angles other than 0 or π to one another, then a state of discontinuous stress is generated across the curve of intersection. Kachanov [Kac 74] proves that stress discontinuities within region MN of the yield surface are statically admissible only for parallel characteristics ($\sigma_1 = 2k$, discontinuous σ_2).

Point B of Fig. 1.1-3 is a location on the elastic–plastic interface where a characteristic is tangent to the boundary. This point occurs for $\hat{\theta} = 2\sin^{-1}(2/3)$. By the statements of the previous paragraph, we may infer that equilibrium cannot exist where the range of influence of the initial data of side DCB overlaps the range of influence from side OAB. This region begins along curve GF of Fig. 1.1-3.

Therefore, without having to determine the stresses in regions $FBEF$ and $OHGDO$, we can conclude that the solution ϕ^*, which was determined in the previous subsection, must be rejected on the basis of equilibrium.

A different solution that has the same tractions on boundary $\partial\Omega$ is ruled out by the uniqueness theorem.

We have therefore proved that the small-scale yielding stresses do not provide a mode I elastic–plastic boundary for a well-posed elastoplastic problem involving the Tresca yield condition under plane stress loading conditions.

1.2 DEVELOPABLE SURFACES

A necessary and sufficient condition that a surface be developable is that its Gaussian curvature vanishes over its entirety [Str 88]. All developable surface are classified as ruled surfaces, i.e., surfaces that can be generated by the motion of a straight line. Not all ruled surfaces, however, are developable surfaces. A ruled surface with nonzero Gaussian curvature is sometimes called a skew surface or a scroll.

Any developable surface in three-dimensional space can be cut and then flattened into a plane in a manner that preserves distance on its contiguous surface. Because of this property, a model of a developable surface can be made by distorting a plane sheet of paper. As cones and cylinders can be formed from paper in this fashion, they serve as examples of simple developable surfaces.

Gaspard Monge [Kli 72] derived the following nonlinear, second-order partial differential equation for a developable surface $z = \psi(x, y)$:

$$\psi_{,xx} \psi_{,yy} = \psi_{,xy}^2 . \tag{1.2-1}$$

The only developable surfaces that do not satisfy (1.2-1) are cylinders whose generators are perpendicular to the xy plane.

Equation (1.2-1) is parabolic in the usual classification of second-order partial differential equations, and as such it has only one family of characteristics. The parabolic nature of equation (1.2-1) can be demonstrated in a novel fashion. Under a transformation of coordinates from real to complex variables ($z = x + iy$ and $\bar{z} = x - iy$), equation (1.2-1) maps into an identical form

$$\psi_{,zz} \psi_{,\bar{z}\bar{z}} = \psi_{,z\bar{z}}^2 . \tag{1.2-2}$$

In contrast to this result, if z and $\bar{z}$ are substituted into a second-order elliptic equation for x and y, then a hyperbolic equation is obtained, and vice versa [CH 62, pp. 499–501].

An intermediate integral to equation (1.2-1) has the following representation [CH 62, p. 10]:

$$\psi_{,x} = G(\psi_{,y}) \tag{1.2-3}$$

where $G(\ )$ is an arbitrary function. By taking partial derivatives of (1.2-3), i.e.,

$$\psi_{,xx} = G'(\psi_{,y})\psi_{,xy}, \qquad \psi_{,xy} = G'(\psi_{,y})\psi_{,yy} \qquad (1.2\text{-}4)$$

and eliminating $G'(\psi_{,y})$ between equations (1.2-4), we obtain (1.2-1).

It is evident that the governing equation (1.1-6) for the plastic stress function $\phi(x, y)$ of the mode III fracture mechanics problem has the form (1.2-3); hence any solution to (1.2-3) represents a surface that is developable.

The functions $\phi^{E}(x, y)$ and $\phi(x, y)$ of (1.1-1) and (1.1-23) for the mode III problem are shown in Fig. 1.2-1 for $y \geq 0$, where ϕ^{E} is represented by a grid, and ϕ by a ruled surface (the conical fan of straight lines). The elastoplastic boundary is shown both in space and as a projection on the xy plane (circle of radius R).

The governing equation for the plastic stress function $\phi(x, y)$ of the mode I elastoplastic fracture problem for plane stress under the Tresca yield condition for a perfectly plastic material is

$$\phi_{,xx} + \phi_{,yy} + \left[(\phi_{,xx} - \phi_{,yy})^{2} + 4\phi_{,xy}^{2}\right]^{1/2} = 4k, \qquad (1.2\text{-}5)$$

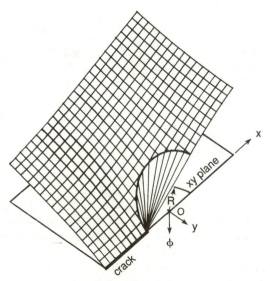

FIGURE 1.2-1

Mode III elastic–plastic stress functions. Adapted from [Ung 91] by permission of Kluwer Academic Publishers.

provided $\sigma_1 \geq \sigma_2 \geq 0$, $\sigma_3 = 0$ where σ_1, σ_2, and σ_3 are the principal stresses.

Because (1.2-5) is not of the form (1.2-1), ϕ is not a developable surface. However, if we make the substitution

$$\phi(x, y) = \psi(x, y) + \psi_0 + k(x - x_0)^2 + k(y - y_0)^2 \qquad (1.2\text{-}6)$$

where (x_0, y_0, ψ_0) are constants, we can bring (1.2-5) into the form of the developable equation (1.2-1). This is accomplished by moving the variables under the radical in (1.2-5) to one side of the equals sign, squaring the expression, and simplifying the result.

It is easily verified that the projection of characteristics of $\psi(x, y)$ on the xy plane are identical to those for the projections of $\phi(x, y)$; i.e., the individual slip lines of Fig. 1.1-3 do not change when ψ is introduced in place of ϕ, as (1.1-90) does not change. In space, however, the characteristics of ϕ are curves, whereas the characteristics of ψ are straight lines (the generators of the ruled surface).

Whether or not the mode I plastic solution obtained previously (1.1-130) can approximate the stress field of a well-posed mode I problem over a particular region has not been determined. It is open to investigation both numerically and analytically.

In this connection, we mention that because $\psi_0 + k(x - x_0)^2 + k(y - y_0)^2$ satisfies the biharmonic equation, the elastic portion of a mode I elastoplastic problem can be transformed as follows:

$$\nabla^4 \phi^E = 0,$$

$$\psi^E(x, y) \equiv \phi^E(x, y) - \psi_0 - k(x - x_0)^2 - k(y - y_0)^2 \rightarrow \nabla^4 \psi^E = 0.$$

$$(1.2\text{-}7)$$

Through the formulation of an elastic–plastic problem with ψ^E and ψ instead of ϕ^E and ϕ, we eliminate the inhomogeneous equation (1.2-5) and substitute in its place the simpler homogeneous equation (1.2-1).

The alternative stress functions $\psi^E(x, y)$, $\psi(x, y)$ for the mode I elastoplastic problem [Ung 91] for the solutions $\phi^E(x, y)$, $\phi(x, y)$ obtained in Section 1.1 are plotted in Fig. 1.2-2 for the half-plane $y \geq 0$. The elastic function $\psi(x, y)$ is represented by a grid, and the plastic function $\psi(x, y)$ is represented by ruled surface. The elastic–plastic boundary (intersection of surfaces ψ^E and ψ) is marked by a space curve and by its projection on the xy plane. The origin of the characteristics is also marked with a space

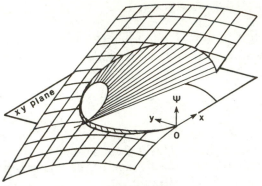

FIGURE 1.2-2

Mode I alternative elastic–plastic stress functions. Adapted from [Ung 91] by permission of Kluwer Academic Publishers Ltd.

curve and it represents the parabolic–hyperbolic plastic interface, (1.1-94)–(1.1-96). The arbitrary constants x_0, y_0, and ψ_0 were set equal to zero for this analysis.

As a final exercise, let us substitute ϕ from (1.2-6) into (1.1-56) and set the arbitrary constants x_0 and y_0 equal to zero. We find

$$\psi = \hat{\psi} + (x - \hat{x})P(a) + (y - \hat{y})Q(a) \qquad (1.2\text{-}8)$$

where $\hat{\psi}$ is the value of ψ on the elastic–plastic boundary and $P(a)$ and $Q(a)$ are defined by (1.1-63) and (1.1-64). The functions $P(a)$ and $Q(a)$ are the first partial derivatives of ψ with respect to x and y on the elastic–plastic boundary. Hence the solution for ϕ of the mode III problem (1.1-15) is similar in form (along a slip line) to the solution for ψ of the mode I problem (1.2-8). This similarity occurs because surfaces with generators of constant slope (1.1-15) are a subfamily of developable surfaces (variable-slope generators). We need only compare the governing first-order equations (1.1-6) with (1.2-3) to prove this assertion.

Equation (1.1-6) can be interpreted as the governing equation of a surface ϕ of constant slope with respect to the xy plane by the following reasoning:

$$p^2 + q^2 = k^2 \rightarrow \nabla\phi \cdot \nabla\phi = k^2 \rightarrow |\nabla\phi| = k, \qquad (1.2\text{-}9)$$

where $|\ |$ represents the magnitude of the gradient of ϕ (i.e., $\nabla\phi$).

1.3 STRAIN RATES FOR PLANE STRESS UNDER THE TRESCA YIELD CONDITION

In this section we derive the expressions for the plastic strain rates for a perfectly plastic material under plane stress loading conditions for region MN of the Tresca yield condition (Fig. 1.1-2).

The maximum shear stress τ_{max} for any stress field is equal to one-half of the greatest difference in the principal stresses; i.e.,

$$\tau_{max} = (\sigma_{max} - \sigma_{min})/2, \qquad (1.3\text{-}1)$$

where σ_{max} and σ_{min} are the maximum and minimum principal stresses, respectively. A plastic potential $h(\sigma_i)$ is now defined that represents the maximum shear stress in the Haigh–Westergaard principal stress space $(\sigma_1, \sigma_2, \sigma_3)$. For a perfectly plastic material the plastic potential for the Tresca yield condition is equal to the yield stress in pure shear k. For region MN of the yield surface in Fig. 1.1-2 we have

$$h(\sigma_i) = (\sigma_1 - \sigma_3)/2 \qquad \text{maximum shear stress on } MN \quad (1.3\text{-}2)$$

$$h(\sigma_i) = k \qquad \text{Tresca yield condition} \qquad (1.3\text{-}3)$$

$$\sigma_3 = \sigma_z = 0 \qquad \text{plane stress condition} \qquad (1.3\text{-}4)$$

where the symbol σ_i denotes a function of principal stresses.

Incremental plastic strains $d\epsilon_1^P$, $d\epsilon_2^P$, and $d\epsilon_3^P$ in the principal stress directions must be orthogonal to the plastic yield surface defined by (1.3-3) by Drucker's postulate of a stable plastic material [Kac 74]. They can be found from the gradient of the plastic potential (1.3-2) as follows [Men 68]:

$$d\epsilon_1^P = [\partial h(\sigma_i)/\partial\sigma_1] d\lambda = \tfrac{1}{2} d\lambda, \qquad (1.3\text{-}5)$$

$$d\epsilon_2^P = [\partial h(\sigma_i)/\partial\sigma_2] d\lambda = 0, \qquad (1.3\text{-}6)$$

$$d\epsilon_3^P = [\partial h(\sigma_i)/\partial\sigma_3] d\lambda = -\tfrac{1}{2} d\lambda \qquad (1.3\text{-}7)$$

where $d\lambda$ is defined as the incremental loading parameter (flow theory).

If we employ the notation that a dot over a variable means differentiation (d/dt) with respect to time t (or some other loading parameter), we can deduce the plastic strain rates from (1.3-5)–(1.3-7) as

$$\dot{\epsilon}_1^P = \tfrac{1}{2}\dot{\lambda}, \qquad (1.3\text{-}8)$$

$$\dot{\epsilon}_2^P = 0, \qquad (1.3\text{-}9)$$

$$\dot{\epsilon}_3^P = -\tfrac{1}{2}\dot{\lambda}. \qquad (1.3\text{-}10)$$

Relationships (1.3-8) and (1.3-9) are consistent with the strain rate direction shown in Fig. 1.1-2 along side MN of the Tresca yield condition.

The incompressibility condition for plastic flow (1.3-11),

$$\dot{\epsilon}_1^P + \dot{\epsilon}_2^P + \dot{\epsilon}_3^P = 0, \tag{1.3-11}$$

is also satisfied by strain rates (1.3-8)–(1.3-10).

From (1.3-3) we show that components of the plastic strain rate tensor in Cartesian coordinates (x, y) are proportional to the second derivatives of the alternative stress function ψ with respect to those coordinates. We must first note, however, the following relationships between ψ, defined by (1.2-6) in terms of ϕ, and the following stresses:

$$\sigma_x = \phi_{,yy} = \psi_{,yy} + 2k, \tag{1.3-12}$$

$$\sigma_y = \phi_{,xx} = \psi_{,xx} + 2k, \tag{1.3-13}$$

$$\tau_{xy} = -\phi_{,xy} = -\psi_{,xy} \tag{1.3-14}$$

The strain rate in the x direction is

$$\dot{\epsilon}_x^P = \dot{\lambda}[\partial h(\sigma_i)/\partial\sigma_x)] \tag{1.3-15}$$

$$= \dot{\lambda}\sum_{i=1}^{3}[\partial h(\sigma_i)/\partial\sigma_i](\partial\sigma_i/\partial\sigma_x) \tag{1.3-16}$$

$$= \dot{\lambda}[(\partial h/\partial\sigma_1)(\partial\sigma_1/\partial\sigma_x)$$
$$+ (\partial h/\partial\sigma_2)(\partial\sigma_2/\partial\sigma_x)$$
$$+ (\partial h/\partial\sigma_3)(\partial\sigma_3/\partial\sigma_x)]. \tag{1.3-17}$$

The evaluation of the various partial derivatives that appear in (1.3-17) follow from (1.1-33) and (1.3-2)–(1.3-4). Only those contributions that are necessary to evaluate (1.3-17) are given below:

$$\partial h/\partial\sigma_1 = \tfrac{1}{2}, \qquad \partial h/\partial\sigma_2 = 0, \qquad \partial\sigma_3/\partial\sigma_x = 0, \tag{1.3-18}$$

$$\partial\sigma_1/\partial\sigma_x = \tfrac{1}{2} + \tfrac{1}{2}(\sigma_x - \sigma_y)\Big/\big[(\sigma_x - \sigma_y)^2 + 4\tau_{xy}^2\big]^{1/2}. \tag{1.3-19}$$

The radical appearing in (1.3-19) can be eliminated through (1.1-37) to yield a simpler expression,

$$\partial\sigma_1/\partial\sigma_x = \tfrac{1}{2} + \tfrac{1}{2}(\sigma_x - \sigma_y)/[4k - \sigma_x - \sigma_y], \tag{1.3-20}$$

$$= (2k - \sigma_y)/(4k - \sigma_x - \sigma_y). \tag{1.3-21}$$

Through the use (1.3-12) and (1.3-13), equation (1.3-21) can be expressed entirely in terms of partial derivatives of ψ, i.e.,

$$\partial\sigma_1/\partial\sigma_x = \psi_{,xx}/(\psi_{,xx} + \psi_{,yy}). \tag{1.3-22}$$

By substituting (1.3-18) and (1.3-22) into (1.3-17), we obtain $\dot{\epsilon}_x^P$ as given in (1.3-25).

Similarly, the other two strain rates in the plane can be determined from the convexity of the yield surface as

$$\dot{\epsilon}_y^P = \dot{\lambda}\big[\partial h(\sigma_i)/\partial\sigma_y\big] \tag{1.3-23}$$

and

$$\dot{\gamma}_{xy}^P = 2\dot{\epsilon}_{xy}^P = \dot{\lambda}\big[\partial h(\sigma_i)/\partial\tau_{xy}\big]. \tag{1.3-24}$$

We omit the details of the evaluation and give the results below.

The three in-plane strain rates in terms of $\dot{\lambda}$ and the second partial derivatives of ψ are

$$\dot{\epsilon}_x^P = \tfrac{1}{2}\dot{\lambda}\psi_{,xx}/(\psi_{,xx} + \psi_{,yy}), \tag{1.3-25}$$

$$\dot{\epsilon}_y^P = \tfrac{1}{2}\dot{\lambda}\psi_{,yy}/(\psi_{,xx} + \psi_{,yy}), \tag{1.3-26}$$

$$\dot{\epsilon}_{xy}^P = \tfrac{1}{2}\dot{\lambda}\psi_{,xy}/(\psi_{,xx} + \psi_{,yy}). \tag{1.3-27}$$

If we now call α the angle that a principal direction makes relative to the x-axis in the xy plane, then the general plane stress relationship

$$-\cot 2\alpha = (\sigma_y - \sigma_x)/(2\tau_{xy}) \tag{1.3-28}$$

exists between the principal directions of stress. By substituting (1.3-12)–(1.3-14) into (1.3-28), we also find that

$$-\cot 2\alpha = (\psi_{,yy} - \psi_{,xx})/(2\psi_{,xy}). \tag{1.3-29}$$

But

$$(\psi_{,yy} - \psi_{,xx})/(2\psi_{,xy}) = \big(\dot{\epsilon}_y^P - \dot{\epsilon}_x^P\big)/\big(2\dot{\epsilon}_{xy}^P\big), \tag{1.3-30}$$

via (1.3-25)–(1.3-27). Thus the principal stress and strain rate directions coincide, i.e.,

$$-\cot 2\alpha = (\sigma_y - \sigma_x)/(2\tau_{xy}) = \big(\dot{\epsilon}_y^P - \dot{\epsilon}_x^P\big)/\big(2\dot{\epsilon}_{xy}^P\big). \tag{1.3-31}$$

Furthermore, the principal strain rates (1.3-8) and (1.3-9) can be recovered from the Cartesian strain rates (1.3-25)–(1.3-27) through the use of tensor formulas found in any elementary strength of materials text. The principal strain rates $\dot\epsilon_1^P$ and $\dot\epsilon_2^P$ can be obtained from the relationships

$$2\dot\epsilon_i^P = \dot\epsilon_x^P + \dot\epsilon_y^P \pm \left[\left(\dot\epsilon_x^P - \dot\epsilon_y^P\right)^2 + 4\dot\epsilon_{xy}^{P\,2}\right]^{1/2}, \qquad i = 1, 2. \quad (1.3\text{-}32)$$

We employ a Laplacian operator symbol in the subsequent analysis in deriving the principal strain rates from (1.3-32),

$$\nabla^2\psi \equiv \psi_{,xx} + \psi_{,yy}. \tag{1.3-33}$$

By substituting (1.3-25)–(1.3-27) and (1.3-33) into (1.3-32), we find

$$2\dot\epsilon_i^P = \left(\dot\lambda/2\nabla^2\psi\right)\left\{\nabla^2\psi \pm \left[\left(\psi_{,xx} - \psi_{,yy}\right)^2 + 4\psi_{,xy}^2\right]^{1/2}\right\} \tag{1.3-34}$$

$$= \left(\dot\lambda/2\nabla^2\psi\right)\left\{\nabla^2\psi \pm \left[\left(\nabla^2\psi\right)^2 + 4\left(\psi_{,xy}^2 - \psi_{,xx}\,\psi_{,yy}\right)\right]^{1/2}\right\}. \tag{1.3-35}$$

Through the use of (1.2-1), equation (1.3-35) reduces to

$$2\dot\epsilon_i^P = \left(\dot\lambda/2\nabla^2\psi\right)\{\nabla^2\psi \pm \nabla^2\psi\}. \tag{1.3-36}$$

Thus we recover (1.3-8) and (1.3-9) from (1.3-36), as indicated below:

$$\dot\epsilon_i^P = \dot\lambda(1 \pm 1)/4 \to \dot\epsilon_1^P = \tfrac{1}{2}\dot\lambda, \qquad \dot\epsilon_2^P = 0. \tag{1.3-37}$$

The last equality in (1.3-37) suggests that no plastic strain rate exists in the direction of a slip line. Thus the component of velocity for a perfectly plastic material is constant in the direction of a slip line along that slip line.

For a general discussion of plane stress relationships for the Tresca yield condition, the reader is directed to [Kac 74].

1.4 MODE I DISPLACEMENTS

We now analytically continue the linear elastic displacements of the mode I fracture mechanics problem of Section 1.1 for an incompressible body into the plastic region. A deformation theory of plasticity is assumed involving small displacements and a perfectly plastic material.

A normalized polar coordinate system (R, θ) is first introduced. It is defined in terms of the dimensionless Cartesian coordinates (X, Y) of (1.1-84) as

$$R \equiv (X^2 + Y^2)^{1/2} = 2\pi r(\sigma_0/K_I)^2, \qquad \tan\theta \equiv Y/X = y/x, \quad (1.4\text{-}1)$$

where σ_0 is the yield stress in tension ($2k$ for the Tresca yield condition).

From the elementary strength of materials formula (1.3-28) and the elastic, small-scale yielding stresses (1.1-30)–(1.1-32), the following relationship can be established between α, the angle a slip line makes relative to the x-axis (Figs. 1.4-1 and 1.4-2), and the polar coordinate angle $\hat{\theta}$ on the elastic–plastic boundary $\partial\Omega$ for the upper half plane:

$$\alpha = 3(\hat{\theta} + \pi)/4, \qquad 0 \le \hat{\theta} \le \pi. \tag{1.4-2}$$

A caret above a variable in this section signifies a function of α that lies on the elastic–plastic boundary. From (1.4-2) we can determine the following relationship between the function a and the angle α:

$$a \equiv \sin \hat{\theta}/2 = -\cos 2\alpha/3. \tag{1.4-3}$$

We now develop a natural coordinate system (α, β) which is composed of the slip lines α and their orthogonal trajectories β. The reason for introducing this new coordinate system is that a simple solution for plastic strain is admissible within it. The strain field we propose is compatible with a deformation theory of plasticity. We assume that the only component of strain that exists in the xy plane is a normal strain in the α direction. This assumption reduces considerably the complexity of the mathematics needed to determine the displacement field, as the strain–displacement equations become integrable as a consequence. We need only apply the boundary condition of continuous displacement at the elastic–plastic interface to determine two arbitrary functions that result from the integration of the partial differential equations that relate displacement to strain.

The family of the orthogonal trajectories β that we seek must meet the slip lines at a slope (dY/dX) which is the negative reciprocal of the slope of the characteristics $(\tan \alpha)$, i.e.,

$$dY/dX = -\cot \alpha. \tag{1.4-4}$$

Through the use of trigonometric identities and (1.4-3), the equation of the characteristics (1.1-90) may be rewritten in terms of α as

$$X \sin \alpha - Y \cos \alpha = \Pi(\alpha), \tag{1.4-5}$$

where $\Pi(\alpha)$ is defined as

$$\Pi(\alpha) \equiv 16 \cos^2\alpha/3 \sin^7\alpha/3. \tag{1.4-6}$$

The function $\Pi(\alpha)$ can be identified as the normalized distance (OV in Fig. 1.4-1) between a given slip line α (UVW in Fig. 1.4-1) and the origin of the Cartesian coordinate system O. (In the subsequent analysis, we occasionally drop the argument symbol on $\Pi(\alpha)$ when its dependence on α is inconsequential.)

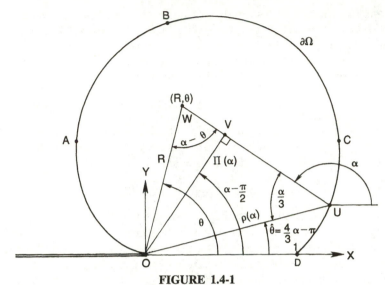

FIGURE 1.4-1

Plastic zone angles and radii.

Relationship (1.4-5) is transformed into

$$R \sin(\alpha - \theta) = \Pi(\alpha), \qquad (1.4\text{-}7)$$

when expressed in polar coordinates. This can also be inferred from the geometry shown in Fig. 1.4-1.

The normalized distance between the common origin of the polar and Cartesian coordinate systems O and the point (U of Fig. 1.4-1) where a given characteristic α intersects the elastic–plastic boundary $\partial\Omega$ is designated by the symbol $\rho(\alpha)$. This distance has the following relationship to previously defined parameters:

$$\rho(\alpha) = \Pi(\alpha) \csc \alpha/3, \qquad (1.4\text{-}8)$$

as can be easily deduced from trigonometry and Fig. 1.4-1.

The polar equivalent of (1.4-4) is

$$dR/R = -\tan(\alpha - \theta)\, d\theta. \qquad (1.4\text{-}9)$$

We then multiply (1.4-7) by (1.4-9) to obtain

$$\cos(\alpha - \theta)\, dR = -\Pi(\alpha)\, d\theta. \qquad (1.4\text{-}10)$$

Now the differential form of (1.4-7) is

$$dR \sin(\alpha - \theta) + R \cos(\alpha - \theta)(d\alpha - d\theta) = d\Pi. \quad (1.4\text{-}11)$$

By substituting R from (1.4-7) and dR from (1.4-9) into (1.4-11), we find

$$d\theta = \cos(\alpha - \theta)[\cos(\alpha - \theta)\,d\alpha - \sin(\alpha - \theta)\,d\Pi/\Pi]. \quad (1.4\text{-}12)$$

Now we eliminate $d\theta$ from (1.4-9) and (1.4-12) to obtain

$$dR/R = \mp \sin(\alpha - \theta)[1 - \sin^2(\alpha - \theta)]^{1/2}\,d\alpha + \sin^2(\alpha - \theta)\,d\Pi/\Pi. \quad (1.4\text{-}13)$$

Note that in the derivation of (1.4-13) an elementary trigonometric identity was used to replace the $\cos(\alpha - \theta)$ with $\sin(\alpha - \theta)$. Accompanying this substitution was the introduction of a plus/minus sign. The upper sign is chosen when $|\alpha - \theta| < \pi/2$ and the lower sign is chosen when $|\alpha - \theta| \geq \pi/2$. Eventually this plus/minus sign convention will be replaced by the re-introduction of the $\cos(\alpha - \theta)$ in (1.4-18), which occurs after the integration of a simple algebraic integrand that was generated by this procedure.

From (1.4-13) we eliminate $\sin(\alpha - \theta)$ via (1.4-7) to infer

$$dR/R = \mp(\Pi/R)\left[1 - (\Pi/R)^2\right]^{1/2}\,d\alpha + \Pi/R^2\,d\Pi. \quad (1.4\text{-}14)$$

Equation (1.4-14) can also be rewritten in a way that separates variables for the purpose of integration, i.e.,

$$\mp d(R^2 - \Pi^2)/(R^2 - \Pi^2)^{1/2} = 2\Pi(\alpha)\,d\alpha. \quad (1.4\text{-}15)$$

Integrating (1.4-15), we find

$$\pm(R^2 - \Pi^2)^{1/2} + \int \Pi(\alpha)\,d\alpha = B \equiv 2\pi\beta\sigma_0^2/K_I^2, \quad (1.4\text{-}16)$$

where B is a dimensionless constant of integration. The indefinite integral appearing in (1.4-16) is evaluated using equation (2.510 5) of [GR 65] as

$$\int \Pi(\alpha)\,d\alpha = 16/3 \cos \alpha/3\{\sin^8\alpha/3 - 1/7[\sin^6\alpha/3 + 2/5(3 \sin^4\alpha/3$$

$$+ 4\sin^2\alpha/3 + 8)]\}. \quad (1.4\text{-}17)$$

Alternatively, B may be interpreted as the dimensionless counterpart of β in an orthogonal coordinate system (α, β), where β is defined in terms of B by the second equality in (1.4-16).

We now substitute $\Pi(\alpha)$ from (1.4-7) into (1.4-16) for Π to obtain

$$R\cos(\alpha - \theta) = B - \int \Pi(\alpha)\,d\alpha. \qquad (1.4\text{-}18)$$

Reverting to Cartesian coordinates, we determine that (1.4-18) becomes

$$X\cos\alpha + Y\sin\alpha = B - \int \Pi(\alpha)\,d\alpha. \qquad (1.4\text{-}19)$$

By solving the simultaneous equations (1.4-5) and (1.4-19) for X and Y, we determine the transformation from the newly defined orthogonal system to Cartesian coordinates as

$$X = \cos\alpha\left(B - \int \Pi(\alpha)\,d\alpha\right) + \Pi(\alpha)\sin\alpha \qquad (1.4\text{-}20)$$

$$Y = \sin\alpha\left(B - \int \Pi(\alpha)\,d\alpha\right) - \Pi(\alpha)\cos\alpha. \qquad (1.4\text{-}21)$$

It can be shown that lines of constant α and curves of constant β are geodesics [Str 88] on the surface ψ of (1.2-6); i.e., they are the shortest paths between two points on the surface.

We note that previous representations for stress from Section 1.1 can now be expressed explicitly in terms of two coordinates (α, β) rather than parametrically in terms of a by the substitution of (1.4-20) and (1.4-21) for X and Y, and (1.4-3) for a. We further note that the principal stresses (1.1-91) and (1.1-92) are the normal stresses $\sigma_\alpha = \sigma_1$ and $\sigma_\beta = \sigma_2$ in the (α, β) coordinate system.

The coordinate system (α, β) is depicted in Fig. 1.4-2 in dimensionless form (α, B). It should be pointed out that the (α, β) coordinate system is right-handed for slip lines that originate from points D to B on $\partial\Omega$ in Fig. 1.4-2; however, the coordinate system becomes left-handed for slip lines that originate from O to B. The behavior is shown explicitly at points K and I of Fig. 1.4-2 by unit vectors $\boldsymbol{\alpha}$ and $\boldsymbol{\beta}$ which point in the directions of increasing α or β.

The change from right-handedness to left-handedness occurs at point B on $\partial\Omega$. This is the location where a slip line is tangent to the elastic–plastic boundary. The numerical value of α at this inflection point is $(3/2)\cos^{-1}(-2/3)$.

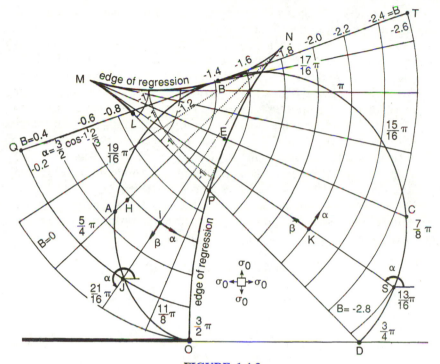

FIGURE 1.4-2

Characteristic coordinate system.

Geometrically a curve of constant β is an involute of the curve labeled "edge of regression" in Fig. 1.4-2, i.e., the curve *LMBNPO*. This edge of regression has cusps at points *M* and *N*. It is also the evolute (envelope) of the slip lines.

Physically, the involutes mentioned above are generated as traces of points on line *QBT* that *QBT* leaves in the plane as it rolls without slip along the stationary edge of regression. A clockwise rotation of *QBT* generates the right-handed coordinates (α, β), while a counterclockwise rotation of *QBT* generates the left-handed coordinates (α, β).

Note the curve $B = -1$ which is plotted in Fig. 1.4-2. The solid portion of curve $B = -1$ and the dotted portion of curve $B = -1$ meet the upper portion of the edge of regression orthogonally. This behavior is related to the generation of β curves through the clockwise or counterclockwise motion of line *QBT* on the edge of regression.

The term *edge of regression* comes from differential geometry terminology concerning developable surfaces. We recall from Section 1.2 that the stress function $\phi(x, y)$ is related to a developable surface $\psi(x, y)$ through a simple transformation. We have also mentioned that the projection of characteristics on the xy plane (slip lines) of $\phi(x, y)$ and $\psi(x, y)$ are identical. The edge of regression is formed in space as the locus of the intersection of "neighboring" generators of the developable surface. In Fig. 1.4-2 we are viewing the projection of this space curve, which touches $\psi(x, y)$, on the xy plane. The edge of regression can be described in Cartesian coordinates in parametric form provided the equation of the developable surface is known as a one-parameter family of planes [Sne 57, p. 314]. For us, its locus is where the metric coefficient $g_{\alpha\alpha} = 0$.

The relationship for the square of differential arc length in the two coordinate systems, (x, y) and (α, β), is determined from (1.1-84), (1.4-20), (1.4-21), and the second equality in (1.4-16) as

$$(dx)^2 + (dy)^2 = (2\pi)^{-2}(K_I/\sigma_0)^4[(dX)^2 + (dY)^2]$$

$$= (2\pi)^{-2}(K_I/\sigma_0)^4\left[B - \Pi'(\alpha) - \int\Pi(\alpha)\,d\alpha\right]^2(d\alpha)^2$$

$$+ (d\beta)^2 \tag{1.4-22}$$

$$= g_{\alpha\alpha}(d\alpha)^2 + (g_{\alpha\beta} + g_{\beta\alpha})(d\alpha)(d\beta) + g_{\beta\beta}(d\beta)^2 \tag{1.4-23}$$

where g_{ij} are metric coefficients. By comparing (1.4-22) and (1.4-23), we can conclude that

$$g_{\alpha\alpha} = (2\pi)^{-2}(K_I/\sigma_0)^4\left[B - \Pi'(\alpha) - \int\Pi(\alpha)\,d\alpha\right]^2, \qquad g_{\beta\beta} = 1 \tag{1.4-24}$$

$$g_{\alpha\beta} + g_{\beta\alpha} = 0 \tag{1.4-25}$$

where the function $\Pi'(\alpha)$ is evaluated by differentiating (1.4-6) with respect to α, i.e.,

$$\Pi'(\alpha) = 16\cos\alpha/3\sin^6\alpha/3\,(7/3 - 3\sin^2\alpha/3). \tag{1.4-26}$$

Condition (1.4-25) above verifies that the (α, β) system is orthogonal.

The normal strains ϵ_α and ϵ_β and the engineering shear strain $\gamma_{\alpha\beta} = 2\epsilon_{\alpha\beta}$ in the (α, β) coordinates are readily expressed in terms of displacements in that system (u_α, u_β) by the following expressions [Sok 56]:

$$\epsilon_\alpha = (u_\alpha g_{\alpha\alpha}^{-1/2})_{,\alpha}$$

$$+ (1/2) g_{\alpha\alpha}^{-1} \{ g_{\alpha\alpha}^{-1/2} u_\alpha g_{\alpha\alpha,\alpha} + g_{\beta\beta}^{-1/2} u_\beta g_{\alpha\alpha,\beta} \} \qquad (1.4\text{-}27)$$

$$\epsilon_\beta = \left(u_\beta g_{\beta\beta}^{-1/2} \right)_{,\beta}$$

$$+ (1/2) g_{\beta\beta}^{-1} \{ g_{\beta\beta}^{-1/2} u_\beta g_{\beta\beta,\beta} + g_{\alpha\alpha}^{-1/2} u_\alpha g_{\beta\beta,\alpha} \} \qquad (1.4\text{-}28)$$

$$\gamma_{\alpha\beta} = (g_{\alpha\alpha} g_{\beta\beta})^{-1/2} \{ g_{\alpha\alpha} (u_\alpha g_{\alpha\alpha}^{-1/2})_{,\beta} + g_{\beta\beta} \left(u_\beta g_{\beta\beta}^{-1/2} \right)_{,\alpha} \} \quad (1.4\text{-}29)$$

where the positive square root of the metric coefficient $g_{\alpha\alpha}$ is given by

$$g_{\alpha\alpha}^{1/2} = \pm (2\pi)^{-1} (K_I/\sigma_0)^2 \left[B - \Pi'(\alpha) - \int \Pi(\alpha) \, d\alpha \right] \quad (1.4\text{-}30)$$

$$= \pm (2\pi)^{-1} (K_I/\sigma_0)^2 [B - B_0] = \pm [\beta - \beta_0] \qquad (1.4\text{-}31)$$

$$= |\beta - \beta_0|, \qquad (1.4\text{-}32)$$

and the value of β for $g_{\alpha\alpha} = 0$ (edge of regression) is

$$\beta_0 = (2\pi)^{-1} (K_I/\sigma_0)^2 B_0 \qquad (1.4\text{-}33)$$

with

$$B_0 \equiv \Pi'(\alpha) + \int \Pi(\alpha) \, d\alpha$$

$$= 32 \cos \alpha / 3 \{ -4/3 \sin^8\alpha/3$$

$$+ 1/7 [8 \sin^6\alpha/3 - 1/15 (3 \sin^4\alpha/3 + 4 \sin^2\alpha/3 + 8)] \}. \quad (1.4\text{-}34)$$

The function β_0 (and correspondingly B_0 in dimensionless form) is the β coordinate of the edge of regression for a particular value of α.

The following sign convention for $\pm$ and $\mp$ is employed in (1.4-30) and in the remainder of this section. The upper sign is chosen for $3/2 \cos^{-1}(-2/3) < \alpha \leq 3\pi/2$, and the lower sign is chosen for $3\pi/4 \leq \alpha < 3/2 \cos^{-1}(-2/3)$. This change in sign is necessary due to the right-handed to left-handed transition in the coordinate system (α, β).

By substituting the metric coefficients (1.4-24) and (1.4-30) into (1.4-27)–(1.4-29), we find that they reduce to

$$\epsilon_\alpha = g_{\alpha\alpha}^{-1/2} [u_{\alpha,\alpha} \pm u_\beta] \qquad (1.4\text{-}35)$$

$$\epsilon_\beta = u_{\beta,\beta} \qquad (1.4\text{-}36)$$

$$\gamma_{\alpha\beta} = g_{\alpha\alpha}^{-1/2} \left[g_{\alpha\alpha} (u_\alpha g_{\alpha\alpha}^{-1/2})_{,\beta} + u_{\beta,\alpha} \right]. \qquad (1.4\text{-}37)$$

We now propose the ansatz that plastic strain develops only for ϵ_α in the $\alpha\beta$ plane. This assumption is admissible within the restrictions imposed by (1.3-5) and (1.3-6), where the first principal direction is the α direction and the second principal direction is the β direction.

We then integrate (1.4-36) to obtain the result that the displacement in the β direction is a function only of α, i.e.,

$$\epsilon_\beta = 0 \rightarrow u_\beta = \hat{u}_\beta(\alpha). \tag{1.4-38}$$

This arbitrary function of α, however, is subject to the physically motivated boundary condition of continuous displacement at the elastic–plastic interface, which is determined from the linear elastic solution. We designate the displacement in the β direction at the elastic–plastic boundary, $\hat{u}_\beta(\alpha)$.

The assumption of no engineering shear strain in the $\alpha\beta$ plane implies the following:

$$\gamma_{\alpha\beta} = 0 \rightarrow g_{\alpha\alpha}(u_\alpha g_{\alpha\alpha}^{-1/2})_{,\beta} + u_{\beta,\alpha} = 0. \tag{1.4-39}$$

We conclude from (1.4-38) and (1.4-39) that

$$(u_\alpha g_{\alpha\alpha}^{-1/2})_{,\beta} = -\hat{u}_\beta'(\alpha)/g_{\alpha\alpha} \tag{1.4-40}$$

where the prime in (1.4-40) denotes differentiation with respect to α.

Now (1.4-40) can be integrated with respect to β, i.e.,

$$u_\alpha g_{\alpha\alpha}^{-1/2} = -\hat{u}_\beta'(\alpha)\int(\beta - \beta_0)^{-2}\, d\beta + h(\alpha), \tag{1.4-41}$$

where $h(\alpha)$ is an arbitrary function of α. The evaluation of the indefinite integral in (1.4-41) is elementary. Upon integration this relationship yields

$$u_\alpha = g_{\alpha\alpha}^{1/2}\left[\hat{u}_\beta'(\alpha)/(\beta - \beta_0) + h(\alpha)\right]. \tag{1.4-42}$$

We may determine the specific form of the function $h(\alpha)$ from the second component of displacement at the elastic–plastic interface $\hat{u}_\alpha(\alpha)$.

The elastic, small-scale yielding solution for an incompressible material (Poisson's ratio $\nu = 1/2$) is, from [Ric 78, Cher 79, KP 85],

$$u_x^{\mathrm{E}} = (K_\mathrm{I}/3G)(r/2\pi)^{1/2}\cos\theta/2(1 + 3\sin^2\theta/2) \tag{1.4-43}$$

$$u_y^{\mathrm{E}} = (K_\mathrm{I}/3G)(r/2\pi)^{1/2}\sin\theta/2(1 + 3\sin^2\theta/2) \tag{1.4-44}$$

where G is the shear modulus. The elastic–plastic boundary is from (1.1-38)

$$\partial\Omega: \qquad r = (2\pi)^{-1}(K_I/\sigma_0)^2\cos^2\theta/2(1 + \sin\theta/2)^2,$$

$$0 \le \theta \le \pi. \quad (1.4\text{-}45)$$

By substituting r from (1.4-45) into (1.4-43) and (1.4-44) and employing (1.4-3), we obtain

$$\hat{u}_x = (K_I^2/6\pi G\sigma_0)(1 - a^2)(1 + a)(1 + 3a^2), \qquad (1.4\text{-}46)$$

$$\hat{u}_y = (K_I^2/6\pi G\sigma_0)a(1 - a^2)^{1/2}(1 + a)(1 + 3a^2). \qquad (1.4\text{-}47)$$

Resolving the x and y components of displacement on $\partial\Omega$ into the α and β directions, we find

$$\hat{u}_\alpha = \mp\hat{u}_x\sin\alpha \pm \hat{u}_y\cos\alpha, \qquad (1.4\text{-}48)$$

$$\hat{u}_\beta = \hat{u}_x\cos\alpha + \hat{u}_y\sin\alpha. \qquad (1.4\text{-}49)$$

Differentiating (1.4-49), we obtain by using the chain rule

$$\hat{u}_\beta'(\alpha) = \hat{u}_x'(\alpha)\cos\alpha - \hat{u}_x\sin\alpha + \hat{u}_y'(\alpha)\sin\alpha + \hat{u}_y\cos\alpha \quad (1.4\text{-}50)$$

$$= (d\hat{u}_x/da)(da/d\alpha)\cos\alpha - \hat{u}_x\sin\alpha$$

$$+ (d\hat{u}_y/da)(da/d\alpha)\sin\alpha + \hat{u}_y\cos\alpha. \qquad (1.4\text{-}51)$$

Since

$$a = -\cos 2\alpha/3 \rightarrow da/d\alpha = (2/3)\sin 2\alpha/3. \qquad (1.4\text{-}52)$$

By differentiating (1.4-46) and (1.4-47) with respect to a, we deduce

$$d\hat{u}_x/da = (K_I^2/6\pi G\sigma_0)(1 + a)[1 + 3a + 3a^2 - 15a^3], \qquad (1.4\text{-}53)$$

$$d\hat{u}_y/da = (K_I^2/6\pi G\sigma_0)[(1 + a)/(1 - a)]^{1/2}[1 + a + 6a^2 + 3a^3 - 15a^4].$$

$$(1.4\text{-}54)$$

Now by (1.4-31), (1.4-42), (1.4-50), and (1.4-51) the undetermined function $h(\alpha)$ becomes

$$h(\alpha) = \left[\pm\hat{u}_\alpha(\alpha) - \hat{u}_\beta'(\alpha)\right]/(\hat{\beta} - \beta_0) \qquad (1.4\text{-}55)$$

$$= -(da/d\alpha)\left[(d\hat{u}_x/da)\cos\alpha + (d\hat{u}_y/da)\sin\alpha\right]/(\hat{\beta} - \beta_0)$$

$$(1.4\text{-}56)$$

where the value of β on the elastic–plastic boundary is given below

$$\hat{\beta} \equiv (2\pi)^{-1}\hat{B}(K_{\mathrm{I}}/\sigma_0)^2, \qquad \hat{B} = -\Pi(\alpha)\cot \alpha/3 + \int \Pi(\alpha)\,d\alpha.$$

$$(1.4\text{-}57)$$

The variable $\hat{B}$ in (1.4-57) was found by substituting $R = \rho(\alpha)$ from (1.4-8) into (1.4-16). Note that on the elastic–plastic boundary $\pi/2 \leq \alpha - \hat{\theta} \leq 3\pi/4$ by (1.4-2), and therefore the lower sign on the radical in (1.4-16) is used.

Now

$$\hat{\beta} - \beta_0 = (2\pi)^{-1}(K_{\mathrm{I}}/\sigma_0)^2(\hat{B} - B_0) \qquad (1.4\text{-}58)$$

where $\hat{B} - B_0$ is evaluated from (1.4-6), (1.4-34), and (1.4-57) as

$$\hat{B} - B_0 = 32/3\cos \alpha/3 \sin^6\alpha/3(1 - 6\cos^2\alpha/3), \qquad 3\pi/4 \leq \alpha \leq 3\pi/2.$$

$$(1.4\text{-}59)$$

Through the use of (1.4-42), (1.4-55), (1.4-56), and (1.4-58), we have

$$u_\alpha = \pm(da/d\alpha)\big[\cos \alpha(d\hat{u}_x/da) + \sin \alpha(d\hat{u}_y/da)\big]$$
$$\times\big[(\hat{B} - B)/(\hat{B} - B_0)\big] + \hat{u}_\alpha(\alpha), \qquad (1.4\text{-}60)$$
$$= \pm(2/3)\sin 2\alpha/3\big[\cos \alpha(d\hat{u}_x/da) + \sin \alpha(d\hat{u}_y/da)\big]$$
$$\times\big[(\beta - \hat{\beta})/(\beta_0 - \hat{\beta})\big] + \hat{u}_\alpha(\alpha). \qquad (1.4\text{-}61)$$

Resolving the components of displacement from the (α, β) system into the Cartesian system, we find

$$u_x(\alpha, \beta) = \mp u_\alpha(\alpha, \beta)\sin \alpha + \hat{u}_\beta(\alpha)\cos \alpha, \qquad (1.4\text{-}62)$$
$$u_y(\alpha, \beta) = \pm u_\alpha(\alpha, \beta)\cos \alpha + \hat{u}_\beta(\alpha)\sin \alpha. \qquad (1.4\text{-}63)$$

For the purpose of comparison, let us define the normalized displacements

$$U_x^{\mathrm{P}} \equiv 6\pi G\sigma_0 u_x/K_{\mathrm{I}}^2, \qquad U_y^{\mathrm{P}} \equiv 6\pi G\sigma_0 u_y/K_{\mathrm{I}}^2 \qquad (1.4\text{-}64)$$
$$(U_x^{\mathrm{E}})_{\mathrm{ssy}} \equiv 6\pi G\sigma_0 u_x^{\mathrm{E}}/K_{\mathrm{I}}^2, \qquad (U_y^{\mathrm{E}})_{\mathrm{ssy}} \equiv 6\pi G\sigma_0 u_y^{\mathrm{E}}/K_{\mathrm{I}}^2. \qquad (1.4\text{-}65)$$

We now compare in tabular form the perfectly plastic displacement field versus the linear elastic, small-scale yielding displacement field along two particular slip lines CE and AH of Fig. 1.4-2. Note that we have chosen

TABLE 1.4-1
Comparison of Normalized Mode I Displacements along Slip Line CE,
$$\alpha = 7\pi / 8$$

B	$(U_x^E)_{ssy}$	U_x^P	$(U_y^E)_{ssy}$	U_y^P
$-2.678\,(C)$	1.411	1.411	0.378	0.378
-2.6	1.419	1.422	0.413	0.406
-2.4	1.457	1.451	0.524	0.476
-2.2	1.522	1.481	0.673	0.547
-2.0	1.613	1.510	0.872	0.618
-1.8	1.722	1.539	1.127	0.688
-1.6	1.835	1.568	1.437	0.759
$-1.512\,(E)$	1.884	1.581	1.588	0.790
-1.4	1.941	1.598	1.790	0.830
-1.2	2.031	1.627	2.168	0.900
-1.0	2.102	1.656	2.553	0.971

slip lines which emanate from two distinct regions of the elastic–plastic boundary, i.e., regions DCB and OAB. These regions are characterized by right-handed and left-handed (α, β) coordinate systems, respectively. Correspondingly, the lower signs (of $\pm$ or $\mp$) are used in all displacement formulas related to slip line CE, and the upper signs are chosen for all formulas related to slip line AH.

From Tables 1.4-1 and 1.4-2, we observe that general trends of growth or decay between elastic and plastic components of displacement are

TABLE 1.4-2
Comparison of Normalized Mode I Displacements along Slip Line AH,
$$\alpha = 5\pi / 4$$

β	$(U_x^E)_{ssy}$	U_x^P	$(U_y^E)_{ssy}$	U_y^P
$-0.471\,(A)$	1.516	1.516	2.626	2.626
-0.485	1.530	1.530	2.603	2.612
-0.5	1.545	1.544	2.580	2.598
-0.535	1.578	1.578	2.525	2.564
$-0.567\,(H)$	1.606	1.608	2.477	2.534
-0.6	1.634	1.640	2.430	2.502
-0.7	1.711	1.736	2.296	2.406
-0.8	1.777	1.832	2.179	2.310
-0.9	1.835	1.928	2.078	2.214
-1.0	1.887	2.024	1.992	2.118

similar as one moves away from the elastic–plastic boundary, although the magnitudes themselves vary considerably.

The plastic displacement field, (1.4-64) and (1.4-65), is multi-valued in the region where slip lines originating from opposite sides of the elastic–plastic boundary cross. The region begins on curve GF of Fig. 1.1-3. By comparing analyses for stress and displacement, we find that where a disequilibrated stress discontinuity exists, a multiplicity of displacement also exists.

The presence of a $O(1/r)$ strain singularity at a crack tip is indicative of deformation theory for a perfectly plastic material. It is observed in the Prandtl perfectly plastic solution for mode I [Ric 68a] and in the Hult and McClintock elastoplastic solution for mode III [Ric 68a]. The possibility of a plastic strain singularity $O(1/r)$ at the crack tip in our analysis (point O of Fig. 1.4-2) is implied by (1.4-31) and (1.4-35).

This singularity would appear to propagate along the edge of regression provided the bracketed term in (1.4-35) is finite. However, assuming that the Tresca yield condition governs, we infer from the locus of the parabolic–hyperbolic plastic boundary $\partial \omega$ (Fig. 1.1-3) that there are only two possible locations for this singularity. One position is the crack tip and the other position is the point of tangency of the slip line QBT to the elastic–plastic interface $\partial \Omega$ (point B of Fig. 1.4-2), which is where a cusp in a β curve occurs. A strain singularity of order $O(1/r)$ is also found at the cusp of an analogous β curve for a mode III problem in Section 2.2 (Refer specifically to equation (2.2-16) and the paragraph that follows it.)

Most of the results that were obtained in Chapter 1 for the Tresca yield condition are equally valid for the Rankine (maximum principal stress) yield condition.

The Rankine yield surface for plane stress is shown schematically as $LMNOPQRSL$ in Fig. 1.4-3. It is depicted superposed over the Tresca yield surface $LMNPQRL$. We note that the two yield surfaces coincide along side MN. Therefore, the predicted elastic–plastic boundary $\partial \Omega$ for mode I is identical for Tresca and Rankine yield conditions because the elastic stresses reach yield along MN. This has been reported previously in [CZ 91].

However, the parabolic–hyperbolic plastic boundary $\partial \omega$, which is found in the Tresca analysis, would not exist under the Rankine yield criterion as there is no hyperbolic region. The slip lines found under the Tresca yield condition would extend beyond $\partial \omega$ under the Rankine yield condition. This is due to the absence of side NP (a hyperbolic region) and the addition of side NO to side MN to form side MNO (a parabolic region) on the Rankine yield surface.

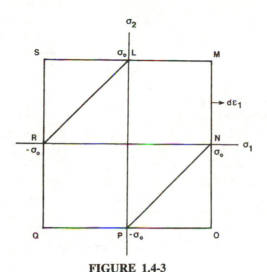

FIGURE 1.4-3

Rankine yield condition superposed over Tresca yield condition.

As a final note on the (α, β) coordinate system, we observe that the solution for $\psi(x, y)$, given as (1.2-8), assumes a particularly simple form in it, i.e.,

$$\psi(\alpha, \beta) = \hat{\psi}(\alpha) + (\beta - \hat{\beta})(\partial \psi/\partial \beta)|_{\partial \Omega}, \qquad (1.4\text{-}66)$$

where the value of the partial derivative of ψ with respect to β on the elastic–plastic boundary $\partial \Omega$ is

$$(\partial \psi/\partial \beta)|_{\partial \Omega} = P(\alpha)\cos \alpha + Q(\alpha)\sin \alpha. \qquad (1.4\text{-}67)$$

The functions $P(\alpha)$ and $Q(\alpha)$ that appear in (1.4-67) were defined for equation (1.2-8). They were also given explicitly in terms of a by (1.1-63) and (1.1-64).

1.5 SPECULATIONS CONCERNING AN ANALYTICAL MODE I ELASTOPLASTIC SOLUTION

Until a few years ago no analytical solutions were available for mode I elastoplastic fracture problems. Previous analytical solutions were confined either to completely elastic problems or to completely plastic problems.

With the publication of [Ung 90a], however, the stresses of the mode I, small-scale yielding, linearly elastic solution under plane stress loading conditions, were continued across the elastic–plastic boundary into the plastic region. The locus of the prescribed elastoplastic interface was found by substituting the stress field of the purely elastic problem into the Tresca yield condition for a perfectly plastic material. The initial value problem for the plastic stress function was then obtained analytically by exploiting the exceptional properties of the governing Monge–Ampere equation. This technique used a complete solution of an intermediate integral of the nonlinear, second-order equation of the plastic stress function. From a one-parameter subsystem of the complete solution, a plastic stress function was found which, if interpreted geometrically as a surface, circumscribed the elastic stress surface (Airy function) of the small–scale yielding, mode I solution. By differentiating the plastic stress function, the stresses were determined in parametric form. These analyses have been reproduced here as Section 1.1.

This mode I solution scheme extended a technique used to solve the analogous mode III problem of Chapter 1. The elastoplastic mode III problem was, of course, previously solved by Hult and McClintock, using a different method. Unlike the Hult and McClintock solution, however, the mode I elastoplastic solution exhibits a disequilibrated stress discontinuity in the trailing portion of the plastic zone. This discontinuity indicates that the mode I, small-scale yielding solution cannot be used as the elastic solution of the elastoplastic problem. This situation is in contrast to the mode III small-scale yielding solution where the linear elastic stress field, found for the purely elastic problem, can serve as the elastic solution of the elastoplastic problem. The mode I solution of the plastic, initial value problem indicates that probable elastic unloading occurs in the vicinity of the stress discontinuity. However, the extent of the unloading and its effect on the stress field ahead of the crack tip is unknown. It is conceivable that the plastic stress field may remain virtually intact in a particular region of the plastic zone. There is some evidence to suggest that the leading edge of a plastic zone might be less susceptible to unloading than the trailing portion.

For example, in steady-state crack propagation for mode III, the Hult and McClintock plastic stress field is no longer valid in the trailing portion of the plastic zone (plastic wake). However, the plastic stress field ahead of the crack tip, as predicted by the stationary Hult and McClintock solution, is a good approximation of the actual stress field, as indicated by both numerical and asymptotic solutions [CM 71].

Another demonstration of the susceptibility of the trailing portion of the plastic zone to unloading comes from a perfectly plastic, plane strain, mode I problem [RDS 80]. This problem involves the Prandtl stress field as a model of crack tip plasticity (Section I.8). For the stationary crack problem, the Prandtl stress field is a statically admissible solution. However, for steady-state crack propagation the same stress distribution predicts negative plastic work in a trailing portion of the plastic zone, which is physically unrealistic as plastic flow dissipates energy. It was shown subsequently that unloading must occur in a sector that lies in the trailing portion of the plastic zone. This sector separates two active plastic regions whose stresses can be approximated by the Prandtl field.

For a stationary crack, a finite-element analysis [DH 91], which was discussed in Section I.9, found that the sector under which the Prandtl solution was valid, in their elastoplastic analysis, varied with the T stress (stresses parallel to the crack faces). However, for all loads investigated, the state of yield of the plastic material ahead of the crack tip, which has a uniform state of stress in the Prandtl solution ($\sigma_x = \pi k$, $\sigma_y = (2 + \pi)k$, $\tau_{xy} = 0$) was shown to be unaffected by the T stress. Somewhat similar to this situation, in Fig. 1.4-2, a state of uniform pressure σ_0 is shown as the continuance of the stress field across DP, albeit for plane stress rather than plane strain loading conditions.

Two criteria were used by Du and Hancock to determine where the Prandtl field applied to their non–work-hardening material. In the fan of the Prandtl solution, the slip lines coincide with the coordinates (r, θ) and the polar shear stress $\tau_{r\theta}$ has the value k. This was the first criterion used by Du and Hancock to find the extent of the Prandtl solution in their finite-element elastoplastic analysis. These loci are indicated in Fig. 1.5-1 (reproduced from [DH 91], also in [Han 92]) by where the radial slip line of the fans terminate as a function of the T stress (see Section I.9 for the definition of T stress). It is seen from the figure that as the T stress decreases, the region over which the Prandtl field applies (the active plastic region) also decreases. Their finite-element solution indicates that for $T/\sigma_0 < 0.446$ the stresses around the crack faces are elastic, i.e., those sectors of Fig. 1.5-1 that have no slip line meshes shown.

Now the plastic yield criterion for plane strain of a non–work-hardening material in polar coordinates is

$$\left[(\sigma_r - \sigma_\theta)^2 + 4\tau_{r\theta}^2\right]^{1/2} = 2k, \tag{1.5-1}$$

and the hydrostatic or mean stress is

$$\sigma = \tfrac{1}{2}(\sigma_r + \sigma_\theta). \tag{1.5-2}$$

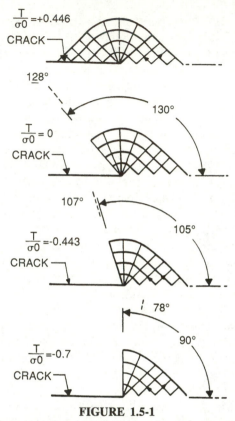

FIGURE 1.5-1

A slip line field representation of the crack tip stresses for various ratios of T stress (stress parallel to crack) to tensile yield stress σ_0. Reprinted from *J. Mech. Phys. Solids*, **39**. Z.-Z. Du and J. W. Hancock, The effect of non-singular stresses on crack-tip constraint, 555–567 (1991), with kind permission from Elsevier Science Ltd., The Boulevard, Langford Lane, Kidlington OX5 1GB, UK.

Du and Hancock discovered that the stresses within the plastic zone were tensile. In order for the principal stresses σ_i to be tensile, the hydrostatic stress σ must be greater than or equal to k. The rationale behind this assumption is given below:

The principal stresses in the plane σ_i $(i = 1, 2)$ in polar form are

$$\sigma_i = \tfrac{1}{2}(\sigma_r + \sigma_\theta) \pm \tfrac{1}{2}\left[(\sigma_r - \sigma_\theta)^2 + 4\tau_{r\theta}^2\right]^{1/2}. \tag{1.5-3}$$

This implies by (1.5-1)–(1.5-2) substituted into (1.5-3) that

$$\sigma \pm k \geq 0 \rightarrow \sigma \geq k. \tag{1.5-4}$$

This was the second criterion that Du and Hancock used to determine the Prandtl field limits. These loci are given in terms of an angle (measured as θ in Fig. I.8-4) as broken radial lines in Fig. 1.5-1. We see similar behavior by this criterion to the previous criterion in Fig. 1.5-1, except at low levels of T stress. Again we note that the leading edge of the plastic zone is less susceptible than the trailing portion of the plastic zone to unloading.

It is also known from a numerical analysis of an elastic/non−work-hardening plastic material involving a U-shaped notch that unloading occurs in the trailing portion of the plastic zone [TF 89]. These results were obtained from the monotonic tensile loading of a cracklike flaw having a semicircular tip. In Fig. 1.5-2 (taken from figure 6 of reference [TF 89]), the active plastic zone behind the crack tip is shown to decrease as a remotely applied tensile traction is applied from 0.14 of the yield stress to 0.28 of the yield stress (in the figures T is the far-field load σ_∞ and Y is the tensile yield stress σ_0). Yield was determined for this mode I

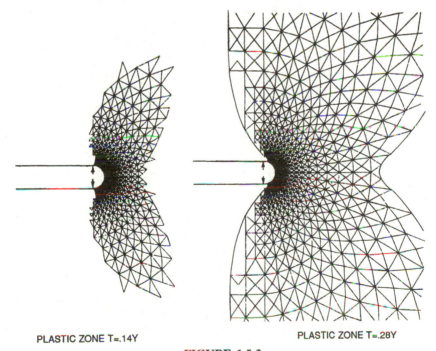

PLASTIC ZONE T=.14Y   PLASTIC ZONE T=.28Y

FIGURE 1.5-2

Plastic zones at the end of U-tipped flaws at two load levels. At $T = 0.28Y$, the active plastic zone does not extend to the arrows, as it does at $T = 0.14Y$, which indicates that unloading occurs at the flaw tip during monotonic increase in T. (T applied load; Y tensile yield stress). Reprinted from [TF 89] by permission of the American Society for Testing and Materials.

problem using the Mises condition under plane strain loading conditions. The general topic of crack tip blunting for perfectly plastic and power-law hardening materials is addressed in [RJ 70]. The strain ahead of crack tips for blunted cracks is focused and results in high strain levels, unlike the Prandtl solution.

As another indication of elastic unloading in the trailing portion of the plastic zone, a stress discontinuity appears in the trailing portion of the plastic zone for the perfectly plastic plane stress crack problem analyzed by Hutchinson under the Mises yield criteria (see Section I.9.). We recall that a stress discontinuity in a perfectly plastic solution indicates the last remnant of an elastic zone. In Section 1.1, we encountered a disequilibrated stress discontinuity in the trailing portion of the plastic zone for the mode I elastoplastic problem, under the Tresca yield criterion and plane stress loading conditions.

Thus there are some indications that the stress field obtained in Chapter 1 may prove to be a satisfactory approximation for the leading edge of a mode I elastic–plastic boundary for a static or steadily moving crack, provided a non–work-hardening model is an appropriate description of the material behavior. As previous mode I numerical analyses have used the Mises yield condition under predominantly plane strain loading conditions, new computations that employ the Tresca yield condition under plane stress loading conditions are needed to confirm or negate this conjecture.

Color Plates   (see inside front and back covers)

Plates 1 and 2 represent the mode III stress functions $\phi^E(x, y)$ of equation (1.1-1) and $\phi(x, y)$ of (1.1-23) for $y \leq 0$. The blue-violet grid is the elastic function and the magenta ruled surface is the plastic function. The xy plane is marked by a brown outline. The elastic–plastic boundary of the surfaces is shown as a yellow space curve. Plate 2 shows the same surfaces in profile. Notice that at the elastic–plastic boundary the height and slope of each function are continuous. One can also observe that the magenta surface forms an envelope for the blue-violet surface. In all color plates the elastic surface is continued into the plastic region and vice versa. For the location of Cartesian axes, compare Plate 1 with Fig. 1.2-1.

It is curious to note that when $\phi^E(x, y)$ of mode III is expressed in parabolic coordinates (u, v) [LSU 79], it assumes the simple form $\phi^E = -|\text{const} \times u|$.

Plates 3 and 4 show the mode I functions $\phi^E(x, y)$ and $\phi(x, y)$ of (1.1-26) and (1.1-56) for $y \geq 0$. The elastic surface is blue-violet and the plastic surface is magenta. The elastic–plastic boundary is green and the parabolic–hyperbolic plastic interface is yellow. One may find it interesting to note that when $\phi^E(x, y)$ of mode I is expressed in parabolic coordinates, it assumes the form $\phi^E = |\text{const} \times u|^3$; i.e., it is proportional to the cube of the magnitude of the mode III stress function.

Plates 5, 6, 7, and 8 represent the alternative mode I stress functions $\psi(x, y)$ and $\psi^P(x, y)$ which respectively correspond to (1.2-6) and (1.2-7). The plastic strain rates are proportional to the second partial derivatives of $\psi(x, y)$ with respect to the Cartesian coordinates by (1.3-25)–(1.3-27). The elastic surface is represented by a grid and the plastic surface is represented by a ruled surface. The color scheme is similar to that in Plates 3 and 4. Notice how the magenta characteristic curves of Plates 3 and 4 transform into the magenta generators of the ruled surfaces in Plates 5–8, through use of the relationship $\phi(x, y) = \psi(x, y) + k(x^2 + y^2)$. For the position of the Cartesian coordinate system, cross-reference Plate 5 with Fig. 1.2-2.

2

Plastic Zone Transitions

In this chapter an analytical solution for mode III cracking is obtained for a finite-width plastic zone model. This model recovers as special cases the small-scale yielding elastic–perfectly plastic solution obtained by Hult and McClintock and a plastic strip model for mode III proposed by Cherepanov, which is analogous in shape to the Dugdale plastic strip model of mode I. The model presented here represents a transitional phase of mode III cracking where the elastic–plastic boundary assumes an elliptical form. The stress, strain, and displacement fields are given for both the elastic and plastic regions. Applications of the model are also discussed.

An infinitesimally thin plastic strip model for the mode I fracture mechanics problem was proposed by Dugdale [Dug 60]. This model assumes the existence of a very narrow region of perfectly plastic material ahead of the crack tip, while material outside of the plastic strip is assumed to be linear elastic. Experiments indicate that the Dugdale model approximates the actual shape of the plastic zone for cracks in thin steel plates subject to plane stress loading conditions. Similar plastic strip models for mode III fracture mechanics problems were later proposed by Cherepanov [Cher 79] and Bilby, Cottrell, and Swinden [BCS 63].

In an elastoplastic problem, there are elastic and plastic domains of finite dimensions. In the elastic domain, the stresses satisfy equilibrium, while the strains satisfy the compatibility equations. In the plastic domain, the stresses satisfy equilibrium and a yield condition, while the strains satisfy either a flow rule in an incremental theory of plasticity or a proportional relationship with stresses in a deformation theory of plasticity. Across the elastic–plastic interface, boundary conditions related to equilibrium and continuous displacement are met.

Hult and McClintock [HM 56] were the first to obtain an analytical mode III elastoplastic solution for an edge crack in a semi-infinite plate. Under the assumptions of small-scale yielding, the shape of the Hult–McClintock elastic–plastic boundary is circular.

In the problem addressed in this chapter, we obtain an analytical elastoplastic solution for a transitional mode III crack problem, under the assumptions of small-scale yielding. The shape of the transition model's plastic zone is an elliptical cylinder. As limiting cases of the transition model, we can recover the Cherepanov plastic strip solution and the Hult–McClintock small-scale yielding elastoplastic solution.

2.1 A FINITE-WIDTH DUGDALE ZONE MODEL FOR MODE III

Schematic representations of various crack tip models are shown in Figs. 2.1-1a–2.1-1d. Figure 2.1-1a represents the Cherepanov model, where the crack tip corresponds to the hollow circle and the end of the plastic zone corresponds to the solid circle. The crack faces are parallel lines to the left of the hollow circle. Figures 2.1-1b and 2.1-1c are representations of the transition model for different ratios of elliptical axes, which correspond to the dimensions of the plastic zone. The semimajor axis is A and the semiminor axis is B. The crack tip is at the hollow circle, and the solid circle is the location of a strain singularity to be discussed later. The inclined lines in the figures represent slip lines. Figure 2.1-1d corresponds to the Hult–McClintock small-scale yield solution, where the elastic–plastic boundary is circular. In this case the crack tip and the aforementioned strain singularity coincide.

Elastic Solution

For the mode III problem, only the antiplane displacement w is nonzero. In addition, all stresses are zero except for the antiplane shear stresses τ_{xz} and τ_{yz}.

The linear elastic stress–strain relationships assume the following form in the Cartesian coordinate system (x, y, z):

$$\tau_{xz}^{E}(x, y) = G\frac{\partial w^{E}(x, y)}{\partial x} = G\gamma_{xz}^{E}(x, y), \qquad (2.1\text{-}1)$$

$$\tau_{yz}^{E}(x, y) = G\frac{\partial w^{E}(x, y)}{\partial y} = G\gamma_{yz}^{E}(x, y), \qquad (2.1\text{-}2)$$

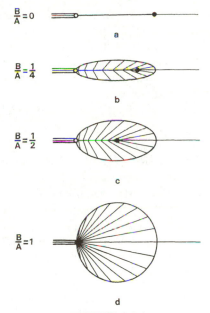

$\dfrac{B}{A} = 0$

a

$\dfrac{B}{A} = \dfrac{1}{4}$

b

$\dfrac{B}{A} = \dfrac{1}{2}$

c

$\dfrac{B}{A} = 1$

d

FIGURE 2.1-1

Plastic zone transition. Reprinted from *Eng. Fract. Mech.*, **34**, D. J. Unger, A finite-width Dugdale zone model for mode III, 977–987 (1989), with permission from Pergamon Press Ltd., Headington Hill Hall, Oxford OX3 OBW, UK.

where τ_{xz}, τ_{yz} are shear stresses and γ_{xz}, γ_{yz} are engineering shear strains, the superscript E denotes a linear elastic state, and G is the shear modulus. All other stresses and strains are zero.

Equilibrium requires that

$$\frac{\partial \tau_{xz}}{\partial x} + \frac{\partial \tau_{yz}}{\partial y} = 0, \tag{2.1-3}$$

and by (2.1-1) and (2.1-2), equation (2.1-3) implies that

$$\frac{\partial^2 w^E(x, y)}{\partial x^2} + \frac{\partial^2 w^E(x, y)}{\partial y^2} = 0, \tag{2.1-4}$$

i.e., $w^E(x, y)$ satisfies Laplace's equation.

An alternative formulation [PM 78] of the mode III problem using complex variables is

$$w^E = (1/G)\mathrm{Im}\, Z_{\mathrm{III}}^*(z), \tag{2.1-5}$$

$$\tau_{xz}^E = \mathrm{Im}\, Z_{\mathrm{III}}(z), \qquad \tau_{yz}^E = \mathrm{Re}\, Z_{\mathrm{III}}(z) \tag{2.1-6}$$

where the argument z is a complex number $z = x + iy$, $Z_{\mathrm{III}}(z)$ is the

Westergaard potential for mode III, and $Z_{III}^*(z)$ denotes integration of the function $Z_{III}(z)$ with respect to the complex variable z. Unfortunately, the traditional symbols for the third Cartesian axis and the complex number have the same symbol z. When z is used as a subscript in this chapter, it will refer to the Cartesian coordinate. When z appears as an argument, it will refer to the complex number.

We can infer from the Westergaard relationship (2.1-6) that

$$Z_{III}(z) = \tau_{yz}^E + i\tau_{xz}^E. \qquad (2.1\text{-}7)$$

Because τ_{yz}^E, τ_{xz}^E are the real $[\text{Re}\, Z_{III}(z)]$ and imaginary $[\text{Im}\, Z_{III}(z)]$ parts of an analytic function of z, respectively, they are conjugate harmonic functions. This suggests that an orthogonal coordinate system $(\tau_{yz}^E, \tau_{xz}^E)$ can be defined. It then follows that the z plane can be conformally mapped onto the Z_{III} plane. Other researchers [Cher 79, HM 56, Ric 68a] have used conformal mapping techniques to obtain mode III solutions.

On the elastic–plastic boundary the stresses satisfy a yield condition. We choose the Mises yield criterion for a perfectly plastic material, i.e.,

$$\tau_{xz}^2 + \tau_{yz}^2 = k^2 \qquad \text{or} \qquad |Z_{III}(z)| = k, \qquad (2.1\text{-}8)$$

where k is the yield stress in pure shear, and the symbol $|\;|$ denotes the magnitude of a complex function. From (2.1-8) we can infer that in the $Z_{III}(z)$ plane the elastic–plastic boundary has the shape of a circular arc.

The elastic–plastic boundary $\partial\Omega$ for the plastic strip model given by Cherepanov [Cher 79] is a straight line. The elastic–plastic boundary $\partial\Omega$ for the small-scale yielding solution of Hult and McClintock [HM 56] is circular. A convenient coordinate system that allows a smooth transition between these two limiting cases is the elliptic coordinate system (u, v) shown in Fig. 2.1-2 [LSU 79]. In this coordinate system the coordinates (u, v) are defined as follows:

$$z \equiv a\cosh(u + iv) \rightarrow x = a\cosh u \cos v, \qquad y = a\sinh u \sin v, \quad (2.1\text{-}9)$$

where $2a$ is the length between foci.

For convenience, let us introduce the following normalized variables and yield condition:

$$X \equiv x/a = \cosh u \cos v, \qquad Y \equiv y/a = \sinh u \sin v \qquad (2.1\text{-}10)$$

$$X + iY = \cosh(u + iv) \qquad (2.1\text{-}11)$$

$$W^E(X, Y) \equiv w^E(x, y)/a \qquad (2.1\text{-}12)$$

$$T_{xz}^E \equiv \tau_{xz}^E/k, \qquad T_{yz}^E \equiv \tau_{yz}^E/k \qquad (2.1\text{-}13)$$

$$Z_{III}/k = T_{yz}^E + iT_{xz}^E \qquad (2.1\text{-}14)$$

$$\partial\Omega: \qquad T_{xz}^2 + T_{yz}^2 = 1, \qquad \text{or} \qquad |Z_{III}/k| = 1. \qquad (2.1\text{-}15)$$

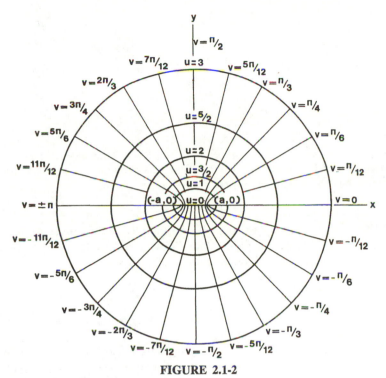

FIGURE 2.1-2

Elliptical coordinate system. Reprinted from *Eng. Fract. Mech.*, **34**, D. J. Unger, A finite-width Dugdale zone model for mode III, 977–987 (1989), with permission from Pergamon Press Ltd., Headington Hill Hall, Oxford OX3 0BW, UK.

The elliptical elastic–plastic boundary $\partial\Omega$ for the transition model in the XY plane, $u = \bar{u}_0$, is shown in Fig. 2.1-3a.

The region exterior to this ellipse $ABCC'B'A$ in Fig. 2.1-3a is the elastic region. From (2.1-4), (2.1-10), and (2.1-12), we can deduce that the normalized displacement in this plane $W^R(X, Y)$ is a harmonic function of X and Y.

The interior of the ellipse $\partial\Omega$ is the plastic region and is subject to the yield condition (2.1-15).

A conformal transformation of the form [Spi 64]

$$X + iY = (-1/2)[S\exp(-u_0) + (1/S)\exp(u_0)] \qquad (2.1\text{-}16)$$

maps the exterior of the ellipse in the $X + iY$ plane to the interior of a circle in the complex S plane (Fig. 2.1-3b).

An additional transformation of the form

$$\sigma^2 = S \qquad (2.1\text{-}17)$$

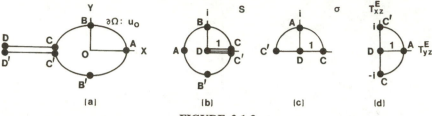

[a]	[b]	[c]	[d]

FIGURE 2.1-3

Conformal mapping sequence. Adapted from *Eng. Fract. Mech.*, **34**, D. J. Unger, A finite-width Dugdale zone model for mode III, 977–987 (1989), with permission from Pergamon Press Ltd., Headington Hill Hall, Oxford OX3 OBW, UK.

maps the circle in the S plane onto the semicircle in the complex σ plane (Fig. 2.1-3c). It is transformation (2.1-17) that gives the elastic stresses $\tau_{xz}^{E}, \tau_{yz}^{E}$ the characteristic asymptotic behavior of small-scale yielding; i.e., $\tau_{xz}^{E} \sim \tau_{yz}^{E} \sim O(r^{-1/2})$ as $r \to \infty$.

The final transform

$$Z_{\mathrm{III}}(z)/k = -i\sigma = T_{yz}^{E} + iT_{xz}^{E} \tag{2.1-18}$$

rotates the semicircle in the σ plane 90° clockwise into the normalized stress plane. This rotation allows the elastic solution to satisfy the traction-less boundary condition along the assumed crack faces CD and $C'D'$ which are shown in Fig. 2.1-3a. Points D and D' are at infinity.

In Fig. 2.1-3d the yield condition (2.1-15) is satisfied along a semicircular boundary, which corresponds to the elliptical boundary in the original Cartesian plane (Fig. 2.1-3a). As a sequence of conformal transformations occurred between Figs. 2.1-3a and 2.1-3d, the displacement in the elastic region of the stress plane, $W^{\langle E \rangle}(T_{yz}, T_{xz}) = W^{E}(X, Y)$, will continue to satisfy Laplace's equation under the transformation of coordinates (X, Y) to (T_{yz}^{E}, T_{xz}^{E}).

Through the series of conformal transformations (2.1-16)–(2.1-18), we obtain the following relationship between the Cartesion coordinates (X, Y), the elastic stresses (T_{yz}^{E}, T_{xz}^{E}), and the elliptic boundary u_0:

$$X + iY = z/a = (1/2)\left[\left(T_{yz}^{E} + iT_{xz}^{E}\right)^{2}\exp(-u_0) + \left(T_{yz}^{E} + iT_{xz}^{E}\right)^{-2}\exp(u_0)\right]. \tag{2.1-19}$$

Solving the quadratic equation (2.1-19) for $(T_{yz}^{E} + iT_{xz}^{E})^{2}\exp(-u_0)$, we find

$$\left(T_{yz}^{E} + iT_{xz}^{E}\right)^{2}\exp(-u_0) = (z/a) \pm \left[(z/a)^{2} - 1\right]^{1/2}. \tag{2.1-20}$$

By substituting the expression for z from (2.1-9) into (2.1-20), we obtain

$$\left(T_{yz}^{E} + iT_{xz}^{E}\right)^{2} \exp(-u_0) = \cosh(u + iv) \pm \sinh(u - iv) = \exp[\pm(u + iv)].$$
$$(2.1-21)$$

The negative sign in relationship (2.1-21) is chosen so that the sign of u_0 agrees with the sign of u along the elastic–plastic boundary. Therefore from (2.1-21) we obtain

$$\left(T_{yz}^{E} + iT_{xz}^{E}\right)^{2} = \exp(u_0 - u - iv). \qquad (2.1-22)$$

Taking the square root of both sides of (2.1-22) and equating real and imaginary parts of the result, we obtain

$$\left.\begin{aligned} T_{xz}^{E} = \tau_{xz}^{E}/k = -\exp[(u_0 - u)/2]\sin(v/2) \\ T_{yz}^{E} = \tau_{yz}^{E}/k = \exp[(u_0 - u)/2]\cos(v/2). \end{aligned}\right\} \quad \begin{aligned} (2.1-23) \\ (2.1-24) \end{aligned}$$

$$u \geq u_0, \quad -\pi \leq v \leq \pi.$$

A second stress field, $-T_{xz}^{E}$ and $-T_{yz}^{E}$, can also be found from (2.1-22). This additional solution reflects the quadratic nature of the yield condition, and it corresponds to an antiplane loading which is opposite to the loading used to generate the stresses in (2.1-23) and (2.1-24). To avoid the introduction of ambiguous signs ($\pm$, $\mp$) throughout this chapter, we limit our analysis to strains and displacements associated with solution (2.1-23)–(2.1-24).

The elastic strains follow immediately from (2.1-23) and (2.1-24) by substitution into (2.1-1) and (2.1-2).

In order to obtain the elastic displacement, we need to obtain the function $Z_{III}^{*}(z)$. From (2.1-18), (2.1-23), and (2.1-24) we can determine that

$$Z_{III}(z) = k \exp[(u_0 - u - iv)/2]. \qquad (2.1-25)$$

Employing the chain rule and using (2.1-9), we find

$$Z_{III}(z) = \frac{dZ_{III}^{*}(z)}{d(u + iv)} \frac{d(u + iv)}{dz} = \frac{dZ_{III}^{*}(z)}{d(u + iv)} \frac{1}{a \sinh(u + iv)}. \qquad (2.1-26)$$

Equating (2.1-25) and (2.1-26), separating variables, and integrating, we obtain

$$Z_{III}^{*}(z) = ak \exp(u_0/2)(\exp[(u + iv)/2] + (1/3)\exp[-3(u + iv)/2]). \qquad (2.1-27)$$

From (2.1-5), (2.1-12), and (2.1-27), we determine the elastic displacement as

$$W^{\mathrm{E}} = (k/G)\exp(u_0/2)[\exp(u/2)\sin(v/2)$$

$$- (1/3)\exp(-3u/2)\sin(3v/2)], \qquad \text{for } u \geq u_0, \quad -\pi \leq v \leq \pi.$$
$$(2.1\text{-}28)$$

Plastic Solution

We seek stresses in the plastic region of the form

$$T_{xz}^{\mathrm{P}} = \tau_{xz}^{\mathrm{P}}/k = -\sin\,\alpha(X,Y), \qquad T_{yz}^{\mathrm{P}} \equiv \tau_{yz}^{\mathrm{P}}/k = \cos\,\alpha(X,Y) \quad (2.1\text{-}29)$$

so that the Mises yield condition (2.1-15) is satisfied.

From the substitution of the stresses from (2.1-29) into (2.1-3), we find the following equilibrium equation in terms of $\alpha(X,Y)$:

$$P + Q\tan\,\alpha(X,Y) = 0, \qquad (2.1\text{-}30)$$

where

$$P \equiv \frac{\partial\alpha(X,Y)}{\partial X}, \qquad Q \equiv \frac{\partial\alpha(X,Y)}{\partial Y}. \qquad (2.1\text{-}31)$$

For continuous stresses across the elastic–plastic border, (2.1-23), (2.1-24), and (2.1-29) require

$$v = 2\alpha \quad \text{on} \quad \partial\Omega \quad \text{or} \quad \alpha = v_0/2 \qquad (2.1\text{-}32)$$

where the subscript 0 denotes a variable on the elastoplastic interface.

The solution of (2.1-30) for $\alpha(X,Y)$ subject to the initial condition (2.1-32) is

$$\frac{Y_0(\alpha) - Y}{X_0(\alpha) - X} = \tan\,\alpha(X,Y), \qquad (2.1\text{-}33)$$

where $X_0(\alpha)$ and $Y_0(\alpha)$ are the normalized coordinates of the elastic–plastic boundary (Fig. 2.1-4). These coordinates are found by substituting the expression for v from (2.1-32) into (2.1-10) to yield $\partial\Omega$:

$$X_0(\alpha) = A\cos 2\alpha, \qquad Y_0(\alpha) = B\sin 2\alpha, \qquad (2.1\text{-}34)$$

where

$$A \equiv \cosh u_0, \qquad B \equiv \sinh u_0, \qquad (2.1\text{-}35)$$

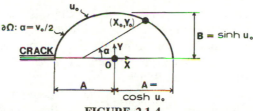

FIGURE 2.1-4

Plastic zone parameters. Reprinted from *Eng. Fract. Mech.*, **34**, D. J. Unger, A finite-width Dugdale zone model for mode III, 977–987 (1989), with permission from Pergamon Press Ltd., Headington Hill Hall, Oxford OX3 OBW, UK.

and u_0 is the elliptical coordinate of the elastic–plastic boundary. From Fig. 2.1-4 we observe that A and B are the semimajor and semiminor axis, respectively, of the elliptical plastic zone in the normalized Cartesian plane.

We now prove that the relationship to α of (2.1-33) satisfies the Cauchy problem as defined by (2.1-30) and (2.1-34).

After taking partial derivatives of (2.1-33) with respect to X and Y, we find

$$\frac{(X_0 - X)Y_0'P + (Y - Y_0)(X_0'P - 1)}{(X - X_0)^2} = P\sec^2\alpha \qquad (2.1\text{-}36)$$

and

$$\frac{(X_0 - X)(Y_0'Q - 1) + (Y - Y_0)X_0'Q}{(X - X_0)^2} = Q\sec^2\alpha, \qquad (2.1\text{-}37)$$

where the prime denotes differential with respect to α. Now by eliminating $(X - X_0)^2\sec^2\alpha$ between (2.1-36) and (2.1-37), we obtain

$$P + \frac{Y_0 - Y}{X_0 - X}Q = 0. \qquad (2.1\text{-}38)$$

Notice that the primed quantities of (2.1-36) and (2.1-37), X_0' and Y_0', cancel. Finally, by substituting (2.1-33) into (2.1-38), we recover the original partial differential equation (2.1-30) to complete the proof.

A line of constant α (Fig. 2.1-4) comprises a characteristic of partial differential equation (2.1-30). We obtain the following equation of a characteristic line (slip line) from (2.1-33) and (2.1-34):

$$Y = [X + 2B - A + 2(A - B)\sin^2\alpha]\tan\alpha, \qquad (2.1\text{-}39)$$

where A and B are defined in terms of u_0 by (2.1-35).

We deduce from (2.1-29) and (2.1-39) that there is a stress discontinuity in T_{xz}^{P} on the X-axis starting at $X = A - 2B$ and continuing to the crack tip at $X = -A$. A similar discontinuity exists in the Cherepanov model ($u_0 = B = 0$). As T_{yz}^{P} is an even function of α, equilibrium is satisfied across the line of discontinuous stress.

The Hencky deformation theory of plasticity requires that the total strains (elastic plus plastic) be proportional to the stresses. This assumption requires that

$$\gamma_{xz}^{\Omega} \equiv \frac{\partial w^{P}(x, y)}{\partial x} = \lambda(x, y)\tau_{xz}^{P}(x, y) = -\lambda(x, y)k \sin \alpha, \quad (2.1\text{-}40)$$

$$\gamma_{yz}^{\Omega} \equiv \frac{\partial w^{P}(x, y)}{\partial y} = \lambda(x, y)\tau_{yz}^{P}(x, y) = \lambda(x, y)k \cos \alpha \quad (2.1\text{-}41)$$

where $\lambda(x, y)$ is the function of proportionality. In (2.1-40) and (2.1-41) the superscript Ω denotes total quantities within the plastic region, i.e., the sum of the elastic contribution plus the plastic contribution, as opposed to the plastic component alone.

Dividing γ_{xz}^{Ω} by γ_{yz}^{Ω} we find that, in normalized notation,

$$\frac{\partial W^{P}}{\partial X} + \tan \alpha \frac{\partial W^{P}}{\partial Y} = 0, \quad (2.1\text{-}42)$$

where

$$W^{P} \equiv w^{P}/a. \quad (2.1\text{-}43)$$

Partial differential equation (2.1-42) is a compatibility requirement between a statically admissible stress field [reflected by α through eq. (2.1-29)] and a complementary displacement. The displacement across the elastic–plastic boundary $\partial\Omega$ must be continuous. From (2.1-28) and (2.1-32) we find that the normalized interfacial displacement W is $\partial\Omega$:

$$W(\alpha) = (k/G)[\exp(u_0)\sin \alpha - (1/3)\exp(-u_0)\sin 3\alpha]. \quad (2.1\text{-}44)$$

As the displacement on the elastic–plastic interface is a function only of α, it is natural to seek displacements interior to $\partial\Omega$ of the form

$$W^{P} = F(\alpha). \quad (2.1\text{-}45)$$

When (2.1-45) is substituted into (2.1-42), we find

$$F'(\alpha)\left[\frac{\partial \alpha}{\partial X} + \tan \alpha \frac{\partial \alpha}{\partial Y}\right] = 0 \quad \text{or} \quad F'(\alpha)[P + Q \tan \alpha] = 0.$$

$$(2.1\text{-}46)$$

From the equilibrium equation (2.1-30), we see that (2.1-46) is satisfied for any plastic displacement that is a function only of α, where α is defined in terms of Cartesian coordinates by (2.1-39).

As the displacement on the elastic–plastic interface is solely a function of the coordinate α, we can continue (2.1-44) into the plastic zone; i.e.,

$$W^{\mathrm{P}}(\alpha) = F(\alpha) = W(\alpha)$$
$$= (k/G)[\exp(u_0)\sin \alpha - (1/3)\exp(-u_0)\sin 3\alpha],$$
$$-\pi/2 \leq \alpha \leq \pi/2. \quad (2.1\text{-}47)$$

Equation (2.1-47) indicates a displacement discontinuity on the X-axis from $X = -A$ to $X = A - 2B$, as there is in the Cherepanov strip model for mode III ($u_0 = B = 0$). The relative displacement associated with this discontinuity at the crack tip is termed the crack tip opening displacement δ_t.

A similar discontinuity exists in the Dugdale model for mode I and in the mode III strip model by Bilby, Cottrell, and Swinden [BCS 63]. The Bilby–Cottrell–Swinden model is a predecessor of the Cherepanov model. Originally derived from dislocation theory, it has a different solution, which will be discussed toward the end of this chapter.

Profiles of normalized displacement are shown in Fig. 2.1-5 as a function of α for different values of u_0. Notice the change in the shape of the profiles as the transition is made from the Cherepanov model ($u_0 = 0$) to the Hult–McClintock model (the elliptical boundary $u_0 = 3$ is nearly circular and hence approximates the Hult–McClintock elastic–plastic boundary). The value of W related to the crack tip opening displacement appears in Fig. 2.1-5 at $\alpha = 90°$.

Having found the total displacement (2.1-47), we may now obtain the total strains. Equations (2.1-40), (2.1-41), (2.1-43), and (2.1-47) imply that

$$\gamma_{xz}^{\Omega} = \frac{\partial W^{\mathrm{P}}(\alpha)}{\partial X} = F'(\alpha)P, \quad (2.1\text{-}48)$$

$$\gamma_{yz}^{\Omega} = \frac{\partial W^{\mathrm{P}}(\alpha)}{\partial Y} = F'(\alpha)Q, \quad (2.1\text{-}49)$$

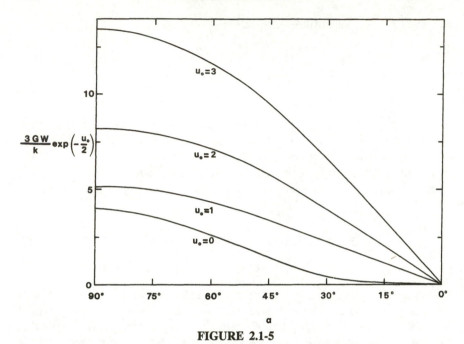

FIGURE 2.1-5

Normalized displacement versus characteristic angle. Reprinted from *Eng. Fract. Mech.*, **34**, D. J. Unger, A finite-width Dugdale zone model for mode III, 977–987 (1989), with permission from Pergamon Press Ltd., Headington Hill Hall, Oxford OX3 0BW, UK.

where the function,

$$F'(\alpha) = (k/G)[\exp(u_0)\cos\alpha - \exp(-u_0)\cos 3\alpha], \quad (2.1\text{-}50)$$

is obtained by differentiating (2.1-47) with respect to α.

From (2.1-33), (2.1-36), and (2.1-37) we solve for P and Q to obtain

$$P = \frac{\tan\alpha}{(X_0 - X)\sec^2\alpha + X_0'\tan\alpha - Y_0'}, \quad (2.1\text{-}51)$$

and

$$Q = \frac{1}{Y_0' - X_0'\tan\alpha + (X - X_0)\sec^2\alpha}, \quad (2.1\text{-}52)$$

where

$$X_0' = -2A\sin 2\alpha, \qquad Y_0' = 2B\cos 2\alpha. \quad (2.1\text{-}53)$$

From (2.1-40), (2.1-41), and (2.1-48)–(2.1-53), we can obtain the proportionality function λ.

When α equals zero, we find from (2.1-49), (2.1-50), and (2.1-52) that

$$\gamma_{yz}^{\Omega}\big|_{\alpha=0} = \frac{2(k/G)\sinh u_0}{X + 2\sinh u_0 - \cosh u_0} = \frac{2(k/G)B}{X + 2B - A}. \quad (2.1\text{-}54)$$

Equation (2.1-54) indicates that a strain singularity of order $O(1/r)$, $r \to 0$ exists at the point $X = A - 2B$, $Y = 0$ for $u_0 > 0$. The only exception is for the case $u_0 = 0$, which is the Cherepanov plastic strip model. In this special case the strain is finite throughout the entire domain, as it is for the Dugdale model of mode I. For the limiting case A equals B (the Hult–McClintock small-scale yielding solution), the strain singularity is coincident with the crack tip [Hut 79]. Notice the movement of the strain singularity (solid circle) to the left in Figs. 2.1-1b–2.1-1d with an increase of the ratio B/A.

Recovery of Previous Solutions

For large u, the following asymptotic relationships hold true:

$$\cosh u \sim \sinh u \sim (1/2)\exp u, \quad \text{as } u \to \infty. \quad (2.1\text{-}55)$$

Equations (2.1-9) and (2.1-55) then imply, in Cartesian coordinates, that

$$x \sim (a/2)\exp u \cos v, \quad y \sim (a/2)\exp u \sin v, \quad \text{as } u \to \infty, \quad (2.1\text{-}56)$$

while in polar coordinates (r, θ), $z = r \exp(i\theta)$, they imply

$$r \sim (a/2)\exp u, \quad \theta \sim v, \quad \text{as } u \to \infty. \quad (2.1\text{-}57)$$

Therefore, for large u, we can substitute (2.1-57) into (2.1-23) and (2.1-24) to obtain

$$\left.\begin{array}{l} T_{xz}^{E} \sim -\exp(u_0/2)[a/(2r)]^{1/2}\sin(\theta/2), \\[6pt] T_{yz}^{E} \sim \exp(u_0/2)[a/(2r)]^{1/2}\cos(\theta/2). \end{array}\right\} \quad \text{as } r \to \infty. \quad \begin{array}{l}(2.1\text{-}58)\\[6pt](2.1\text{-}59)\end{array}$$

Equations (2.1-58) and (2.1-59) provide a means of determining the parameter product, $a \exp u_0$, of the elliptic coordinate system in terms of the stress intensity factor and the shear yield stress k. We know from [PM 78] that the small-scale yielding solution for mode III is

$$(T_{xz}^{E})_{\text{ssy}} = (\tau_{xz}^{E}/k)_{\text{ssy}} = -(K_{\text{III}}/k)(2\pi r)^{-1/2}\sin(\theta/2), \quad (2.1\text{-}60)$$

$$(T_{yz}^{E})_{\text{ssy}} = (\tau_{yz}^{E}/k)_{\text{ssy}} = (K_{\text{III}}/k)(2\pi r)^{-1/2}\cos(\theta/2), \quad (2.1\text{-}61)$$

where K_{III} is the mode III stress intensity factor.

Assuming, as we have, that (2.1-58) and (2.1-59) approach the small-scale yielding solution at a sufficiently large distance from the crack tip, we can identify the elliptic coordinate parameter a in terms of K_{III}, k, and u_0 as

$$a = (K_{III}/k)^2/[\pi \exp u_0]. \tag{2.1-62}$$

We infer from (2.1-62) that as $u_0 \to \infty$, the foci of the elliptic coordinate system coalesce, i.e., $a \to 0$.

Now in elliptic coordinates the eccentricity ϵ of an ellipse for a given dimension u_0 is

$$\epsilon = \text{sech } u_0. \tag{2.1-63}$$

Therefore as $u_0 \to \infty$ $(\epsilon \to 0)$, the elliptic elastic–plastic boundary u_0 approaches a circular shape. In view of (2.1-57), we can replace $\exp(u_0)$ in (2.1-62) by

$$\exp u_0 \sim (2/a)r_0, \quad \text{as } u_0 \to \infty, \tag{2.1-64}$$

to find

$$r_0 = (K_{III}/k)^2/(2\pi), \quad \lim \epsilon \to 0 \quad \text{for } \partial\Omega. \tag{2.1-65}$$

This expression is identical to the Hult–McClintock radius r_0 for the elastic–plastic boundary. The elastic stresses and strains of the Hult–McClintock solution can be recovered from our elastic solution by substituting asymptotic relationships (2.1-57), (2.1-64), and (2.1-65) into the corresponding relationships presented in this section.

The total stresses, strains, and displacements of the Hult–McClintock solution in the plastic region can be obtained by making the following substitution for α:

$$\alpha = \tan^{-1}[Y/(X + A)] \tag{2.1-66}$$

into the corresponding formulas of this section. Equation (2.1-66) is obtained from (2.1-39) by the substitution $B = A$.

In the case of the Cherepanov solution, the elastic–plastic boundary can be specified in terms of the elliptic coordinate parameter a. This boundary, $\partial\Omega$, can be defined so that it spans the distance $X = -1$ to $X = 1$ on the Cartesian axis $Y = 0$. This line segment corresponds to the elliptic coordinate $u = 0$.

To recover Cherepanov's solution, we substitute $u_0 = 0$ into (2.1-23) and (2.1-24). Under a translation of axes $x^* \equiv z + a$ and the introduction of the notation $\tau/k \equiv T_{xz}^E - iT_{yz}^E$, we obtain equation (4-248) of [Cher 79]. Cherepanov did not choose to use elliptic coordinates, nor did he present an explicit solution for the stresses; however, his stresses would take the form of (2.1-23) and (2.1-24) with $u_0 = 0$. Similarly, the strains and displacements of Cherepanov's solution can be determined by the substitution $u_0 = 0$ into their appropriate elastic counterparts.

Crack Tip Opening Displacement

The model presented in this chapter thus far is underdetermined; i.e., the stresses, strains, and displacements cannot be uniquely determined from the imposed boundary conditions. It is this additional degree of freedom, however, that allows us to develop a transition model that accounts for changes in shape of the plastic zone.

A change of shape in the plastic zone may be related to an internal variable such as temperature, or it may be related to a three-dimensional effect such as plate thickness.

If the elastic–plastic boundary u_0 can be specified in terms of a known parameter, then the elastoplastic problem becomes determinate. In this regard, the crack tip opening displacement can serve as a suitable parameter.

The crack tip opening displacement δ_t is obtained from the relative displacement of the crack surfaces at the crack tip, i.e.,

$$\delta_t = a[W^P(\pi/2) - W^P(-\pi/2)]. \tag{2.1-67}$$

With the substitution of the parameter a from (2.1-62) and the evaluation of $W^P(\alpha)$ at the angles $\alpha = \pm\pi/2$, we find from (2.1-67) that

$$\delta_t = \left[2K_{III}^2/(\pi Gk)\right][1 - (1/3)\exp(-2u_0)], \qquad u_0 \geq 0. \tag{2.1-68}$$

In principle, we can use (2.1-68) to determine experimentally the parameter u_0 from values of δ_t, K_{III}, G, and k. This procedure naturally assumes that the Hult–McClintock to Cherepanov plastic zone transition is representative of the material behavior of the specimen.

Because the J integral is related to the stress intensity factor of small-scale yielding [Hut 79] by the formula

$$J = K_{III}^2/(2G), \tag{2.1-69}$$

equation (2.1-68) may be rewritten as

$$\delta_t = [4J/(\pi k)][1 + (1/3)\exp(-2u_0)]. \tag{2.1-70}$$

For $u_0 = 0$, (2.1-70) gives the value of the crack tip opening displacement for the Cherepanov plastic strip model δ_{Ch},

$$\delta_{Ch} = 16J/(3\pi k). \tag{2.1-71}$$

In the limit as $u_0 \to \infty$, we recover from (2.1-70) the Hult–McClintock crack tip opening displacement δ_{HM} [Hut 79] in terms of the corresponding J integral, i.e.,

$$\delta_{HM} = 4J/(\pi k). \tag{2.1-72}$$

We see by comparing (2.1-70) and (2.1-72) that for identical values of J and k, the crack tip opening displacement for the transition model δ_t is always higher than for the Hult–McClintock model δ_{HM}.

It is curious to note the the Bilby–Cottrell–Swinden plastic strip model for mode III has a crack tip opening displacement δ_{BCS} [KP 85] that is lower than the Hult–McClintock, the transition, and the Cherepanov crack tip opening displacements for the same values of J and k, i.e.,

$$\delta_{BCS} = J/k. \tag{2.1-73}$$

Comments

While our mode III elastoplastic solution is not directly applicable to other modes of fracture, it is anticipated that general trends can be established through its analysis. In [McC 58] and as a commentator to an addendum to [Irw 60], McClintock discusses insights that can be gained about mode I from a mode III elastoplastic solution. An analogy for the plane strain to plane stress transition of mode I is given for mode III in the latter reference.

The model presented in this section provides a new analytical tool for the investigation of transition phenomena associated with changes of plastic zone shape ahead of a crack tip. While the solution itself is based on elastoplastic fracture mechanics, additional constitutive equations are required for the transition effect. As the shape of the plastic zone can be related to the crack tip opening displacement, the development of constitutive relationships from standard test procedures is possible.

2.2 AN ENERGY-DISSIPATION ANALYSIS FOR THE TRANSITION MODEL

In this section an exact relationship is obtained for the rate of energy dissipation [Ung 92a] due to plastic work for the transition model of mode III crack propagation. It is found that the rate of energy dissipation increases monotonically as the transition in plastic zone shape changes from the infinitesimally thin line segment of the Cherepanov plastic strip solution to the circular shape of the Hult–McClintock elastoplastic solution.

This analysis might serve as an aid for investigating irreversible fracture processes.

The following equation of a slip line can be determined from (2.1-33)–(2.1-35):

$$\frac{y - a \sinh u_0 \sin 2\alpha}{x - a \cosh u_0 \cos 2\alpha} = \tan \alpha. \tag{2.2-1}$$

As part of the energy-dissipation analysis, it is convenient to develop an orthogonal coordinate system (α, β) where β is the family of orthogonal trajectories to the slip lines α. A procedure for finding orthogonal trajectories is given in [Cha 87]. The slope dy/dx of a trajectory β must be perpendicular to the slip line α, i.e.,

$$\frac{dy}{dx} = -\cot \alpha \tag{2.2-2}$$

where the relationship between α and (x, y) is given by (2.2-1). By differentiating (2.2-1), we may eliminate either dx or dy from (2.2-2). Then by separating variables we may integrate the result over $d\alpha$ and one of the Cartesian coordinates. Upon substituting this relationship into (2.2-1), we find the second coordinate in terms of α. The procedure yields

$$x = \beta \cos \alpha - ae^{-u_0}[(1/3)\cos^4\alpha + \sin^4\alpha] - a \sinh u_0 \tag{2.2-3}$$

$$y = \beta \sin \alpha - (4/3)ae^{-u_0}\sin \alpha \cos^3\alpha \tag{2.2-4}$$

where β is a constant of integration. Equations (2.2-3) and (2.2-4) may also be interpreted as the definition of an orthogonal coordinate system (α, β).

The (α, β) coordinate system is shown in Fig. 2.2-1 for the particular parameter value listed on the figure. The ratio B/A corresponds to the case of the transition model which is shown in Fig. 2.1-1c, i.e., where the strain singularity coincides with the origin of the Cartesian coordinate system (x, y).

The differential arc length ds in three-dimensional coordinates (α, β, z) is derived by differentiating (2.2-3)–(2.2-4) and by substituting the results for dx, dy, and dz into (2.2-5); i.e.,

$$(ds)^2 = (dx)^2 + (dy)^2 + (dz)^2 \tag{2.2-5}$$

$$= g_{\alpha\alpha}(d\alpha)^2 + g_{\beta\beta}(d\beta)^2 + g_{zz}(dz)^2 \tag{2.2-6}$$

where

$$g_{\alpha\alpha} = \{\beta - (4/3)ae^{-u_0}\cos 3\alpha\}^2 \tag{2.2-7}$$

$$g_{\beta\beta} = 1, \qquad g_{zz} = 1. \tag{2.2-8}$$

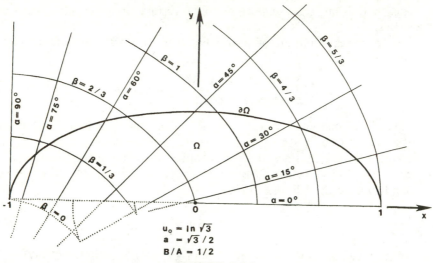

FIGURE 2.2-1

Characteristic coordinate system. Reprinted from *Eng. Fract. Mech.*, **41**, D. J. Unger, An energy dissipation analysis for a transitional model of crack tip plasticity, 457–462 (1992), with permission from Pergamon Press Ltd., Headington Hill, Oxford, OX3 OBW, UK.

It was assumed in [Ung 89b] that all displacements u_i are zero except for those in the z direction; i.e.,

$$u_\alpha = u_\beta = 0, \qquad u_z = w^P(\alpha). \tag{2.2-9}$$

(Notation: the subscripted elliptic coordinate u_0 is not a displacement.)

The relationships between normal strains ϵ_{ii} (no sum for repeated index) and small displacements in orthogonal coordinates are as follows [Sok 56]:

$$\epsilon_{ii} = (u_i/g_{ii}^{1/2})_{,i} + [1/(2g_{ii})]\sum_k g_{ii,k} u_k/g_{kk}^{1/2}. \tag{2.2-10}$$

In our case $i = \alpha, \beta, z$; $k = \alpha, \beta, z$; where the components of the metric tensor g_{ii} are given in (2.2-7)–(2.2-8). Similarly, the relationships between engineering shear strains γ_{ij} and small displacements are

$$\gamma_{ij} = 2\epsilon_{ij} = (g_{ii}g_{jj})^{-1/2}\Big[g_{ii}(u_i/g_{ii}^{1/2})_{,j} + g_{jj}\big(u_j/g_{jj}^{1/2}\big)_{,i}\Big], \qquad i \neq j, \tag{2.2-11}$$

for $i = \alpha, \beta, z$; $j = \alpha, \beta, z$.

In [Ung 89b], no explicit expression was given for the plastic strain as the expression would have been unwieldy in Cartesian coordinates or elliptic coordinates. However, in (α, β, z) coordinates the plastic strain was readily determined [Ung 92a].

Using (2.2-10) and (2.2-11), we find that the only nonzero strain in the plastic region $\gamma_{\alpha z}^{\Omega}$. This strain is composed of an elastic (recoverable) component $\gamma_{\alpha z}^{E}$ and plastic (inelastic) component $\gamma_{\alpha z}^{P}$, such that

$$\gamma_{\alpha z}^{\Omega} = \gamma_{\alpha z}^{E} + \gamma_{\alpha z}^{P}. \tag{2.2-12}$$

From Hooke's law, we may write

$$\gamma_{\alpha z}^{E} = \tau_{\alpha z}^{P}/G = k/G. \tag{2.2-13}$$

The purely plastic component of strain may be obtained from (2.2-11)–(2.2-13) as

$$\gamma_{\alpha z}^{P} = g_{\alpha\alpha}^{-1/2} w_{,\alpha}^{P} - k/G. \tag{2.2-14}$$

By substituting (2.1-43), (2.1-47) and (2.2-7) into (2.2-14) and differentiating w^{P} with respect to α as indicated, we find

$$\gamma_{\alpha z}^{P} = g_{\alpha\alpha}^{-1/2} \left[K_{\text{III}}^{2}/(\pi k G) \right] \{\cos \alpha - e^{-2u_0} \cos 3\alpha\} - k/G \tag{2.2-15}$$

$$= \frac{K_{\text{III}}^{2}[\cos \alpha - e^{-2u_0} \cos 3\alpha]}{\pi k G\{\beta - (4/3) a e^{-u_0} \cos 3\alpha\}} - k/G. \tag{2.2-16}$$

We note from (2.2-16) that a strain singularity of order $O(1/r)$ exists at $\alpha = 0$, $\beta = (4/3) a e^{-u_0}$, $u_0 \neq 0$. The location of this singularity is indicated in Figs. 2.1-1b–2.1-1d by the solid circle on the crack axis. Other potential strain singularities exist at $\beta = (4/3) a e^{-u_0} \cos 3\alpha$, $\alpha \neq 0$; however, these points do not fall in the physical plane of the plastic zone. Two of these points correspond to the cusps of the dotted coordinate curves of Fig. 2.2-1. The denominator of (2.2-16) is also equal to zero at $\alpha = \pi/2$, $\beta = 0$, which is the intersection of the crack with the plastic zone; but in this case the numerator is also equal to zero. Using l'Hospital's rule, we find a finite strain at this position. In the special case $u_0 = 0$ (the Cherepanov model), there is no strain singularity anywhere in the field.

Let us now choose the stress intensity factor as the loading parameter with which the strain rates will be calculated. Partial derivatives of functions with respect to K_{III} are designated by the following:

$$(\dot{\ }) = \frac{\partial(\ )}{\partial K_{\text{III}}}. \tag{2.2-17}$$

Consequently, the function

$$\dot{w}^P = [2K_{III}/(\pi kG)][\sin \alpha - (1/3)e^{-2u_0}\sin 3\alpha] \qquad (2.2\text{-}18)$$

is obtained by the partial differentiation of (2.1-47) with respect to K_{III}.

The inelastic component of the total strain rate is determined in a fashion analogous to (2.2-14) and (2.2-15); i.e.,

$$\dot{\gamma}_{\alpha z}^P = g_{\alpha\alpha}^{-1/2}\dot{w}_{,\alpha}^P - \dot{k}/G \qquad (2.2\text{-}19)$$

$$= g_{\alpha\alpha}^{-1/2}[2K_{III}/(\pi Gk)][\cos \alpha - e^{-2u_0}\cos 3\alpha] \qquad (2.2\text{-}20)$$

where the substitution $\dot{k} = 0$ is made in (2.2-19).

The rate of energy dissipation is related to two distinct components. The first component $\dot{D}_1$ is the work done internally by the stress field, and as such it is related to the volume of plastic material. The second component $\dot{D}_2$ is related to work done by the tractions on the discontinuous surfaces in the plastic stress field (the region on the crack axis between the solid and hollow circular markers of Fig. 2.1-1). The total rate of energy dissipation $\dot{D}$ will therefore be the sum of these two components:

$$\dot{D} = \dot{D}_1 + \dot{D}_2. \qquad (2.2\text{-}21)$$

The first component of the rate of energy dissipation per unit plate thickness is

$$\dot{D}_1 = \int_{\Omega} \tau_{\alpha z}^P \dot{\gamma}_{\alpha z}^P \, dS, \qquad (2.2\text{-}22)$$

where dS is the differential area of plate surface. In (α, β) coordinates, dS becomes

$$dS = g_{\alpha\alpha}^{1/2} \, d\alpha \, d\beta. \qquad (2.2\text{-}23)$$

If we substitute k for $\tau_{\alpha z}^P$, define the limits of integration in the (α, β) plane, and make use of symmetry for the upper and lower half-planes, we find that (2.2-22) and (2.2-23) assume the form

$$\dot{D}_1 = 2k\int_0^{\pi/2} \int_{\beta_i(\alpha)}^{\beta_o(\alpha)} \dot{\gamma}_{\alpha z}^P g_{\alpha\alpha}^{1/2} \, d\beta \, d\alpha \qquad (2.2\text{-}24)$$

where β_i and β_o are the inner and outer limits of the coordinate β, as shown in Fig. 2.2-2.

Now by substituting (2.2-20) for $\dot{\gamma}_{\alpha z}^P$, and (2.2-7) for $g_{\alpha\alpha}^{1/2}$ into (2.2-24), we find

$$\dot{D}_1 = [4K_{III}/(\pi G)]\int_0^{\pi/2} \int_{\beta_i(a)}^{\beta_o(\alpha)} (\cos \alpha - e^{-2u_0}\cos 3\alpha) \, d\beta \, d\alpha. \qquad (2.2\text{-}25)$$

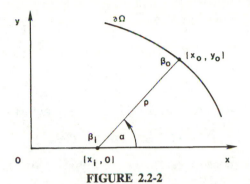

FIGURE 2.2-2

Integration limits. Reprinted from *Eng. Fract. Mech.*, **41**, D. J. Unger, An energy dissipation analysis of a transitional model of crack tip plasticity, 457–462 (1992), with permission from Pergamon Press Ltd., Headington Hill, Oxford, OX3 OBW, UK.

The inner integral of (2.2-25) is trivial. Its evaluation yields

$$\dot{D}_1 = [4K_{\text{III}}/(\pi G)]\int_0^{\pi/2} \rho(\alpha)(\cos\alpha - e^{-2u_0}\cos 3\alpha)\,d\alpha \quad (2.2\text{-}26)$$

where

$$\rho(\alpha) \equiv \beta_o(\alpha) - \beta_i(\alpha). \quad (2.2\text{-}27)$$

From the geometry shown in Fig. 2.2-2, we can deduce the following

$$x_o - x_i = \rho\cos\alpha, \qquad y_o = \rho\sin\alpha \quad (2.2\text{-}28)$$

$$\rho = \left[(x_o - x_i)^2 + y_o^2\right]^{1/2}. \quad (2.2\text{-}29)$$

Equations (2.2-30) can be established by using (2.1-9) and (2.1-32):

$$x_o = a\cosh u_0\cos 2\alpha, \qquad y_0 = a\sinh u_0\sin 2\alpha. \quad (2.2\text{-}30)$$

The coordinate x_i is found by setting $y = 0$ in (2.2-1) and solving for x. We obtain

$$x_i = (a/2)[e^{-u_0}(3 - 4\sin^2\alpha) - e^{u_0}]. \quad (2.2\text{-}31)$$

The additional relationship (2.2-32)–(2.2-33) are derived from (2.2-28)–(2.2-31),

$$x_o - x_i = 2a\sinh u_0\cos^2\alpha \quad (2.2\text{-}32)$$

$$\rho(\alpha) = 2a\sinh u_0\cos\alpha. \quad (2.2\text{-}33)$$

Through (2.2-26) and (2.2-33), we find

$$\dot{D}_1 = [8a \sinh u_0 K_{III}/(\pi G)] \int_0^{\pi/2} (\cos \alpha - e^{-2u_0} \cos 3\alpha) \cos \alpha \, d\alpha.$$

$$(2.2\text{-}34)$$

We substitute (2.1-62) for a in (2.2-34) and integrate to yield

$$\dot{D}_1 = (1 - e^{-2u_0}) K_{III}^3/(G\pi k^2). \qquad (2.2\text{-}35)$$

This relationship constitutes the first component of the rate of energy dissipation.

We will now proceed to evaluate the second component of $\dot{D}$. The extent of the stress/displacement discontinuity along the crack axis is, from Section 2.1, $-A \le x/a \le A - 2B$. In this region, a one-to-one correspondence exists between α and x. We can deduce this relationship between x and α from the characteristic equation (2.2-1) by setting $y = 0$. It follows that

$$x/a = A - 2B + 2(B - A)\sin^2\alpha, \qquad y = 0, \ -A \le x/a \le A - 2B.$$

$$(2.2\text{-}36)$$

The rate of energy dissipation per unit thickness of the plate due to the traction on the faces of the discontinuity is

$$\dot{D}_2 = 2 \int_{-aA}^{a(A-2B)} \tau_{yz}^P \dot{w}^P \, dx \qquad (2.2\text{-}37)$$

where the factor 2 in front of the integral accounts for both lower and upper discontinuities. The term dx in (2.2-37) may be found in terms of α by differentiating (2.2-36). This produces

$$dx = -2ae^{-u_0}\sin 2\alpha \, d\alpha, \qquad -A \le x/a \le A - 2B, \ y = 0. \quad (2.2\text{-}38)$$

Now by substituting (2.2-18), (2.2-38), and $\tau_{yz}^P = k \cos \alpha$ into (2.2-37), we find

$$\dot{D}_2 = [8aK_{III}/(\pi G)]e^{-u_0} \int_0^{\pi/2} \cos \alpha [\sin \alpha - (1/3)e^{-2u_0}\sin 3\alpha]\sin 2\alpha \, d\alpha.$$

$$(2.2\text{-}39)$$

By evaluating integral (2.2-39) and substituting a from (2.1-62) into the result, we come to the conclusion that

$$\dot{D}_2 = [K_{III}^3/(\pi Gk^2)]e^{-2u_0}\{1 - (1/3)e^{-2u_0}\}. \qquad (2.2\text{-}40)$$

Therefore, by (2.2-21), (2.2-35), and (2.2-40), the total rate of energy dissipation per unit thickness of plate is

$$\dot{D} = \left[K_{\mathrm{III}}^3/(\pi Gk^2) \right]\{1 - (1/3)e^{-4u_0}\}. \tag{2.2-41}$$

We note that if we set $u_0 = 0$ in (2.2-41), then we recover the value of $\dot{D}$ for the Cherepanov model [Cher 79]; and if we take the limit of (2.2-41) as $u_0 \rightarrow \infty$, then we recover $\dot{D}$ for the Hult–McClintock model [Cher 79]. Equation (2.2-41) also gives intermediate values of $\dot{D}$ for the transition between these two limiting cases. We can see that the rate of energy dissipation increases uniformly with u_0.

It is intended that the energy dissipation analysis presented here be useful to researchers interested in plastic zone transitions in fracture mechanics.

In the case of mode I, we know that the thickness of the specimen affects the shape of the plastic zone and the fracture toughness. In the case of plane stress, the Dugdale plastic strip model, which is similar in shape to the Cherepanov strip model of mode III, can serve as a reasonable model of crack tip plasticity. However, no mode I counterpart exists for the Hult–McClintock solution.

As there are no exact elastoplastic solutions available for mode I fracture problems with finite-dimensional plastic zones (without a disequilibrated stress discontinuity; see Chapter 1), the relationships provided here may give some insight into this other mode of fracture by analogy. Possible applications include temperature transition phenomena (lower-shelf to upper-shelf transitions).

2.3 EFFECTIVE CRACK LENGTH FOR THE TRANSITION MODEL

Irwin proposed an effective crack length for use in brittle fracture criteria in order to extend the utility of linear elastic fracture mechanics to ductile materials (see [Hel 84, p. 87]). This concept was based in part on an elastoplastic analysis of the mode III fracture mechanics problem by Hult and McClintock.

Under conditions of small-scale yielding, Hult and McClintock's solution predicts an elastic–plastic boundary that is circular. The locus of the elastoplastic boundary can be determined by substituting the stresses from the purely elastic mode III solution into the Mises yield criterion. The plastic stress field that satisfies equilibrium across the elastic–plastic interface requires the crack tip to move from its original position in the purely elastic solution (the center of the circular elastoplastic boundary) to the edge of the plastic zone. The elastic stress field in the elastoplastic problem is consequently equivalent to stresses generated in a purely elastic problem by a crack with an effective length c_{eff} equal to the physical crack length c plus the radius of the plastic zone R_P, i.e.,

$$c_{\text{eff}} = c + R_P. \qquad (2.3\text{-}1)$$

A stress intensity factor that is calculated using the equivalent crack length rather than the actual crack length is called the effective stress intensity factor.

The following relationship has been derived for the Hult–McClintock plastic zone radius R_P (see Chapter 1);

$$R_P = (K_{\text{III}}/k)^2/(2\pi) \qquad (2.3\text{-}2)$$

where K_{III} is the mode III stress intensity factor and k is the yield stress in pure shear.

There are no exact elastoplastic solutions available for the other two modes of fracture from which analogous expressions can be derived for the lengths L of the plastic zones along the crack axes ($L = 2R_P$). However, a simple approximation involving equilibrium in one dimension and an assumed translation of a singular elastic stress field of order $O(r^{-1/2})$ can produce the following result for the plane stress mode I problem (see [Hel 84, p. 18])
Irwin plane stress:

$$L = 2R_P = (K_I/\sigma_0)^2/\pi \approx 0.318(K_I/\sigma_0)^2 \qquad (2.3\text{-}3)$$

where K_I is the mode I stress intensity factor and σ_0 is the tensile yield stress. Irwin suggested the following correction for a plane strain mode I problem on the basis of the Tresca yield condition [Hel 84, p. 18]:
Irwin plane strain:

$$L = 2R_P = (K_I/\sigma_0)^2/(3\pi) \approx 0.106(K_I/\sigma_0)^2. \qquad (2.3\text{-}4)$$

On the other hand, the Dugdale plastic strip model for plane stress gives the following expression for the length of the plastic zone [Hel 84, p. 20]:
Dugdale plane stress:

$$L = (\pi/8)(K_I/\sigma_0)^2 \approx 0.393(K_I/\sigma_0)^2. \qquad (2.3\text{-}5)$$

We see that the two plane stress expressions (2.3-3) and (2.3-5) are comparable in length.

Unger [Ung 89b] proposed a different mode III model in which the elastic–plastic boundary assumes the shape of an ellipse (Fig. 2.3-1). This model can recover as a limited case the small-scale yielding Hult–McClintock solution as the eccentricity of the elliptic elastic–plastic boundary goes to zero. In addition, the Cherepanov [Cher 79] plastic strip model for mode III can also be recovered as a special case by allowing the elliptic elastic–plastic boundary to generate to a slit. In all cases the elastic stresses have the characteristic behavior of small-scale yielding; i.e., they are of the order $O(r^{-1/2})$ as $r \to \infty$.

Following [Ung 89b] and Section 2.1, let us establish an elliptic coordinate system with the origin O at the center of the plastic zone (Fig. 2.3-1). The relationships between Cartesian (x, y) and elliptic coordinates (u, v) are given by (2.1-9).

Curves of constant stress intensity T,

$$T = \left(\tau_{xz}^2 + \tau_{yz}^2\right)^{1/2},\qquad (2.3\text{-}6)$$

fall on the ellipses u, where τ_{xz} and τ_{yz} are the antiplane shear stresses in the x and y directions, respectively.

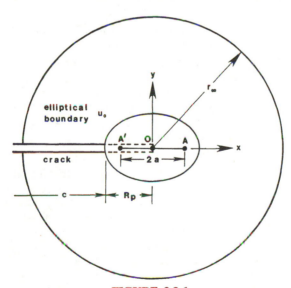

FIGURE 2.3-1

Crack tip geometry of the transition model. Reprinted from [Ung 90b] by permission of Kluwer Academic Publishers.

For higher values of u, a curve of constant T becomes circular (cf. Fig. 2.1-2 and Fig. 2.3-1, locus r_∞). For sufficiently large u, the solution is indistinguishable from the purely elastic small-scale yielding solution which has concentric circles of stress intensity. Thus the far-field stresses are equivalent to those generated by a crack that has been extended the length of the broken lines in Fig. 2.3-1.

The semimajor axis of the plastic zone R_P (Fig. 2.3-1) can be determined from equation (2.1-9) as

$$R_P = |x|_{u=u_0, v=\pi} = |a \cosh u_0 \cos \pi| = a \cosh u_0. \qquad (2.3\text{-}7)$$

By substituting the value of a from (2.1-62) into (2.3-7), we find

$$R_P = (K_{III}/k)^2[1 + \exp(-2u_0)]/(2\pi), \qquad 0 \le u_0 \le \infty. \quad (2.3\text{-}8)$$

For large u_0 the elliptic elastic–plastic boundary asymptotically approaches a circular shape (centered at O). In the limit as $u_0 \to \infty$ the value of the Hult–McClintock elastic–plastic radius (2.3-2) is obtained from (2.3-8).

In the Cherepanov model, the plastic zone reduces to line segment AA' of Fig. 2.3-1. We can obtain the Cherepanov plastic strip value of R_P from (2.3-8) by setting $u_0 = 0$.

We note that the plastic zone length of the Cherepanov model is twice the length of the Hult–McClintock plastic zone along the x-axis (for identical values of k and K_{III}). Any intermediate value of u_0 gives a value of R_P between these limits.

We observe that the Dugdale model of mode I has a value of L that is longer than the length for plane strain. In a way, this resembles the relationship between the plastic zones of Cherepanov and of Hult and McClintock. However, no analogous expression exists for R_P that allows a smooth transition from plane stress to plane strain.

The effective stress intensity factor K_{IIIeff} for a central crack of length $2c_{eff}$ in an infinite plate is

$$K_{IIIeff} = \tau_\infty(\pi c_{eff})^{1/2} = \tau_\infty[\pi(c + R_P)]^{1/2}, \qquad (2.3\text{-}9)$$

where τ_∞ is a remotely applied antiplane stress. By substituting R_P from (2.3-8) into (2.3-9), we find

$$K_{IIIeff} = \tau_\infty\left(\pi c + (K_{IIIeff}/k)^2[1 + \exp(-2u_0)]/2\right)^{1/2}. \quad (2.3\text{-}10)$$

By solving equation (2.3-10) for K_{IIIeff}, we deduce that the effective stress intensity factor for an infinite plate with an internal crack of length $2c$ is

$$K_{\text{IIIeff}} = \tau_\infty(\pi c)^{1/2} \Big/ \left\{ 1 - (1/2)(\tau_\infty/k)^2[1 + \exp(-2u_0)] \right\}^{1/2}. \quad (2.3\text{-}11)$$

We can employ equation (2.3-11) for mode III in a way similar to Irwin's use of the effective stress intensity factor of mode I for predicting critical loads [Hel 84, p. 87]. We can calculate the value of τ_∞ related to failure by substituting a known value of the fracture toughness K_{IIIc} into (2.3-11) for K_{IIIeff} together with a corresponding value for u_0. An experimental technique for determining u_0 from the crack tip opening displacement is discussed in [Ung 89b] and in Section 2.1.

We may find experimentally that K_{IIIc} is a function of temperature, specimen geometry, and phase composition. In mode I, we observe pronounced changes in fracture toughness with temperature (the lower-shelf to upper-shelf transition) and plate thickness (the plane stress to plane strain transition).

As a final comment, we mention that the length of the plastic zone for the Bilby–Cottrell–Swinden plastic strip model [BCS 63, eq. (21)] is Bilby–Cottrell–Swinden:

$$L = (\pi/8)(K_{\text{III}}/k)^2 \approx 0.393(K_{\text{III}}/k)^2. \quad (2.3\text{-}12)$$

We infer from (2.3-8) and (2.3-12) that this model produces a plastic zone that falls between the lower limit ($L \approx 0.318 K_{\text{III}}^2/k^2$) and the upper limit ($L \approx 0.637 K_{\text{III}}^2/k^2$) of plastic zone length $L = 2R_P$ of the transition model. This model [BCS 63] has a stress $\tau_{yz} = k$ on the plastic strip; however, the stress intensity T violates yield ($T > k$) along most of the plastic strip as $\tau_{xz} \neq 0$ except at the forward tip of the plastic zone. See (2.4-9) in Section 2.4.

2.4 FRACTURE ASSESSMENT DIAGRAMS

The fracture (or failure) assessment diagram [DT 75, and HLM 76] is an attempt at combining failure criteria based on linear elastic fracture mechanics and plastic collapse. This failure criterion is a function of two parameters K_r and S_r, which respectively quantify the elastic fracture component and the plastic collapse component. A curve that represents a limit of safe design is plotted in the coordinate system (K_r, S_r). The ordinate of the graph K_r is the ratio of the stress intensity factor K_I to the toughness K_c. The abscissa of the graph S_r is the ratio of the applied tensile traction σ_∞ to the limit load stress σ_L. A particular design is considered safe provided K_r and S_r fall below the failure curve on the fracture assessment diagram.

It has been generally assumed that a curve based on the Dugdale model (plane stress) of crack tip plasticity provides a reasonable lower bound for design loads. The Dugdale model has a plastic zone in the shape of a strip ahead of the crack tip [Dug 60]. In the plastic strip a biaxial state of stress σ_0 (yield) exists. The failure curve (called R6) based on the Dugdale model [HLM 76] predicts that

$$K_r = S_r \left[(8/\pi^2) \ln \sec(\pi S_r/2) \right]^{-1/2}, \qquad (2.4\text{-}1)$$

provided we interpret the limit load σ_L as σ_0. The locus of points based on equation (2.4-1) is plotted in Fig. 2.4-1.

As has been previously observed, there are cases when the R6 criterion proves nonconservative. To show this, a plot of experimental data by Chell [Chel 79] is reproduced here as Fig. 2.4-2. We can see from this figure that some of the experimental data fall below the R6 curve, which is shown as a solid line. To compensate for this, Chell proposed a more conservative

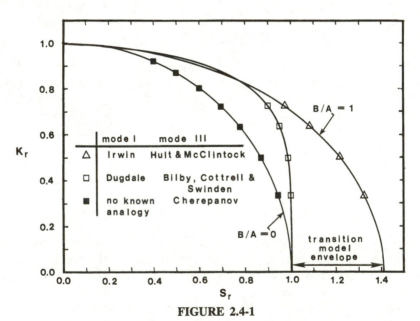

FIGURE 2.4-1

Mode I and mode III fracture assessment diagrams. Reprinted from [Ung 92b] by permission of Kluwer Academic Publishers.

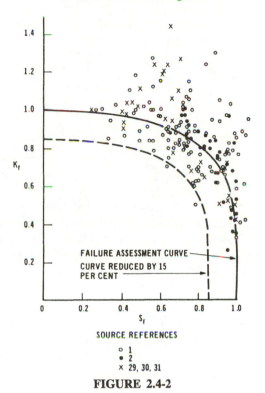

FIGURE 2.4-2

Experimental validation of the failure assessment diagram. Reprinted from [Chel 79] with permission of G. G. Chell.

failure curve which is reduced by 15%. Its locus is also shown on Fig. 2.4-2 as a broken line. Materials represented on this diagram were chosen from titanium alloys, aluminum alloys, and steels. These data come from a number of sources, which are listed below the figure. A key that identifies the references listed by Chell with those contained in this text is provided in Table 2.4-1.

For a comparison of the Dugdale model (R6) with other failure criteria, additional failure curves proposed by different individuals and agencies are given in Table 2.4-2 and plotted in Fig. 2.4-3 [McC 94]. These comparisons were originally made by McCabe [McC 89].

Let us now examine a particular failure curve. When the Irwin failure criterion for plane stress ($\sigma_L = \sigma_0$)

$$K_r = \left[1 - (S_r)^2/2\right]^{1/2} \tag{2.4-2}$$

TABLE 2.4-1
Key to Chell's References in Fig. 2.4-2.

Chell [Chel 79]	This text
[1]	[DT 75]
[2]	[Chel 77]
[29]	[BL 72]
[30]	[LY 58]
[31]	[CS 77]

is compared to the Dugdale failure locus, the Irwin model falls below the Dugdale over a particular region. This behavior is depicted in both Figs. 2.4-1 and 2.4-3. The Irwin model of crack tip plasticity represents a finite-width plastic zone for plane stress, as opposed to the Dugdale plastic strip model, which is infinitesimally thin.

TABLE 2.4-2
Example of Elastic–Plastic Calibrations after [McC 89].

Model [Reference]	K_c Equation	K_r Equation
CEGB R/H/R6 [CEGB 84]	Typical engineering materials	$(1 - 0.14S_r^2)$ $[0.3 + 0.7\exp(-0.65S_r^6)]$
Tangent stress [Mer 81]	$\sigma_0(\pi c)^{1/2} Y\left[\left(\frac{\sigma_\infty}{\sigma_0}\right)^2 + \alpha\left(\frac{\sigma_\infty}{\sigma_0}\right)^{n+1}\right]^{1/2}$	$S_r[S_r^2 + \alpha S_r^{n+1}]^{-1/2}$
Irwin [IKS 58]	$\dfrac{\sigma_\infty(\pi c)^{1/2}}{\left[1 - \dfrac{(\sigma_\infty/\sigma_0)^2}{2}\right]^{1/2}}$	$\left[1 - \dfrac{S_r^2}{2}\right]^{1/2}$
EL-PL HBK [KGS 81]	$\left[EJ(c_e)\left(\frac{P}{P_0}\right)^2 + EJ(c,n)\left(\frac{P}{P_0}\right)^{n+1}\right]^{1/2}$	$S_r[H_eS_r^2 + H_nS_r^{n+1}]^{-1/2}$
Dugdale [Dug 60]	$\left[8\sigma_0^2\left(\frac{c}{\pi}\right)\ln \sec\left(\frac{\pi\sigma_\infty}{2\sigma_0}\right)\right]^{1/2}$	$S_r\left[\frac{8}{\pi^2}\ln \sec\left(\frac{\pi S_r}{2}\right)\right]^{-1/2}$
NUREG-0744 [Joh 82]	$\sigma_\infty(\pi c)^{1/2}\dfrac{Y}{[1 - Y^2/\beta(\sigma_\infty/\sigma_0)^2]^{1/2}}$ where $Y = f(c/W)$	$\left[1 - \dfrac{Y^2}{\beta(S_r)^2}\right]^{1/2}$

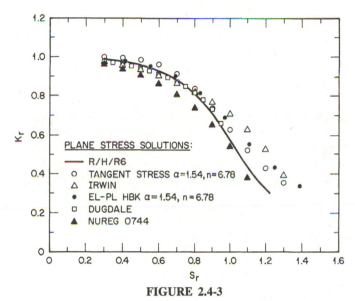

FIGURE 2.4-3

Calibration curves for six elastic–plastic models: center-cracked panel; W (width = 406 mm = 16 in.); $2c/W$ = 0.5. After [McC 89]. Courtesy of Oak Ridge National Laboratory and D. E. McCabe.

By analogy, the Irwin model for mode I crack propagation is supported by the predictions of the Hult–McClintock [HM 56], small-scale yielding, elastoplastic solution for mode III crack propagation. However, this in itself makes it difficult to judge precisely the effect of plastic zone development on failure criteria, as one curve is based on an exact mode I solution (Dugdale) and the other is supported by an exact mode III solution (Hult–McClintock). It would be desirable to compare two analytical solutions with these dissimilar types of plastic zones for the same mode of fracture. This is impossible for mode I as no counterpart to the Hult–McClintock solution has been found. There are, however, plastic strip solutions available for mode III to compare with the Hult–McClintock solution.

Two different plastic strip models for mode III have already been mentioned in this text: one by Cherepanov [Cher 79] and the other by Bilby, Cottrell, and Swinden [BSC 63]. Although both of these mode III models have plastic zones similar in shape to that of the Dugdale model, their stresses and failure predictions differ.

Unger [Ung 89b] has obtained an analytical elastoplastic solution for mode III in a related problem, that models a transition in plastic zone shape from a strip to a circular cylinder (see Sections 2.1 and 2.3).

Correspondingly, the Cherepanov solution and the Hult–McClintock solution can be recovered from the transition model, which has a plastic zone in the shape of an elliptical cylinder.

Unger [Ung 90b] has also developed an effective crack length, similar to Irwin's, for the transition model, which was presented in the previous section as (2.3-1) and (2.3-8). This allows us to model in a continuous fashion the theoretical change between a strip model and a finite-width plastic zone model for the mode III counterpart of the fracture assessment diagram [Ung 92b].

The ratio B/A of the semiminor axis to the semimajor axis of the elliptic plastic zone satisfies the following relationship by (2.1-35):

$$B/A = \tanh u_0. \qquad (2.4\text{-}3)$$

Therefore we can rewrite (2.3-11) as

$$K_{\text{IIIeff}} = \frac{\tau_\infty(\pi c)^{1/2}}{\left(1 - \left[(\tau_\infty/k)^2/(1 + B/A)\right]\right)^{1/2}}, \qquad 0 \le B/A \le 1. \quad (2.4\text{-}4)$$

To obtain the failure criterion for the transition model from (2.4-4), we first redefine K_r and S_r as

$$K_r = K_{\text{III}}/K_{\text{IIIc}}, \qquad S_r = \tau_\infty/\tau_L \qquad (2.4\text{-}5)$$

where K_{III} is a mode III stress intensity factor, K_{IIIc} is the corresponding toughness, τ_∞ is the applied shear traction, and τ_L is the collapse stress in shear.

Then by setting $\tau_L = k$, $K_{\text{IIIeff}} = K_{\text{IIIc}}$, and $\tau_\infty(\pi c)^{1/2} = K_{\text{III}}$, we infer from (2.4-4)–(2.4-5) that the failure criterion for the transition model is

$$K_r = \left\{1 - \left[(S_r)^2/(1 + B/A)\right]\right\}^{1/2}, \qquad 0 \le B/A \le 1. \quad (2.4\text{-}6)$$

We note that if $B/A = 1$, then (2.4-6) produces a result that corresponds to the Hult–McClintock solution. We also see that (2.4-6) with $B/A = 1$ is analogous to the Irwin failure criterion (2.4-2), and represents the upper bound for any ratio of B/A. For $B/A = 0$, equation (2.4-6) predicts the lower bound of the transition model. This locus is a circular arc and it is based on the Cherepanov model of crack tip plasticity. For all other values of B/A, the shape of the failure curve on the fracture assessment diagram is elliptic. This family of elliptic curves expands uniformly on the fracture assessment diagram from the lower bound $B/A = 0$ to the upper bound $B/A = 1$.

We should mention that the second plastic strip model (Bilby–Cottrell–Swinden) is often regarded as the mode III equivalent of the Dugdale model because the crack tip opening displacement is completely analogous to its mode I counterpart [BS 66]. For small-scale yielding, compare equations (I.6-23) to (I.6-65) to see this. It follows that a failure criterion for mode III based on the Bilby–Cottrell–Swinden model has the same form as (2.4-1) provided we change the definitions of (K_r, S_r) to (2.4-5).

We notice in Fig. 2.4-1 that the Bilby–Cottrell–Swinden failure curve lies on or above the Cherepanov curve. Therefore, the Bilby–Cottrell–Swinden model is not the most conservative mode III failure criterion available from a plastic strip model.

The fact that the Cherepanov curve lies below the Bilby–Cottrell–Swinden curve on the fracture assessment diagram might be explained by analyzing the stress fields, the yield condition, and the lower bound theorem of plasticity.

The Bilby–Cottrell–Swinden model has a constant shear traction

$$\tau_{yz} = k \tag{2.4-7}$$

applied ahead of a crack tip as a boundary condition representing a plastic strip in an otherwise purely elastic problem. Now the elastic solution for τ_{xz} along the plastic strip is obtained from the imaginary part of the Westergaard complex function $Z(z)$ from [BS 66], i.e.,

$$Z(z) = (2k/\pi)\cot^{-1}\left\{(c/z)[(z^2 - a^2)/(a^2 - c^2)]^{1/2}\right\}, \tag{2.4-8}$$

where $2c$ is the crack length and $(a - c)$ is the length of one of the two plastic zones. (Note that the definitions of a and c have been interchanged from those of Section I.6.) Taking the imaginary part of (2.4-8), we find that, along the plastic strip $(y = 0)$,

$$\tau_{xz} = -(2k/\pi)\tanh^{-1}\left\{(c/x)[(a^2 - x^2)/(a^2 - c^2)]^{1/2}\right\}, \qquad c < x < a. \tag{2.4-9}$$

We further note that the Mises or Tresca yield condition for a perfectly plastic material has the form of (2.1-8).

It follows from (2.4-7) and (2.4-9) that stresses that exceed yield (2.1-8) must exist along the plastic strip, because $\tau_{yz} = k$ alone satisfies yield and any nonzero contribution for τ_{xz} pushes it over the limit. This implies that the limit load of plastic collapse may have been exceeded. Therefore, the Bilby–Cottrell–Swinden model is inappropriate as a lower limit on the fracture assessment diagram, as it violates the lower bound theorem of plasticity.

On the other hand, the transition solution, which includes the Cherepanov solution and the Hult–McClintock solution as limiting cases, does not have stresses for any ratio of B/A that exceed yield. Thus the Cherepanov solution, which is the most conservative limit of the transitional model solution, can serve as a model for a failure curve known to satisfy the conditions of the lower bound theorem of plasticity.

A similar statement cannot be made about the Dugdale model (see Section I.6) for the mode I fracture assessment diagram because the Dugdale model does not have stresses that exceed yield, as is the case for the Bilby–Cottrell–Swinden model.

The Dugdale model has as its far-field stresses a biaxial state of stress $\sigma_x = \sigma_y = \sigma_\infty$. Lu and Chow [LC 90] have also proposed a different mode I plastic strip model that does not restrict the normal stresses at infinity to equality with one another; i.e.,
Lu–Chow:

$$\sigma_x(\pm\infty, y) = c\sigma_\infty, \qquad \sigma_y(x, \pm\infty) = \sigma_\infty \qquad (2.4\text{-}10)$$

Dugdale:

$$\sigma_x(\pm\infty, y) = \sigma_\infty, \qquad \sigma_y(x, \pm\infty) = \sigma_\infty, \qquad (2.4\text{-}11)$$

where c is a constant of proportionality between the imposed tractions in the x and y directions at infinity.

Along the plastic strip, the Dugdale model's state of stress is represented by point M on the plane stress yield surfaces of Fig. I.9-1.
Dugdale model:

$$\sigma_x(x,0) = \sigma_y(x,0) = \sigma_0, \qquad \tau_{xy}(x,0) = 0. \qquad (2.4\text{-}12)$$

Using the plane stress Mises yield criterion (I.9-31), we find a more general state of yield for use with the Lu–Chow model of the form,

$$\sigma_x(x,0)^2 + \sigma_y(x,0)^2 - \sigma_x(x,0)\sigma_y(x,0) = \sigma_0^2, \qquad \tau_{xy}(x,0) = 0,$$
$$(2.4\text{-}13)$$

where the shear stress τ_{xy} has been set equal to zero due to the symmetry of the mode I problem. This yield condition can be visualized in the principal stress space of Fig. I.9-1 as the Mises ellipse where $\sigma_1 = \sigma_x$ and $\sigma_2 = \sigma_y$. To justify this, we compare (I.9-31) with $\tau_{xy} = 0$ to (I.9-32).

Notice that the Dugdale model stresses along the plastic strip $\sigma_x(x, 0)$ $= \sigma_y(x, 0) = \sigma_0$ also satisfy (2.4-13).

The crack tip opening displacement for the Lu–Chow model [LC 90] is Lu–Chow:

$$\delta_{LC} = [8a\sigma_0^*/(\pi E)]\ln[\sec(\pi\sigma_\infty)/(2\sigma_0^*)], \qquad (2.4\text{-}14)$$

where

$$\sigma_0^* \equiv \sigma_0\Big/\left\{\left[1 - (3/4)(1 - c)^2(\sigma_\infty/\sigma_0)^2\right]^{1/2} + (1 - c)\sigma_\infty/(2\sigma_0)\right\}.$$
$$(2.4\text{-}15)$$

If we compare (2.4-15) to (I.6-22), we find the crack tip opening displacement of the Lu–Chow model to be analogous to the Dugdale model's, where its effective yield stress σ_0^* replaces the yield stress σ_0 in the Dugdale model.

Let us now set $c = 0$ in the Lu–Chow model to obtain the solution for a uniaxial load σ_∞ in the y direction. The analogy between (2.4-14) and (I.6-22) allows us to conclude that Lu–Chow ($c = 0$):

$$K_r = S_r\left\{\left[1 - (3/4)S_r^2\right]^{1/2} + (S_r/2)\right\}$$
$$\times \left\{(8/\pi^2)\ln\sec\left[(\pi/2)S_r\left\{\left[1 - (3/4)S_r^2\right]^{1/2} + (S_r/2)\right\}\right]\right\}^{-1/2}.$$
$$(2.4\text{-}16)$$

Notice from its plot in Fig. 2.4-4 that the Lu–Chow uniaxial load (2.4-16) is conservative relative to the Dugdale model (2.4-1) with its biaxial load. As the Lu–Chow model represents a more realistic loading and a more conservative yield locus, it seems appropriate that this curve should replace the R6 curve as the standard theoretical model for mode I.

Another feature of the fracture assessment diagram is the reserve stress of the material. The reserve stress, or safety factor, is the ratio of length of the line segment going from the origin O through the design state point P and continuing until it reaches the assigned failure locus point Q, divided by the length of the line segment from the origin to point P. In Fig. 2.4-4, for the Lu–Chow failure curve, the reserve stress is the ratio of length OQ divided by length OP.

We can tell from the mode I data provided by Chell in Fig. 2.4-2, that some experimental data still fall below the theoretical Lu–Chow failure curve. Perhaps a more practical yield locus to adopt in its place is a

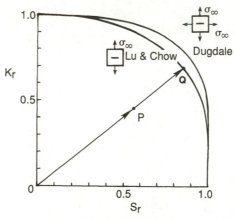

FIGURE 2.4-4

Failure curves related to uniaxial and biaxial loadings and the radii of the reserve stress (OQ/OP) of point P relative to the uniaxial load curve.

circular arc in analogy to the mode III Cherepanov locus. Much of the experimental data by Chell will fall above this arc. A reduced circle could also be used, similar to Chell's reduced curve in Fig. 2.4-2, to ensure that all data fall safely above the reduced arc. Furthermore, the reserve stress of the material would be particularly convenient to calculate using a circular failure locus, because it is the ratio of two radii.

3

Environmental Cracking

Naturam expellas furca tamen usque recurret.[1]

Materials under applied loads in aggressive environments often suffer from some form of subcritical crack growth. Crack propagation can initiate under adverse environmental conditions at relatively small loads. Common materials such as aluminum alloys, ceramics, and steels are subject to environmental cracking through the action of water. All told, environmental cracking is a phenomenon that afflicts many different engineering materials through numerous reactive agents. Brass is adversely affected by ammonia, for example, and titanium alloys are subject to hydrogen-assisted cracking.

Variables that affect environmental crack growth rates include viscous fluid and molecular transport (external), physical and chemical adsorption, chemical reactions, film deposits, and internal diffusion (which is in turn affected by stress, trapping mechanisms, and mobile dislocations).

Common experimental trends can be observed for materials subject to degradation by either stress corrosion cracking (scc) or hydrogen embrittlement. One of these features is the threshold stress intensity factor K_{Iscc} (or K_{th}) below which crack propagation is not observed for fixed environmental conditions. For values of the stress intensity factor above K_{Iscc}, three stages of steady-state crack propagation are typically observed.

In Sections 3.1 and 3.2 we discuss the modeling of hydrogen-assisted crack growth. In this model stage I and stage III crack propagation is

---

[1] Roman proverb: "Though you drive out nature with a pitchfork, it will always return" (recorded by Horace).

clearly observed. In Section 3.3 we solve a moving boundary value problem for stage II stress corrosion cracking that is transport-controlled. Section 3.3 describes what is possibly the first true moving boundary value problem that has been solved analytically for environmental crack propagation, aside from steady-state solutions in Galilean frames of reference and quasi-static solutions.

3.1 HYDROGEN-ASSISTED CRACKING

Hydrogen-assisted cracking is a phenomenon that afflicts both high-strength steels and titanium alloys. Subcritical crack growth can initiate in metals susceptible to hydrogen embrittlement at load levels far below those required for rapid fracture in inert environments. As a consequence, an otherwise conservatively designed steel structure or mechanism can fail when exposed to hydrogen due to the slow growth of a crack that ultimately attains a critical length.

Exposure to hydrogen can take different forms. Direct exposure to hydrogen gas occurs in pipelines and in pressure vessels. Indirect exposure to hydrogen can occur from any physical contact of the metal with liquid water or water vapor. In the latter case a chemical reaction between steel and water produces hydrogen gas, which subsequently enters the metal and embrittles it. Hydrogen can also be introduced into a material during the manufacturing process or by electrochemical charging.

In the case of an aqueous environment, a hydrogen-free specimen can pass through a substantial incubation period before crack propagation begins. This incubation time, as well as the crack velocity itself, $\dot{a}$, is a function of the environment, specimen geometry, crack length, and load [Her 76]. The last three parameters can be recorded through the stress intensity factor K_I, provided small-scale yielding criteria are met.

Two special values of the stress intensity factor exist: a threshold stress intensity factor K_{th}, below which subcritical (slow and incremental) crack propagation is not observed, and a critical stress intensity factor K_{IC} where instantaneous failure occurs.

Laboratory experiments are conducted under both steady-state (time-independent) and unsteady (time-dependent) conditions. In steady-state experiments, the investigator avoids sudden changes in K_I as impulsive changes produce velocity transients and correspondingly time-dependent behavior. In unsteady experiments, transients in velocity are intentionally induced by step or other sudden changes in load. Unsteady data must be recorded as a function of both the stress intensity factor and time. In most investigations steady-state conditions have been assumed, but this assumption can prove false, depending on the magnitude of the initial stress intensity factor relative to K_{th}.

To elaborate on this, we see in Fig. 3.1-1 a plot of experimental data [HW 71] which shows a crack velocity versus time for 4340 steel in distilled water at 298 K (Kelvins) [WNW 72, HW 81]. A special kind of specimen, known as the tapered double-cantilevered beam (DCB), was used for these experiments. A small schematic of one of these is provided in the figure (uniform plate thickness). This type of specimen has the unusual property of maintaining a constant stress intensity factor for constant load. This is achieved by the specimen's unconventional shape, which differs from most others which have rectangular cross sections with uniform plate thicknesses. These data show clearly that transient behavior does occur, but they also show that steady-state velocities are eventually reached for a given stress intensity factor.

The data of Fig. 3.1-1 may now be cross-referenced with data [LW 73] in Fig. 3.1-2 from [WNW 72, LW 73, HW 81], which were obtained from more conventional specimens (center cracked panel) whose stress intensity factors vary under constant load. The tapered DCB specimen's data fall on the solid curve, which corresponds to the envelope of the conventional specimen data, initiated at different stress intensity factors but exposed to

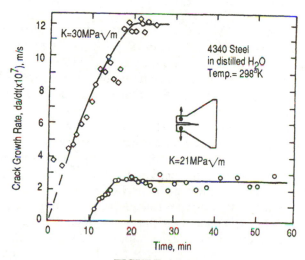

FIGURE 3.1-1

Static load crack growth rates under constant stress intensity factor conditions showing transient and steady-state behavior. Reprinted from [WNW 72] by permission of ASTM and from *Int. J. Pressure Vessels Piping*, 9, S. J. Hudak, Jr., and R. P. Wei, Considerations of non-steady-state crack growth in materials evaluation and design, 63–74 (1981), with permission from Elsevier Science, Ltd., Pergamon Imprint, The Boulevard, Langford Lane, Kidlington OX5 1GB, UK.

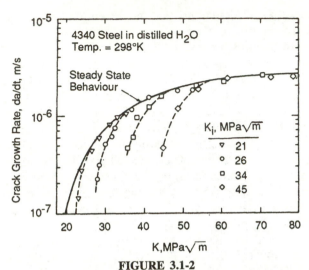

FIGURE 3.1-2

Dependence of static load crack growth kinetics on initially applied stress intensity factor K_I. Reprinted from [LW 73] by permission of Kluwer Academic Publishers, [WNW 72] by ASTM, and from *Int. J. Pressure Vessels Piping*, **9**, S. J. Hudak, Jr., and R. P. Wei, Considerations of non-steady-state crack growth in materials evaluation and design, 63–74 (1981), with permission from Elsevier Science, Ltd., Pergamon Imprint, The Boulevard, Langford Lane, Kidlington, OX5 1GB, UK.

common environments. We can see clearly in this example that stage I growth is not steady-state, as there is no one-to-one-correspondence between stress intensity factor and crack velocity. However, it should also be pointed out that most of the specimens had experienced initial crack growth at stress intensity factors well above K_{th}, so steady-state conditions should not prevail immediately.

Graphs of crack velocity versus stress intensity factor (Fig. 3.1-3) typically show three stages of steady-state crack propagation. The first stage (I) of crack growth, which is the stage nearest to K_{th}, is the region exhibiting an exponential growth of $\dot{a}$ in relation to K_I. The second stage (II) of crack growth is a region in which the crack velocity is less dependent on the stress intensity factor. In the case depicted in Fig. 3.1-3, the crack velocity is virtually independent of the stress intensity factor. The third stage (III) of crack growth is a region close to the critical stress intensity factor. Here the crack velocity increases significantly and is again strongly dependent on K_I. Rapid fracture occurs in hydrogen environments near the same K_{IC} as that found under inert environmental conditions.

Kinetic Processes

A number of kinetic processes may be operating simultaneously in subcritical cracking associated with hydrogen embrittlement. Any one

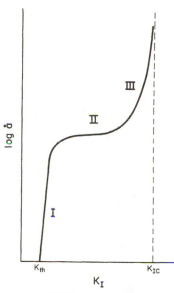

FIGURE 3.1-3

Average crack velocity versus stress intensity factor. Reprinted from *Eng. Fract. Mech.*, **31**, S. L. Lee and D. J. Unger, A decohesion model for hydrogen assisted cracking, 647–660 (1988), with permission from Pergamon Press Ltd., Headington Hill Hall, Oxford OX3 OBW, UK.

process or combination of processes can be rate-limiting and produce the stage II growth noted earlier. For example, fluid transport can be a rate-limiting process. A deleterious substance must migrate from its environmental reservoir to a region near the crack tip. If the supply is slower than the embrittling process itself, then the overall cracking process is rate-limited by transport.

Chemical reactions that occur near the crack tip to produce hydrogen gas can also be rate-limiting. For example, in the case of water and AISI 4340 steel, a chemical reaction associated with the oxidation of metal and release of hydrogen gas has been identified in [SPW 78] for stage II crack propagation. In Fig. 3.1-4, the experimental data for a 4340 steel in water of various temperatures, obtained by [LW 73, HM 75] and discussed in this context in [SPW 78], are reproduced here.

In Fig. 3.1-5, a new set of data reported in [SPW 78] is shown for the same steel as that in Fig. 3.1-4, but subjected to hydrogen gas rather than water. This would, of course, eliminate the oxidation stage of metal with the accompanying release of hydrogen gas as a controlling mechanism of crack growth rates. Fractographic evidence, which was obtained in this study, indicated that the mechanism responsible for fracture was identical to that of the previous study, thereby implicating hydrogen as the underly-

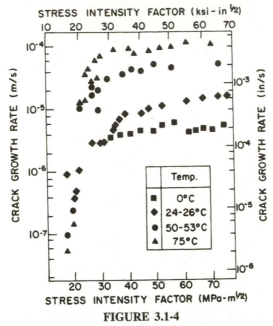

FIGURE 3.1-4

The kinetics of sustained-load crack growth in AISI 4340 steel (tempered at 204°C) in distilled water. Reprinted from [SPW 78] by permission of ASM International.

ing cause of crack growth in both cases. We observe in Fig. 3.1-5 that stage II growth is again present in the experimental data despite the absence of the previous rate-controlling mechanism. It was hypothesized in [SPW 78] that the new controlling mechanism could be one of a number of mechanisms: surface reactions, hydrogen entry, transport to the fracture site, or the fracture process itself.

Figure 3.1-6, a schematic diagram from [GW 77] shows the sequence of events that occurs when exposure to an environment of hydrogen gas causes crack growth in high-strength steels. In this diagram C_H stands for hydrogen concentration, δ is the distance to the region where embrittlement takes place, σ represents an applied stress, and FPZ is the fracture process zone.

Once hydrogen reaches the surface of the crack tip from an external source (1 in Fig. 3.1-6), it must enter the metal by an adsorption process. Two different adsorption processes exist. The first type is a physical adsorption (2) of hydrogen gas, where diatomic molecules, as opposed to ions, are adsorbed. The second stage, called chemical adsorption or chemisorption (3–4), occurs after the molecules dissociate into atoms

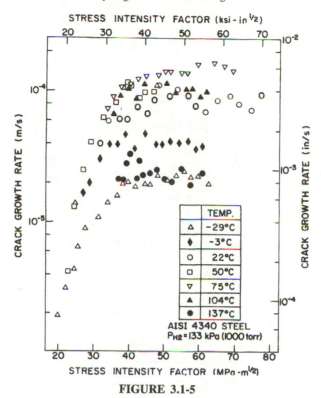

FIGURE 3.1-5

The kinetics of sustained-load crack growth in AISI 4340 steel (tempered at 204°C) in dehumidified hydrogen at 133 Pa. Reprinted from [SPW 78] by permission of ASM International.

under the influence of strong crystal fields [Fuj 85]. At low temperatures the first type can be rate-limiting, and at room temperature the second can be rate-limiting as indicated by studies involving hydrogen gas and 4340 steel [SF 81]. Upon entering the material (5), the hydrogen diffuses under the influence of hydrostatic stress gradients (6).

In [LPWSW 81], crack growth controlled by the internal diffusion of hydrogen in 4340 steel exposed to hydrogen sulfide gas has been reported. Data from their study are shown in Fig. 3.1-7 and 3.1-8. At high pressure, the rate-limiting mechanism is believed to be internal hydrogen diffusion. At the low pressure, the rate-limiting mechanism changes to external transport, where hydrogen sulfide gas from the environment reaches the crack tip through Knudsen diffusion. (This kind of diffusion is discussed in Section 3.3.) The change of rate-limiting mechanisms, between two pres-

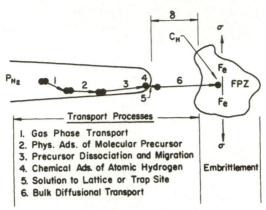

FIGURE 3.1-6

Schematic illustration of the processes involved in gaseous hydrogen embrittlement. Reprinted from [GW 77] by permission of ASM International.

sure extremes of 133 Pa and 2660 Pa, is implied by the change of slope in Fig. 3.1-8, where the log of crack growth rate is plotted inversely proportional to the absolute temperature.

Hydrogen introduced internally into the matrix of the metal during the forming process or by charging [SG 73] can also diffuse to the neighbor-

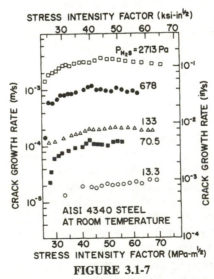

FIGURE 3.1-7

The kinetics of sustained-load crack growth in AISI 4340 steel to hydrogen sulfide at room temperature and at different pressures. Reprinted from [LPWSW 81] by permission of ASM International.

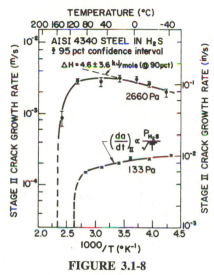

FIGURE 3.1-8

The effect of temperature on the mean stage II crack growth rate at hydrogen sulfide pressures of 133 and 2660 Pa. Reprinted from [LPWSW 81] by permission of ASM International.

hood of the crack tip under the influence of hydrostatic stress gradients to cause cracking. The diffusion process is accelerated by mobile dislocations that carry hydrogen (Cottrell) clouds [HL 82, CJ 49]. The local concentration of hydrogen can also be affected by traps such as voids, dislocations, grain boundaries, and foreign atoms.

Models

The model of hydrogen embrittlement presented here is based on the concept of a degrading cohesive force. This mechanism was originally proposed by Troiano [Tro 60] and his co-workers. It was later applied by Oriani and Josephic [OJ 77] to the modeling of threshold data for 4340 steel in hydrogen gas. In that particular analysis it was assumed that the cohesive force between atoms is lowered in a linear fashion with the hydrogen concentration. The concentration was then related to the stress by an equilibrium relationship.

A different decohesion model of hydrogen embrittlement that is applicable beyond the threshold stage was proposed by Neimitz and Aifantis [NA 85, NA 87a, NA 87b]. These investigators suggested a Barenblatt zone of cohesive force that degrades with time due to the presence of hydrogen. Subcritical crack initiation and arrest criteria are based on the crack tip opening displacement. The crack tip opening displacement is assumed to be a function of the average concentration of hydrogen which is, in turn, a function of time. When a critical average concentration of hydrogen is reached, a discrete jump in the crack length less than or equal to the length of the process zone occurs. Average crack velocities can thus be determined by dividing the increment of crack growth by the increment of time between subcritical initiations.

The model analyzed here is a particular case of a model proposed in [Ung 86]. Assuming a linear degradation between the cohesive force and hydrogen concentration, it incorporates subcritical fracture criteria based on crack tip opening displacement. This model differs most significantly from previous models in that it incorporates a pointwise degradation of cohesive force in relation to hydrogen concentration over the length of the cohesive force zone. The crack tip opening displacement is calculated directly from the degraded cohesive force profile, thus making the distribution of hydrogen in the cohesive zone important as well as the total content of hydrogen. As no attempt was made to solve a specific problem in [NA 85, NA 87a, NA 87b], the relative performance of these two decohesion models cannot be compared.

For a description of some other models of environmental cracking phenomena, the reader is directed to the subsection on previous models.

Growth of the Cohesive Zone

Our first task will be to establish the growth process of the cohesive zone. In the next subsection, we demonstrate that this growth is concurrent with an increase in the crack tip opening displacement, which ultimately provides a measure of the damage due to the presence of hydrogen in the metal. Although a specific boundary value problem for a particular initial condition is analyzed in this section, the model can readily accommodate other initial and boundary conditions. The kinetic model for a propagating crack proposed in the next subsection is consistent with the model presented here for the growth of the cohesive zone. The rate-limiting kinetic processes, which were mentioned earlier, can also be incorporated into this model.

In a Barenblatt model [SL 69], the cohesive force provides an additional contribution to the stress intensity factor so that the total stress intensity factor remains zero. This assumption is based on the physical assumption that stresses at the crack tip remain finite. If we denote this additional contribution due to the cohesive force with the symbol K_0, then this condition reads

$$K_I = K_0 \qquad (3.1\text{-}1)$$

where K_I is identified as the usual stress intensity factor. To determine K_0 we must substitute an expression for the cohesive force (traction) $\sigma_c(x,t)$ into the following integral [SL 69]:

$$K_0 = 2(c/\pi)^{1/2} \int_a^c \sigma_c(x,t)/(c^2 - x^2)^{1/2} \, dx \qquad (3.1\text{-}2)$$

where x is the coordinate shown in Fig. 3.1-9, a is the crack length, t is time, and $c = a + d$ where d is the length of the cohesive zone.

The cohesive force is, in general, a function of the distance between atoms (idealized as surfaces) between a and c. However, in order to simplify the analysis, we assume that the cohesive force is independent of the displacement of the crack surfaces. This should be sufficient to demonstrate hydrogen's quantitative effect on the cohesive force. Thus the cohesive force before the introduction of hydrogen is uniform.

The cohesive force is assumed to degrade linearly with the concentration of hydrogen $C(x,t)$, i.e.,

$$\sigma_c(x,t) = \sigma_{c0} - \gamma C(x,t), \qquad (3.1\text{-}3)$$

where σ_{c0} is the cohesive force in the absence of hydrogen and γ is a constant. We assume that the initial concentration of hydrogen $C(x,0)$ is zero. Thus we are modeling hydrogen that is introduced from the environment, rather than hydrogen initially present in the specimen. At time $t = 0^+$ a constant concentration of hydrogen C_0 is imposed at the crack tip. The concentration of hydrogen is governed by the heat equation

$$\frac{\partial C(x,t)}{\partial t} = D\frac{\partial^2 C(x,t)}{\partial x^2}, \qquad (3.1\text{-}4)$$

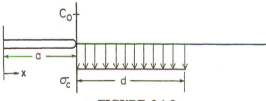

FIGURE 3.1-9

Crack length, cohesive zone, and coordinate. Reprinted from *Eng Fract. Mech*, **31**, S. L. Lee and D. J. Unger, A decohesion model for hydrogen assisted cracking, 647–660 (1988), with permission from Pergamon Press Ltd., Headington Hill Hall, Oxford, OX3 OBW, UK.

where D is the diffusivity. The use of the heat equation in (3.1-4) represents the simplest possible model of hydrogen diffusion, although the model itself is not inherently restricted to this equation. Equation (3.1-4) can be replaced by a stress-assisted diffusion equation such as that proposed in [Aif 80]. Here we are trying to establish only qualitative behavior due to the decohesion mechanism. As such, D in (3.1-4) should be understood as representing an apparent or effective diffusivity. In the same light, $C(x, t)$ should be interpreted as a quantity representing the total damage due to hydrogen and not necessarily the actual concentration of hydrogen.

The solution of the heat equation in one dimension for an initial hydrogen concentration of zero and a constant boundary condition C_0 is

$$C(x, t) = C_0 \text{erfc}\left[(x - a)/(4Dt)^{1/2}\right], \tag{3.1-5}$$

where erfc[ ] is the complementary error function, which is related to the error function erf[ ] by erfc[ ] $= 1 - $ erf[ ].

For this particular analysis, let us assume that the stress intensity factor is that of an infinite plate subject to a tensile traction σ_∞ with an internal crack of length $2c$; i.e.,

$$K_{\text{I}} = \sigma_\infty(\pi c)^{1/2}. \tag{3.1-6}$$

Note that in our notation a is one-half of the crack length and c is the length a plus the length of the cohesive zone d. Mathematically, however, the Barenblatt model treats the crack as if it were physically of length $2c$ with tractions due to the cohesive forces applied over the crack surfaces from $x = \pm a$ to $x = \pm c$.

The substitution of equations (3.1-2), (3.1-3), (3.1-5), and (3.1-6) into (3.1-1) gives the Barenblatt condition as

$$\int_a^c \left\{\sigma_{c0} - \gamma C_0 \text{erfc}\left[(x - a)/(4Dt)^{1/2}\right]\right\} \Big/ (c^2 - x^2)^{1/2} \, dx = (\pi/2)\sigma_\infty. \tag{3.1-7}$$

Now the first part of integral (3.1-7) may be readily evaluated to yield

$$\sigma_{c0}\cos^{-1}(a/c) - \gamma C_0 \int_a^c \text{erfc}\left[(x - a)/(4Dt)^{1/2}\right] \Big/ (c^2 - x^2)^{1/2} \, dx$$

$$= (\pi/2)\sigma_\infty. \tag{3.1-8}$$

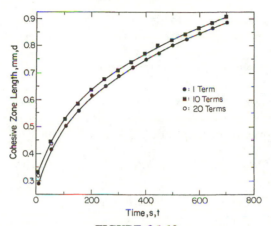

FIGURE 3.1-10

Cohesive zone length versus time. Reprinted from *Eng Fract. Mech*, **31**, S. L. Lee and D. J. Unger, A decohesion model for hydrogen assisted cracking, 647–660 (1988), with permission from Pergamon Press Ltd., Headington Hill Hall, Oxford OX3 OBW, UK.

The remaining integral in (3.1-8) can be approximated by the quadrature formula (25.4.37) of [AS 64] to give the first-order approximation.

$$\sigma_{c0}\cos^{-1}(a/c) - 2\gamma C_0[3(c-a)/(5c+a)]^{1/2}\mathrm{erfc}\left[(c-a)/(9Dt)^{1/2}\right]$$

$$= (\pi/2)\sigma_\infty. \tag{3.1-9}$$

A comparison [LU 88] between this one-term approximation, a ten-term approximation, and a twenty-term approximation can be found in Fig. 3.1-10 for the representative coefficient values appearing in Table 3.1-1 with the crack length $a = 1.016 \times 10^{-2}$ m. We can see that a twenty-term expansion is virtually indistinguishable from a ten-term expansion. We can also see that a one-term approximation is adequate for analyzing qualitative behavior. In all cases the accuracy of the approximations improves with time.

TABLE 3.1-1

Parameters

$D = 6.45 \times 10^{-10}$ m^2/s	$\sigma_{c0} = 1.31 \times 10^9$ Pa
$\sigma_\infty = 1.72 \times 10^8$ Pa	$\gamma C_0 = 0.9\sigma_{c0}$

Table 3.1-2 shows how closely two different functions appearing in (3.1-9) agree for c/a. Therefore, in (3.1-9) we can replace the second function appearing in the table by the first with little loss in accuracy. This leads to the following convenient form, which replaces (3.1-9):

$$\cos^{-1}(a/c) = (\pi/2)\sigma_\infty \Big/ \Big\{ \sigma_{c0} - \gamma C_0 \mathrm{erfc}\big[(c - a)/(9Dt)^{1/2}\big] \Big\}. \quad (3.1\text{-}10)$$

Taking the cosine of both sides of (3.1-10), we obtain

$$a/c = \cos\Big\{ (\pi/2)\sigma_\infty \Big/ \Big(\sigma_{c0} - \gamma C_0 \mathrm{erfc}\big[(c - a)/(9Dt)^{1/2}\big] \Big) \Big\}. \quad (3.1\text{-}11)$$

Let us now define an effective cohesive force $\sigma_{c\mathrm{EFF}}$:

$$\sigma_{c\mathrm{EFF}} \equiv \sigma_{c0} - \gamma C_0 \mathrm{erfc}\big[(c - a)/(9Dt)^{1/2}\big]. \quad (3.1\text{-}12)$$

By rearranging (3.1-11) and substituting (3.1-12) into (3.1-11), we find

$$c/a = \sec[(\pi/2)(\sigma_\infty/\sigma_{c\mathrm{EFF}})]. \quad (3.1\text{-}13)$$

Equation (3.1-13) has the form familiar in fracture mechanics literature. An expression similar to (3.1-13) has been used to determine the length of a plastic zone d (Dugdale model [Dug 60]), where the time-dependent $\sigma_{c\mathrm{EFF}}$ is replaced by a constant yield stress σ_0. Being a function of time, however, (3.1-13) predicts a monotonically increasing cohesive zone instead of a constant length as in the Dugdale model.

Crack Propagation

In the previous subsection, we described a decohesion model of hydrogen embrittlement in which a Barenblatt zone of cohesive force degrades

TABLE 3.1-2
A Comparison of Two Functions Appearing in (3.1-9)

c/a	$\cos^{-1}(a/c)$	$2[3(c - a)/(5c + a)]^{1/2}$
1.00	0.000000	0.000000
1.01	0.140836	0.140836
1.05	0.309845	0.309839
1.10	0.429700	0.429669
1.20	0.585686	0.585540
2.00	1.047198	1.044466
10.00	1.470629	1.455214
∞	1.570796	1.549193

linearly with the concentration of hydrogen. In this model, the cohesive zone grows to compensate for the loss of cohesion subject to the Barenblatt (finite-stress) condition. We now introduce criteria for crack initiation and arrest into the model. We also discuss the incorporation of various rate-limiting kinetic processes, and the model's multistage crack growth capability.

Figure 3.1-11a shows a schematic representation of the initial conditions of a specimen exposed to hydrogen: an initial crack length a_0, an initial cohesive zone length d_0, and a constant cohesive force σ_c. The specimen is assumed to be initially free of hydrogen with a boundary condition of hydrogen concentrations C_0 imposed at the crack tip.

Figure 3.1-11b represents an early stage of material degradation. The material has been damaged by hydrogen diffusing from the crack tip. The cohesive zone extends due to the degraded cohesive force subject to the Barenblatt condition (3.1-1).

The crack tip opening displacement δ may now be used as the damage criterion for this model.

In general, the crack tip opening displacement can be calculated numerically using equation (2.3.13) found in [SL 69], i.e., a double integration over the cohesive force σ_c. Accordingly, we have

$$\delta = -\Lambda \int_a^c x/(x^2 - a^2)^{1/2} \int_a^x \sigma_c(x,t)/(x^2 - \zeta^2)^{1/2} \, d\zeta \, dx + \delta_E \quad (3.1\text{-}14)$$

with $\Lambda = 8(1 - \nu^2)/(\pi E)$ for plane strain and $\Lambda = 8/(\pi E)$ for plane stress, where E is Young's modulus, $\nu =$ Poisson's ratio, x is the spatial coordinate, t is time, and $c = a + d$. The term δ_E in (3.1-14) is the elastic contribution to the crack tip opening displacement whose form is dependent on the geometry of the specimen and load. For example, an infinite plate with a crack of length $2a$ subject to a tensile force σ_∞ has

$$\delta_E = \Lambda(\pi/2)\sigma_\infty(c^2 - a^2)^{1/2}. \quad (3.1\text{-}15)$$

Refer to (3.2-12) and (3.2-14) for the evaluation of the integral used to generate (3.1-15).

At the early stage of degradation represented in Fig. 3.1-11b (defined by the broken-line region (b) in Fig. 3.1-12), the cohesive zone has extended to the length d_1, but the crack tip opening displacement is below a postulated critical value δ_c where subcritical crack propagation begins. For us, it is assumed that δ_c is constant, i.e., free of environmental and material effects. However, variable criteria can be readily introduced into the model.

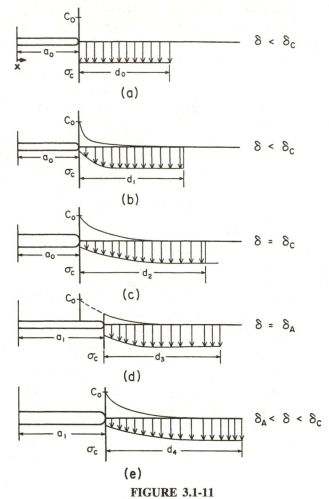

FIGURE 3.1-11

Crack propagation sequence. Reprinted from *Eng Fract. Mech*, **31**, S. L. Lee and D. J. Unger, A decohesion model for hydrogen assisted cracking, 647–660 (1988), with permission from Pergamon Press Ltd., Headington Hill Hall, Oxford OX3 OBW, UK.

In Fig. 3.1-11c (point c of Fig. 3.1-12), the degradation of the cohesive force has reached a state where crack propagation initiates, i.e., where the crack tip opening displacement has grown to the critical value, $\delta = \delta_c$. The time it takes to reach this state from the corresponding state shown in Fig. 3.1-11a may be interpreted as the incubation time, which is observed experimentally.

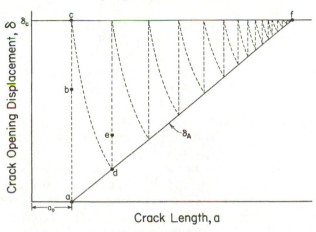

FIGURE 3.1-12

Crack tip opening displacement versus crack length. Reprinted from *Eng Fract. Mech*, **31**, S. L. Lee and D. J. Unger, A decohesion model for hydrogen assisted cracking, 647–660 (1988), with permission from Pergamon Press Ltd., Headington Hill Hall, Oxford OX3 OBW, UK.

We know that as the crack tip advances, it moves from very damaged material into much "healthier" material over a short distance. In the healthy material, the cohesive force is near its original strength; consequently, subcritical growth is initially accompanied by a drop in δ as the material undergoes a large effective increase in cohesive force. However, the crack tip opening displacement cannot fall indefinitely with crack advance. Once the bulk of the hydrogen damage has been passed, the effective cohesive force becomes essentially constant and any increase in crack length is subsequently accompanied by an increase in δ, as is normally observed under inert environmental conditions. This transition, shown by a solid line in Fig. 3.1-12, represents a natural lower bound for δ, which we term δ_A.

Figure 3.1-11d (point d of Fig. 3.1-12) show a crack that has arrested. It is proposed that the crack arrests when the crack tip opening displacement falls to δ_A. To find the new crack length a_1 and the new cohesive zone length d_3, subject to the Barenblatt condition and (3.1-1) requires a numerical procedure.

It is assumed that the time it takes to go from crack initiation shown in Fig. 3.1-11c to crack arrest shown in Fig. 3.1-11d is very short. As no significant time passed between crack initiation and arrest, the hydrogen concentration profile in Fig. 3.1-11d is the same as that in Fig. 3.1-11c. However, only the hydrogen beyond the new crack tip a_1 contributes to the subsequent degradation of the material, i.e., the initial concentration of hydrogen for the second increment of crack growth. For the most part, it is believed that this remnant of hydrogen is small.

We are now faced with the problem of imposing a new boundary condition of hydrogen concentration at the new crack tip at $x = a_1$. If we assume that the kinetic processes that supply the hydrogen to the crack tip are not rate-limiting, then imposing the same concentration C_0 as before is not an unreasonable assumption. As we are concentrating on the decohesion mechanism for the present, let us assume that this particular assumption holds.

In Figure 3.1-11e (point e in Fig. 3.1-12), we observe a state in which the cohesive zone and crack tip opening displacement are again expanding due to hydrogen decohesion following the first increment of crack advance. The hydrogen from the state shown in Fig. 3.1-11d remains as the initial concentration profile, and the boundary condition C_0 has been imposed at the new crack tip a_1. The crack is not currently moving, as δ is temporarily below δ_c.

A cycle of subcritical crack initiation and arrest then follows until the crack grows to a length where the lower bound δ_A coincides with δ_c. At this point, the crack tip opening displacement is forced to rise above δ_c and instantaneous failure occurs. This is point f on Fig. 3.1-12.

Average crack velocities can be calculated by dividing the increment of crack growth by the increment of time between subcritical crack initiations. The shortening path shown in Fig. 3.1-12 causes higher crack velocities.

Computer codes were developed independently to test the qualitative behavior of the model described previously [LU 88] followed by [SU 88].

The computer programs used analytic solution (3.1-5) of the diffusion equation (3.1-4) to quantify the evolution of hydrogen in the specimen. After each increment of crack growth, the time and initial concentration of hydrogen were reset to zero for the next increment of crack growth. This is a reasonable assumption provided the crack advances into virtually undamaged material with each increment of crack growth.

As the hydrogen content in the specimen increases with time, the code calculates corresponding cohesive zone lengths and crack tip opening displacements. The cohesive zone must be determined using (3.1-1), followed by the crack tip opening displacement using (3.1-14). The numerical integrations of (3.1-1) and the inner integral of (3.1-14) employed equation (25.4.37) of [AS 64] and ten Gaussian weights. This numerical integration scheme was chosen as it allows naturally for the square-root singularities encountered in the integrations. A Romberg integration scheme was used for the outer integration of (3.1-14).

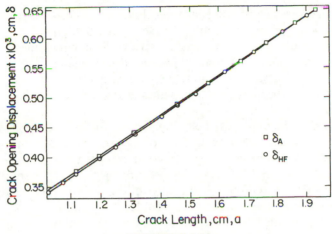

FIGURE 3.1-13

Comparison of arrest and hydrogen-free crack tip opening displacement. Reprinted from *Eng Fract. Mech*, **31**, S. L. Lee and D. J. Unger, A decohesion model for hydrogen assisted cracking, 647–660 (1988), with permission from Pergamon Press Ltd., Headington Hill Hall, Oxford OX3 OBW, UK.

The computer code used an incremental, path-dependent procedure. Using small increments of time, the program determines when the crack tip opening displacement first reaches δ_c from its initial state. The crack length a is then allowed to grow in small increments. The cohesive zone length and crack tip opening displacement are calculated for each incremental increase in crack length. When the crack tip opening displacement falls to δ_A, the crack arrests. The value δ_A is determined numerically and occurs when δ begins to increase with the crack length. It was verified numerically that δ_c approaches the hydrogen-free crack tip opening displacement δ_{HF}:

$$\delta_{HF} = \Lambda a \sigma_{c0} \ln\{\sec[\pi\sigma_\infty/(2\sigma_{c0})]\}. \tag{3.1-16}$$

A representative comparison [LU 88] between δ_A and δ_{HF} is shown in Fig. 3.1-13 for the parameters in Tables 3.1-1 and 3.1-3. The close proximity of

TABLE 3.1-3
Parameters

$E = 2.01 \times 10^{11}$ Pa	$K_{IC} = 4.62 \times 10^7$ Pa m$^{1/2}$	$a_0 = 1.016 \times 10^{-2}$ m
$\nu = 0.25$	$\delta_c = 7.60 \times 10^{-6}$ m	

these two curves suggests that little residual hydrogen remains after each increment of crack growth to affect subsequent crack growth.

Average crack velocities are calculated by dividing increments of crack growth by increments of time between critical events. Only the time between the previous arrest and the new initiation is considered. The extremely short period of time that passes during the actual propagation is neglected.

The external load σ_∞ was held constant in the computer programs to model steady-state crack growth. The stress intensity factor for an infinite plate subject to an external tensile traction σ_∞ was used.

In Figs. 3.1-14 and 3.1-15 crack tip opening displacements are plotted as functions of time and displacement, respectively, for the first increment of crack growth using the parameters of Tables 3.1-1 and 3.1-3. As expected, δ increases with time before attaining the critical value δ_c (Fig. 3.1-14), and δ decreases with the crack length following the attainment of δ_c (Fig. 3.1-15). The markers on the various graphs represent numerical data points.

In Fig. 3.1-16, computed average crack velocities are plotted for a variation of temperature (270–377 K) on a semilog scale. Here γC_0 was chosen as $0.65\sigma_{c0}$ and δ_∞ was chosen as 159 MPa. We also assume that the apparent diffusivity allows an Arrhenius representation

$$D = D_0 \exp[-Q/(RT)], \qquad (3.1\text{-}17)$$

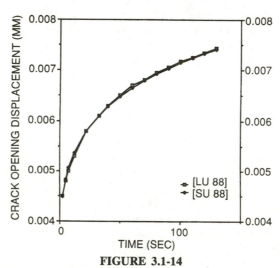

FIGURE 3.1-14

Crack tip opening displacement versus time for a stationary crack [SU 88].

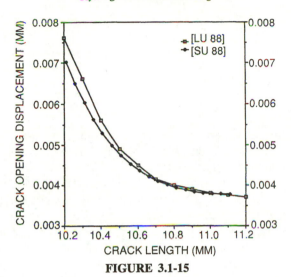

FIGURE 3.1-15

Crack tip opening displacement versus crack length during propagation [SU 88].

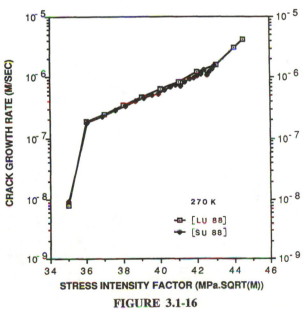

FIGURE 3.1-16

Average crack velocity versus stress intensity factor [SU 88].

TABLE 3.1-4

Parameters

$D_0 = 6.45 \times 10^{-2}$ m^2/s	$\sigma_{c0} = 1.31 \times 10^9$ Pa
$Q = 4.94 \times 10^4$ J/mol	$R = 8.32$ J/(mol K)

where Q is the activation energy, R is the gas constant, T is absolute temperature, and D_0 is a constant. A compilation of the other parameters used in this analysis is found in Tables 3.1-3 and 3.1-4.

We note that the curves in Figs. 3.1-16, 3.1-17, and 3.1-18 show the characteristic three stages of steady-state crack growth for all temperatures. The changes that occur in Figs. 3.1-16 to 3.1-18 with temperature are consistent with experimental trends. For mechanisms that do not follow an Arrhenius representation, alternative relationships between apparent diffusivity and temperature can be substituted in place of (3.1-17).

We have chosen a value of initial cohesive traction that is approximately the yield stress of high-strength steel. With this stress, and the calculation of a critical crack tip opening displacement based on a plane strain Dugdale model, we can obtain stage III growth as we approach K_{IC}.

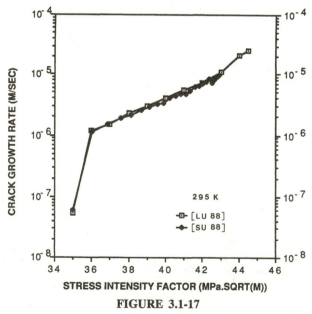

FIGURE 3.1-17

Average crack velocity versus stress intensity factor [SU 88].

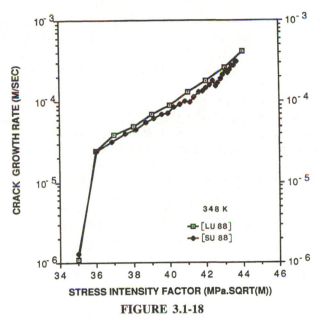

FIGURE 3.1-18

Average crack velocity versus stress intensity factor [SU 88].

Naturally, this "cohesive force" must be interpreted as an effective rather than an actual cohesive force as it is about 15 times less than the theoretical value $E/10$. As we are ignoring the details of the process zone, which are to a large extent unknown, this is a reasonable phenomenological approach.

The stage II growth exhibited in Figs. 3.1-16 to 3.1-18 is not a plateau variety as shown in Fig. 3.1-3. This might be expected as that type of stage II growth is often attributed to rate-limiting kinetic processes that are not incorporated into the computer code. (See the section on the Stefan problem in this text for transport-controlled stress corrosion cracking.)

In some cases a change in the activation energy Q can occur as the crack grows. For example, this change could occur if the activation energy were a function of the state of stress. The effect of such changes on crack velocity can be shown qualitatively by using a variable Q [LU 88]. The appearance of plateau regions in these curves demonstrates that stage II growth can occur from activation energy changes.

We might also add that plateau stage II crack growth can result from changes in the boundary condition C_0. These numerical results were documented in [Lee 86] for a boundary condition that decreases with crack length. Physically a decrease in the boundary condition of hydrogen can occur if the supply is being limited by transport along the outer crack surfaces, a chemical reaction at the crack tip, or an adsorption process.

It is possible to determine the parameter product γC_0 from a knowledge of the threshold stress intensity factor K_{th}. The following analysis explains the procedure.

As time goes to infinity, the cohesive force σ_c becomes the constant $\sigma_{c0} - \gamma C_0$, provided crack propagation does not occur. As the cohesive force becomes constant, the integral in (3.1-1) may be readily evaluated analytically to give the Barenblatt condition as

$$a/c = \cos\{(\pi/2)[\sigma_\infty/(\sigma_{c0} - \gamma C_0)]\}. \tag{3.1-18}$$

Similarly the integral in (3.1-14) may be evaluated analytically (the symbolic computer program MACSYMA[2] was used) to give the crack tip opening displacement as

$$\delta_\infty = \Lambda(\sigma_{c0} - \gamma C_0)\left[a\ln(c/a) - (c^2 - a^2)^{1/2}\cos^{-1}(a/c)\right] + \delta_E. \tag{3.1-19}$$

Now if we substitute (3.1-15) and (3.1-18) into (3.1-2) assume further that $\delta_\infty \ll \delta_c$, then we find δ_∞ is approximately

$$\delta_\infty = \Lambda\pi^2\sigma_\infty^2 a/[8(\sigma_{c0} - \gamma C_0)]. \tag{3.1-20}$$

If d is small compared to a, and if we assume plane strain conditions, then (3.1-20) becomes

$$\delta_\infty = (1 - \nu^2)K_I^2/[E(\sigma_{c0} - \gamma C_0)]. \tag{3.1-21}$$

The crack tip opening displacement δ_∞ represents the largest value of δ that a stationary crack can attain. If δ_∞ is less than δ_c, the crack will never propagate. If δ_∞ is greater than δ_c, the crack will begin to propagate before δ_∞ is reached. The special case $\delta_\infty = \delta_c$ corresponds to the threshold condition.

We note that given K_{th} from experimental data, we can, in principle, solve for γC_0 from (3.1-21) as all other parameters are assumed known from data collected under inert environmental conditions. Extreme care and patience are required to obtain a K_{th} that is truly the lowest possible value; i.e., the crack will grow for that particular value of stress intensity factor only as time approaches infinity. In light of this, published values of K_{th} may not be appropriate for use in (3.1-21) to find γC_0.

[2] Macsyma, Inc., Arlington, MA.

Overview of Some Previous Models of Environmental Cracking

The work of Charles and Hilig [CHi 62] was an early attempt to quantify steady-state crack velocity as a function of the applied stress in the presence of an aggressive environment. These investigators assumed an Eyring rate relationship of the form

$$\dot{a} = V_0 \exp(\beta\sigma), \tag{3.1-22}$$

where $\dot{a}$ is the velocity of the crack tip, V_0 and β are phenomenological coefficients, and σ is the applied stress. This relationship (3.1-22) was based on the assumption that activation energy is proportional to stress. Experimentally, a relationship of this form fits data very well for stress corrosion crack of glass in water. For temperature variations, the coefficient V_0 can be assumed to change in an Arrhenius fashion

$$V_0 = \text{const} \exp[-Q/(RT)], \tag{3.1-23}$$

where Q is the activation energy, R is the gas constant, and T is absolute temperature. This assumption also fits data well for temperature variations in glass subjected to water or water vapor.

Other investigators have developed relationships similar in form to (3.1-22) through various justifications. For example, Liu [Liu 70] solved a steady-state stress-assisted diffusion equation to obtain the concentration of a degrading solute of the form

$$C = C_0 \exp(\beta\sigma), \tag{3.1-24}$$

where β and C_0 are constants and σ is the hydrostatic stress. He then proposed that crack velocity was proportional to C to produce a relationship similar to (3.1-22) for stress corrosion cracking problems.

Gerberich *et al.* [GCS 75] proposed a relationship similar to (3.1-23) for hydrogen-assisted cracking by using an equilibrium solution like (3.1-24). Terms related to grain and plastic zone size were then incorporated into the model.

Oriani [Ori 72] proposed a decohesion model of hydrogen embrittlement, based on ideas due to Troiano [Tro 60], that cohesive forces between atoms are reduced by hydrogen. Oriani and Josephic [OJ 77] proposed that the cohesive force σ_c is reduced by hydrogen concentration as follows:

$$\sigma_c = \text{const} - kC, \tag{3.1-25}$$

where k is a constant and C has the form of (3.1-24) with σ being the applied traction. They then applied this relationship to threshold data for 4340 steel subjected to hydrogen gas.

In general, a relationship like (3.1-22) will model steady-state environmental cracking data if stage II and stage III growth are absent. Various glasses [WB 70] subjected to water have this characteristic, but many materials do not.

Lawn and Wilshaw [LW 75] discuss a model based on Knudsen diffusion and reaction rates. They were able to model both stage I and II crack growth for water and glass.

Krausz [Kra 79] and Brown [Bro 79] independently proposed theories employing systems of parallel and series rate relationships of the form (3.1-22). It was shown that individual relationships of this type could be combined to fit all three stages of steady-state crack growth.

Cherepanov [Cher 79] proposed a simple steady-state model of continuous crack growth based on the diffusion of hydrogen. He assumed a constant flux of protons located at the crack tip. Cherepanov [Cher 79] also proposed a quasi-static incremental model based on the diffusion of hydrogen. Crack propagation was assumed to initiate when a critical concentration of hydrogen was reached.

Van Leeuwen [vLe 75] proposed a different quasi-static model of incremental crack growth where stress gradients were included in the diffusion equation of the form

$$C_{,t} = D \nabla^2 C - M \nabla\sigma \cdot \nabla C - MC \nabla^2\sigma, \qquad (3.1\text{-}26)$$

where D and M are constants. An approximate solution was obtained.

Note that a solution of the form (3.1-24) will solve (3.1-26) under steady-state conditions; i.e., $C_{,t} \to 0$, provided $\beta = M/D$ and $\nabla^2\sigma = 0$. The latter relationship is true of all hydrostatic stresses determined from linear elastic stress fields neglecting body forces and inertia.

Hirose and Mura [HM 84] proposed a fracture model for stress corrosion cracking that employs a stress-assisted diffusion equation similar to (3.1-26) with a hydrostatic stress related to a dislocation pile-up.

Rice [Ric 78] proposed a thermodynamic foundation for stress corrosion cracking.

Stevens *et al.* [SDP 74] proposed a theory of the chemical potential of defects, and Puls *et al.* [PDS 74] applied this theory to obtain the velocity of a crack growing by the diffusion of vacancies.

Raj and Varadan [RV 77] proposed a model of hydrogen embrittlement based on the growth of a small secondary crack ahead of a primary crack.

Unger and Aifantis [UA 83] proposed a model applicable to hydrogen-assisted crack propagation based on an equilibrium solution of a steady-state, stress-assisted diffusion equation of the form [Aif 80]

$$(D + N\sigma) \nabla^2 C - (M - N) \nabla\sigma \cdot \nabla C = 0, \qquad (3.1\text{-}27)$$

where D, M, and N are constants and σ is the hydrostatic stress of the mode I crack problem. They predicted a power law between crack velocity and stress intensity factors of the form

$$\dot{a} = V_0 K_I^n, \qquad (3.1\text{-}28)$$

where n is the ratio of the two diffusion coefficients M/N and V_0 is a constant.

Neimitz and Aifantis [NA 85, NA 87a, NA 87b] proposed an incremental model of hydrogen-assisted cracking with crack tip opening displacement as a damage criterion. The additional crack tip opening displacement due to the presence of hydrogen δ_H was related to the average concentration of hydrogen C_m in the process zone as follows

$$\delta_H = \text{const } C_m^3(\delta_0 + \delta_c), \qquad (3.1\text{-}29)$$

where δ_0 is the arrest crack tip opening displacement and δ_c is the critical crack tip opening displacement.

Markworth and McCoy [MMc 88] explored a model of hydrogen decohesion at the atomic level. They incorporated the idea of a chaotic motion of atoms at the crack tip. This motion is induced by a slight reduction of cohesive strength between atoms. Ultimately, separation occurs between atoms, thereby resulting in crack growth.

Creager and Paris [CP 67] discuss the effect of crack tip blunting on stress corrosion cracking and provide a linear elastic solution for the blunted crack.

Sofronis and McMeeking [SM 89] solved numerically a large deformation elastic–plastic problem coupled to a nonlinear diffusion equation for hydrogen. Their conclusion was that hydrostatic stresses are less important than traps and plastic straining insofar as hydrogen concentration is concerned around the mode I crack tip.

Garud [Gar 91] discusses corrosion fatigue and creep fatigue modeling together with damage accumulation.

3.2 ANALYSIS FOR IMPENDING HYDROGEN-ASSISTED CRACK PROPAGATION

An analytic solution [Ung 89a] is obtained for the initial phase of crack propagation for the decohesion model of hydrogen embrittlement discussed in Section 3.1. Error bounds are set on certain simplifications of integrals of the theory. Benchmarks are established for comparison with numerical solutions.

The integrand in (3.1-2) can be factored to obtain

$$K_0 = 2(c/\pi)^{1/2} \int_a^c \sigma_c(x,t)(c+x)^{-1/2}(c-x)^{-1/2} \, dx. \quad (3.2\text{-}1)$$

We can approximate the integral in (3.2-1) in two simple ways be substituting either

$$(c+x)^{-1/2} \approx (c+c)^{-1/2} \quad \text{or} \quad (c+x)^{-1/2} \approx (c+a)^{-1/2}. \quad (3.2\text{-}2)$$

Both of these relationships produce good approximations for integral (3.2-1), as these two functions vary little over the interval a to c. The first relationship in (3.2-2), when substituted in (3.2-1), gives a lower bound for that integral. Similarly, the second relationship of (3.2-2) gives an upper bound for integral (3.2-1). From these substitutions, we can infer the following about K_0:

$$(2/\pi)^{1/2} \int_a^c \sigma_c(x,t)(c-x)^{-1/2} \, dx$$

$$< K_0 < 2\{c/[\pi(c+a)]\}^{1/2} \int_a^c \sigma_c(x,t)(c-x)^{-1/2} \, dx, \quad (3.2\text{-}3)$$

provided $\sigma_c(x,t)$ is positive and finite. Equation (3.2-3) can be rewritten as the following inequality by employing $c = a + d$:

$$1 < \frac{K_0}{(2/\pi)^{1/2} \int_a^c \sigma_c(x,t)(c-x)^{-1/2} \, dx} < [1 - d/(2c)]^{-1/2}. \quad (3.2\text{-}4)$$

We now expand the right side of (3.2-4) in a Taylor series to obtain

$$[1 - d/(2c)]^{-1/2} = 1 + d/(4c) + \cdots$$

$$= 1 + O(d/c) \quad \text{as } d/c \to 0. \quad (3.2\text{-}5)$$

The series is convergent provided $d/(2c) \le 1$. The order symbol $O(\ )$ in (3.2-5) has the usual meaning [DeB 81]. From (3.2-5) we can come to the conclusion that

$$\frac{K_0}{(2/\pi)^{1/2} \int_a^c \sigma_c(x,t)(c-x)^{-1/2} \, dx} - 1 = O(d/c) \quad \text{as } d/c \to 0.$$

$$(3.2\text{-}6)$$

Therefore, we can approximate integral (3.2-1) by [LW 75]

$$K_0 \approx (2/\pi)^{1/2} \int_a^c \sigma_c(x, t)(c - x)^{-1/2} \, dx, \qquad \text{for } d \ll c. \quad (3.2\text{-}7)$$

The advantage of using (3.2-7) over (3.1-2) is that it is generally easier to evaluate (3.2-7) analytically.

We now assume that the initial concentration of hydrogen is zero. At time $t = 0^+$ a concentration of hydrogen C_0 is imposed at the crack tip. The hydrogen then diffuses into the material and causes damage in the form of a reduction in cohesive force. We assume here the simplest possible model of diffusion, i.e., Fick's law. This law has the heat equation as the governing partial differential equation. The solution to the heat equation for the semi-infinite boundary value problem with zero initial concentration was given as (3.1-5).

When (3.1-6), (3.2-7), (3.1-3), and (3.1-5) are substituted into the Barenblatt/Dugdale condition (3.1-1), we obtain

$$\sigma_\infty(\pi c)^{1/2} = (2/\pi)^{1/2}(\sigma_{c0} - \gamma C_0) \int_a^c (c - x)^{-1/2} \, dx$$

$$+ (2/\pi)^{1/2} \gamma C_0 \int_a^c \text{erf}[\alpha(x - a)](c - x)^{-1/2} \, dx. \quad (3.2\text{-}8)$$

The first integral appearing in (3.2-8) is easily evaluated as $2d^{1/2}$. The second integral in (3.2-8) is evaluated in terms of the function $\psi(c, a, \alpha)$ of (3.2-41). Evaluating the first integral and substituting $\psi(c, a, \alpha)$ in place of the second integral in (3.2-8), we obtain

$$\sigma_\infty(\pi c)^{1/2} = 2(2d/\pi)^{1/2}(\sigma_{c0} - \gamma C_0) + (2/\pi)^{1/2} \gamma C_0 \psi(c, a, \alpha) \quad (3.2\text{-}9)$$

where

$$\psi(c, a, \alpha) \equiv \int_a^c \text{erf}[\alpha(x - a)](c - x)^{-1/2} \, dx.$$

From (3.2-40) we see that $\psi(c, a, \alpha)$ is related to the generalized hypergeometric function $_2F_2(1/2, 1; 5/4, 7/4; -\alpha^2 d^2)$. By substituting (3.2-40) into (3.2-9), we obtain

$$\sigma_\infty \pi (c/2)^{1/2} = d^{1/2} \{ 2(\sigma_{c0} - \gamma C_0) $$

$$+ (8/3)\alpha d\pi^{-1/2} \gamma C_0 \, _2F_2(1/2, 1; 5/4, 7/4; -\alpha^2 d^2) \}.$$

$$(3.2\text{-}10)$$

The generalized hypergeometric function in (3.2-10) can be expanded in a series to obtain

$$\sigma_\infty \pi (c/2)^{1/2} = d^{1/2}\{2(\sigma_{c0} - \gamma C_0)$$

$$+ (8/3)\alpha d\pi^{-1/2}\gamma C_0[1 - (8/35)\alpha^2 d^2 + (64/1155)\alpha^4 d^4$$

$$- (512/45{,}045)\alpha^6 d^6 + (4096/2{,}078{,}505)\alpha^8 d^8 - \cdots]\}$$

$$(3.2\text{-}11)$$

where $\alpha \equiv (4Dt)^{-1/2}$.

For long times $t \to \infty$, i.e., $\alpha \to 0$, only a few terms of (3.2-11) need be retained. For short times $t \to 0$, i.e., $\alpha \to \infty$, an asymptotic expression for $\psi(c, a, \alpha)$, equation (3.2-58), can be substituted in place of (3.2-40) in (3.2-9). The first few terms of this expression can then be used for short times.

In the schematic diagram Fig. 3.1-11b, we can see the cohesive zone expanding, due to loss of cohesion, in relation to the increasing hydrogen concentration. This process is assumed to continue until the degradation is severe enough to cause crack propagation. The degradation parameter used to determine this critical state is the crack tip opening displacement δ_c. The evaluation of the crack tip opening displacement δ will be discussed shortly.

The time it takes for the specimen to go from the initial condition shown in Fig. 3.1-11a to the time corresponding to δ_c in Fig. 3.1-11c may be interpreted as the incubation period, which is observed experimentally. As time goes to infinity, (3.1-3) and (3.1-5) predict that the cohesive force becomes the constant $\sigma_{c0} - \gamma C_0$. If a critical δ cannot be obtained with this degraded value of cohesive force, the crack will never propagate. In Section 3.1 and [LU 88] it is described how the material parameter γC_0 can be obtained from an experimental value of the threshold stress intensity factor K_{th}.

In our model the value of d must be obtained from the Barenblatt/Dugdale condition (3.2-11). In general, for a given set of material parameters, a specific time t, and crack length a, this value of d must be obtained by an iterative root scheme such as Newton's method or the bisection method. For $t \to \infty$, however, truncating the hypergeometric series in (3.2-11) after one term can allow an explicit algebraic solution for d (from a cubic equation in $d^{1/2}$), provided we make the assumption $c \approx a$ in the left side of (3.2-11). A similar explicit solution for short times $t \to 0$ can be obtained by substituting the asymptotic formula for $\psi(c, a, \alpha)$ (3.2-57) into (3.2-9) and then limiting the series to the first two or three terms of

$\gamma(c, a, \alpha)$ (a quadratic or quartic equation in $d^{1/2}$), again provided the assumption $c \approx a$ is made in the formula for stress intensity factor K_{I}.

Crack Tip Opening Displacement

The crack tip opening displacement is used as the criterion for crack initiation and crack arrest in this model. The crack initiates when the crack opening displacement reaches the critical value δ_{c}. This condition corresponds to that shown in Fig. 3.1-11c, which is a schematic representation of the crack tip, and to point c in Fig. 3.1-12, which is a plot of the crack tip opening displacement versus crack length. As the crack propagates, the crack tip opening displacement initially drops as the crack advances out of the damaged region of the material. However, this drop in δ does not continue indefinitely.

We have shown that the arrest value δ_{A} approaches the hydrogen-free curve of crack opening displacement versus crack length, which is theoretically a straight line. The fact that δ_{A} is very close to the hydrogen-free curve means that almost all hydrogen-damaged material is left behind after each increment of crack growth; i.e., the residual hydrogen shown in Fig. 3.1-11d is negligible as the initial condition for the next increment of crack propagation, thereby making the problem self-similar. Average crack velocities are then determined in the model by dividing the increment of crack growth by the increment of time between critical events, i.e., when $\delta = \delta_{\mathrm{c}}$.

The analysis discussed in this section is restricted to the threshold stage of crack growth; i.e., crack growth is confined to conditions represented in Figs. 3.1-11a through 3.1-11c, and to regions a, b, and c shown in Fig. 3.1-12.

The crack opening displacement for the problem we are addressing can be obtained from the following double integral [SL 69]:

$$\delta = \Lambda \sigma_{\infty} \int_{a}^{c} x(x^2 - a^2)^{-1/2} \int_{0}^{x} (x^2 - \xi^2)^{-1/2} \, d\xi \, dx$$

$$- \Lambda \int_{a}^{c} x(x^2 - a^2)^{-1/2} \int_{a}^{x} \sigma_{\mathrm{c}}(\xi, t)(x^2 - \xi^2)^{-1/2} \, d\xi \, dx \quad (3.2\text{-}12)$$

where

$$\Lambda = 8(1 - \nu^2)/(\pi E) \qquad \text{for plane strain}$$

$$= 8/(\pi E) \qquad \text{for plane stress.} \qquad (3.2\text{-}13)$$

The first integral appearing in (3.2-12) is elementary and can be easily evaluated to give the expression we previously called δ_{E}, which is defined as (3.1-15). Two terms in the second double integral of (3.2-12) may be factored to give the following expression for δ:

$$\delta = \delta_E - \Lambda \int_a^c x(x + a)^{-1/2}(x - a)^{-1/2}$$

$$\times \int_a^x \sigma_c(\xi, t)(x + \xi)^{-1/2}(x - \xi)^{-1/2} \, d\xi \, dx, \qquad (3.2\text{-}14)$$

where

$$\delta_E \equiv \Lambda(\pi/2)(c^2 - a^2)^{1/2} \sigma_\infty. \qquad (3.2\text{-}15)$$

We can find an approximation for (3.2-14) analogously to the approximation in the previous section for K_0. To this end, we can use the following approximations for the double integral appearing in (3.2-14):
Inner integral:

$$(x + \xi)^{-1/2} \approx (x + x)^{-1/2} = (2x)^{-1/2} \qquad (3.2\text{-}16)$$

$$(x + \xi)^{-1/2} \approx (x + a)^{-1/2} \qquad (3.2\text{-}17)$$

Outer integral:

$$x/(x + a) \approx a/(a + a) = 1/2 \qquad (3.2\text{-}18)$$

$$x/(x + a) \approx c/(c + a) = (1/2)[1 - d/(2c)]. \qquad (3.2\text{-}19)$$

There are four possible combinations of approximations: {(3.2-16), (3.2-18)}, {(3.2-17), (3.2-18)}, {(3.2-17), (3.2-19)}, and {(3.2-16), (3.2-19)}. The combinations {(3.2-16), (3.2-18)} and {(3.2-17), (3.2-19)} give redundant results. From these approximations of the functions appearing in (3.2-14), we can infer the following inequalities:

$$1 < \frac{2(\delta_E - \delta)}{\Lambda \int_a^c (x - a)^{-1/2} \int_a^x \sigma_c(\xi, t)(x - \xi)^{-1/2} \, d\xi \, dx}$$

$$< \left[1 - \frac{d}{(2c)}\right]^{-1/2} < \left[1 - \frac{d}{(2c)}\right]^{-1}. \qquad (3.2\text{-}20)$$

Because

$$[1 - d/(2c)]^{-1} \approx 1 + d/(2c) + \cdots = 1 + O(d/c) \qquad (3.2\text{-}21)$$

we can establish

$$\frac{2(\delta_E - \delta)}{\Lambda \int_a^c (x-a)^{-1/2} \int_a^x \sigma_c(\xi,t)(x-\xi)^{-1/2} \, d\xi \, dx} - 1 = O\left(\frac{d}{c}\right)$$

$$\text{as } d/c \to 0. \quad (3.2\text{-}22)$$

As indicated by (3.2-22), we can approximate (3.2-14) by the following expression:

$$\delta \approx \delta_E - (\Lambda/2) \int_a^c (x-a)^{-1/2} \int_a^x \sigma_c(\xi,t)(x-\xi)^{-1/2} \, d\xi \, dx \quad \text{for } d \ll c.$$

$$(3.2\text{-}23)$$

The advantage of using (3.2-23) instead of (3.2-14) is that it is usually easier to evaluate analytically the double integral appearing in (3.2-23).
    We now substitute (3.1-3) and (3.1-5) into (3.2-23) to find

$$\delta = \delta_E - \Lambda \int_a^c (x-a)^{-1/2}$$

$$\times \int_a^x \{\sigma_{c0} - \gamma C_0 + \gamma C_0 \text{erf}[\,\alpha(\xi-a)]\}(x-\xi)^{-1/2} \, d\xi \, dx. \quad (3.2\text{-}24)$$

The constant term in (3.2-24) is easy to evaluate. The term containing the error function may be expressed in terms of the function $\psi(x,a,\alpha)$, which is defined as (3.2-31). In place of (3.2-24), we obtain

$$\delta = \delta_E - \Lambda(\sigma_{c0} - \gamma C_0)d - (\Lambda/2)\gamma C_0 \int_a^c (x-a)^{-1/2} \psi(x,a,\alpha) \, dx.$$

$$(3.2\text{-}25)$$

Now substituting into (3.2-25) the expression for $\psi(x,a,\alpha)$ given in (3.2-40), we find

$$\delta = \delta_E - \Lambda(\sigma_{c0} - \gamma C_0)d - (4\Lambda/3)\alpha\gamma C_0 \pi^{-1/2}$$

$$\times \int_a^c (x-a)\,_2F_2(1/2, 1; 5/4, 7/4; -\alpha^2(x-a)^2) \, dx. \quad (3.2\text{-}26)$$

We define a new variable

$$\chi \equiv [(x-a)/d]^2. \quad (3.2\text{-}27)$$

Substitution of (3.2-27) into (3.2-26) leads to

$$\delta = \delta_E - \Lambda(\sigma_{c0} - \gamma C_0)d - (2\Lambda/3)\alpha d^2 \gamma C_0 \pi^{-1/2}$$

$$\times \int_0^1 {}_2F_2(1/2, 1; 5/4, 7/4; -\alpha^2 d^2 \chi) \, d\chi. \qquad (3.2-28)$$

Evaluating the integral in (3.2-28) with the aid of the tabulated integral (7.512 12) found in [GR 65], we get the following:

$$\delta = \delta_E - \Lambda(\sigma_{c0} - \gamma C_0)d$$

$$- (2\Lambda/3)\alpha d^2 \gamma C_0 \pi^{-1/2} {}_3F_3(1, 1/2, 1; 2, 5/4, 7/4; -\alpha^2 d^2), \qquad (3.2-29)$$

where ${}_3F_3(\,,\,;\,,\,;)$ is a generalized hypergeometric function.

The first five terms of the series associated with the generalized hypergeometric function in (3.2-24) are given explicitly as follows:

$$\delta = \delta_E - \Lambda(\sigma_{c0} - \gamma C_0)d$$

$$- (2\Lambda/3)\alpha d^2 \gamma C_0 \pi^{-1/2}[1 - (4/35)\alpha^2 d^2 + (64/3465)\alpha^4 d^4$$

$$- (128/45,045)\alpha^6 d^6 + (4096/10,392,525)\alpha^8 d^8 - \cdots], \qquad (3.2-30)$$

where $\alpha \equiv (4Dt)^{-1/2}$.

Function $\psi(c, a, \alpha)$

The function $\psi(c, a, \alpha)$ is an important function in our model of hydrogen-assisted cracking. It appears first in connection with the growth of the cohesive zone. The function $\psi(x, a, \alpha)$ is also used to determine the crack tip opening displacement. As such, it is convenient to dedicate a separate subsection for its evaluation.

The function $\psi(c, a, \alpha)$ is not immediately recognizable as a standard special function. However, we show in this subsection that it is related to the generalized hypergeometric series. We also find an asymptotic series to represent the function $\psi(c, a, \alpha)$ for large values of α.

The function $\psi(c, a, \alpha)$ is defined as follows:

$$\psi(c, a, \alpha) \equiv \int_a^c \text{erf}[\alpha(x - a)](c - x)^{-1/2} \, dx. \qquad (3.2-31)$$

To facilitate the evaluation of (3.2-31), we first integrate the expression by parts, where

$$u(x) = \text{erf}[\alpha(x - a)], \qquad dv(x) = (c - x)^{-1/2} \, dx \qquad (3.2-32)$$

which gives

$$\psi(c, a, \alpha) = \int_a^c u(x)v'(x)\, dx = u(x)v(x)\big|_a^c - \int_a^c v(x)u'(x)\, dx \quad (3.2\text{-}33)$$

where the prime in (3.2-33) denotes differentiation with respect to x. From (3.2-33) we find that the expression $u(x)v(x)$ evaluated from $x = a$ to $x = c$ disappears, except for the degenerate case, $\alpha = \infty$. From (3.2-33) we find

$$\psi(c, a, \alpha) = 4\alpha\pi^{-1/2} \int_a^c (c - x)^{1/2} \exp[-\alpha^2(x - a)^2]\, dx, \qquad \alpha < \infty.$$
$$(3.2\text{-}34)$$

Changing the variable x in (3.2-34) to

$$X \equiv x - a, \qquad\qquad (3.2\text{-}35)$$

we obtain

$$\psi(c, a, \alpha) = 4\alpha\pi^{-1/2} \int_0^d (d - X)^{1/2} \exp(-\alpha^2 X^2)\, dX. \quad (3.2\text{-}36)$$

Now expanding the exponential term in (3.2-36) in a Taylor series, it follows that

$$\psi(c, a, \alpha) = 4\alpha\pi^{-1/2} \int_0^d (d - X)^{1/2}(1 - \alpha^2 X^2 \cdots)\, dX. \quad (3.2\text{-}37)$$

Upon integrating the first two terms, we find

$$\psi(c, a, \alpha) = 4\alpha\pi^{-1/2}\Big\{ -(2/3)(d - X)^{3/2}\big|_0^d$$
$$+ (2/105)\alpha^2(15X^2 + 12dX + 8d^2)(d - X)^{3/2}\big|_0^d + \cdots \Big\}$$
$$(3.2\text{-}38)$$

which becomes

$$\psi(c, a, \alpha) = (8/3)\alpha d^{3/2}\pi^{-1/2}\{1 - (8/35)\alpha^2 d^2 + \cdots\}. \quad (3.2\text{-}39)$$

The recursion relationship for higher order terms in (3.2-39) is not immediately obvious; however, Gradshteyn and Ryzhik [GR 65] provide an expression for the evaluation of integral (3.2-36). This yields

$$\psi(c, a, \alpha) = (8/3)\alpha d^{3/2}\pi^{-1/2}\,_2F_2(1/2, 1; 5/4, 7/4; -\alpha^2 d^2) \quad (3.2\text{-}40)$$

where $_2F_2(,;,;)$ is a generalized hypergeometric function. The integral used is listed as (3.478 3) in [GR 65].

The expansion of the generalized hypergeometric function as a series follows:

$$\psi(c, a, \alpha) = (8/3)\alpha d^{3/2}\pi^{-1/2} \sum_{k=0}^{\infty} \frac{(1/2)_k(1)_k[-\alpha^2 d^2]^k}{(5/4)_k(7/4)_k k!}, \quad (3.2\text{-}41)$$

where

$$(\mu)_0 \equiv 1, \quad (\mu)_k \equiv \mu(\mu + 1)(\mu + 2) \cdots (\mu + k - 1). \quad (3.2\text{-}42)$$

We note that the first two terms of this series are identical to those appearing in (3.2-39).

The series (3.2-41), however, can be slowly converging for large values of α, i.e., $(t \rightarrow 0)$. For these cases it is better to use an asymptotic expansion of $\psi(c, a, \alpha)$ rather than (3.2-41). This expansion is derived in the subsequent subsection.

Asymptotic Expansion

By noting that erf(∞) = 1, we can see from (3.2-31) that

$$\lim \alpha \rightarrow \infty \psi(c, a, \alpha) = \int_a^c (c - x)^{-1/2} dx = 2(c - a)^{1/2} = 2d^{1/2}.$$

$$(3.2\text{-}43)$$

In order to find a general relationship for $\psi(c, a, \alpha)$ for large but finite values of α, we expand the function in (3.2-36) to find

$$[1 - (X/d)]^{1/2} = 1 - \frac{1}{2}(X/d) - \frac{1}{2 \cdot 4}(X/d)^2$$

$$- \frac{1 \cdot 3}{2 \cdot 4 \cdot 6}(X/d)^3 - \frac{1 \cdot 3 \cdot 5}{2 \cdot 4 \cdot 6 \cdot 8}(X/d)^4 - \cdots$$

$$= \sum_{k=0}^{\infty} \frac{(2k)!}{(1 - 2k)(k!)^2}[X/(4d)]^k. \quad (3.2\text{-}44)$$

Series (3.2-44) is convergent for $0 < X \leq d$. A discussion of the technique we use in this section to develop an asymptotic series for $\psi(c, a, \alpha)$ is given in Section 4.4 of [DeB 81]. This is a Laplace method that applies to series expansions which are convergent over a limited domain, as in the case of the power series in (3.2-44).

If truncated after N terms, the series (3.2-44) has a remainder R_N of the following order:

$$[1 - (X/d)]^{1/2} = \sum_{k=0}^{N} \frac{(2k)!}{(1 - 2k)(k!)^2} [X/(4d)]^k + R_N, \quad (3.2\text{-}45)$$

where

$$R_N = O([X/d]^{N+1}). \qquad (3.2\text{-}46)$$

Upon substitution of (3.2-45) into (3.2-36), we obtain

$$\psi(c, a, \alpha) = 4\alpha(d/\pi)^{-1/2} \sum_{k=0}^{N} \frac{(2k)!}{(1 - 2k)(k!)^2(4d)^k}$$

$$\times \int_0^d X^k \exp(-\alpha^2 X^2)\, dX$$

$$+ O\left(\int_0^d [X/d]^{N+1} \exp[-\alpha^2 X^2]\, dX \right). \qquad (3.2\text{-}47)$$

Let us now note the following two identities:

$$\int_0^d X^k \exp[-\alpha^2 X^2]\, dX = \int_0^\infty X^k \exp[-\alpha^2 X^2]\, dX - \int_d^\infty X^k \exp[-\alpha^2 X^2]\, dX$$

$$(3.2\text{-}48)$$

and

$$\int_d^\infty X^k \exp[-\alpha^2 X^2]\, dX = \int_d^\infty X^k \exp(-X^2) \exp[(1 - \alpha^2)X^2]\, dX. \quad (3.2\text{-}49)$$

It follows from the inequality

$$0 < d \leq X \rightarrow d^2 \leq X^2 \qquad (3.2\text{-}50)$$

that

$$\int_d^\infty X^k \exp(-X^2) \exp[(1 - \alpha^2)X^2]\, dX$$

$$< \exp[(1 - \alpha^2)d^2] \int_d^\infty X^k \exp(-X^2)\, dX \qquad (3.2\text{-}51)$$

provided $\alpha > 1$. Changing the limits of integration from d to 0 on the lower limit of the right side of (3.2-51) increases the value of the integral; therefore,

$$\int_d^\infty X^k \exp(-X^2) \exp[(1 - \alpha^2 X^2)] \, dX$$

$$< \exp[(1 - \alpha^2)d^2] \int_0^\infty X^k \exp(-X^2) \, dX. \qquad (3.2\text{-}52)$$

The integral on the right side of (3.2-52) can be evaluated to obtain

$$\int_d^\infty X^k \exp(-X^2) \exp[(1 - \alpha^2 X^2)] \, dX < \exp[(1 - \alpha^2)d^2] \Gamma([k + 1]/2)/2$$

$$(3.2\text{-}53)$$

We can see from (3.2-53) that the integral on the left will be of order $O(\exp[-\alpha^2 d^2])$ as $\alpha \to \infty$. Therefore, we can infer from (3.2-48), (3.2-49), and (3.2-53) that

$$\int_0^d X^k \exp[-\alpha^2 X^2] \, dX = \int_0^\infty X^k \exp[-\alpha^2 X^2] \, dX + O(\exp[-\alpha^2 d^2]).$$

$$(3.2\text{-}54)$$

A similar technique to that used to generate (3.2-54) was discussed in [Wil 78].

By substituting (3.2-54) into (3.2-47), we obtain

$$\psi(c, a, \alpha) = 4\alpha(d/\pi)^{1/2} \left\{ \sum_{k=0}^N \frac{(2k)!}{(1 - 2k)(k!)^2 (4d)^k} \right.$$

$$\times \left[\int_0^\infty X^k \exp(-\alpha^2 X^2) \, dX + O(\exp[-\alpha^2 d^2]) \right]$$

$$+ O\left(d^{-N-1} \left[\int_0^\infty X^{N+1} \exp[-\alpha^2 X^2] \, dX \right. \right.$$

$$\left. \left. \left. + O(\exp[-\alpha^2 d^2]) \right] \right) \right\}. \qquad (3.2\text{-}55)$$

Performing the definite integrations and making use of a relationship from [BH 86], i.e., $O(O(\epsilon)) = O(\epsilon)$, we find that (3.2-55) reduces to

$$\psi(c, a, \alpha) = 2(d/\pi)^{1/2} \sum_{k=0}^{N} \frac{(2k)! \Gamma[(k+1)/2]}{(1-2k)(k!)^2 (4\alpha d)^k} + O\left(\frac{1}{(\alpha d)^{N+1}}\right)$$
$$+ O(\alpha \exp[-\alpha^2 d^2]). \tag{3.2-56}$$

The first four terms of (3.2-56) are explicitly

$$\psi(c, a, \alpha)|_{\alpha \to \infty} \sim 2d^{1/2}\left[1 - \frac{1}{2\pi^{1/2}\alpha d} - \frac{1}{16\alpha^2 d^2} - \frac{1}{16\pi^{1/2}\alpha^3 d^3} - \cdots\right].$$
$$\tag{3.2-57}$$

Letting N go to infinity in (3.2-56), we find that the asymptotic series for $\psi(c, a, \alpha)$ is

$$\psi(c, a, \alpha)|_{\alpha \to \infty} \sim 2(d/\pi)^{1/2} \sum_{k=0}^{\infty} \frac{(2k)! \Gamma[(k+1)/2]}{(1-2k)(k!)^2 (4\alpha d)^k} \tag{3.2-58}$$

where $\alpha \equiv (4Dt)^{-1/2}$.

Discussion

In Unger and co-authors [LU 88, SU 88], numerical studies employing both Gauss–Chebyshev and Romberg integration schemes were used to evaluate (3.1-2) and (3.2-12) for the cohesive force $\sigma_c(x, t)$ given by (3.1-3) and (3.1-5). As no previous analytical solution existed for use as a benchmark, the accurancy of these schemes remained to some degree uncertain. In the present study, we have obtained analytic results in the form of generalized hypergeometric functions for simplifications of the two integrals involved: namely, (3.2-7) and (3.2-23). Error bounds are also provided from these simplifications in the form of (3.2-4) and (3.2-20), from which the possible error can be estimated. We can then obtain solutions to the problem, which are given in the form of series, i.e., (3.2-11) and (3.2-30), to within the numerical precision of the machine.

Tables 3.1-1 and 3.1-3 contain parameters that were used in [LU 88, SU 88]. We can see from Tables 3.2-1 and 3.2-2 that values obtained from numerical integrations do not differ appreciably from values obtained from the series expansion of d and δ using (3.2-11) and (3.2-30), respectively. In this analysis the first ten terms of the series were used.

Of course there is intrinsic value in having an analytic solution. For example, it permits us to see better how various parameters affect the

TABLE 3.2-1

Comparison of Cohesive Zone Values d

t (sec)	d (mm)		
	Lee and Unger [LU 88][a]	Seo and Unger [SU 88]	Eq. (3.2-11)
10	0.33	0.30	0.31
50	0.44	0.43	0.44
100	0.53	0.51	0.52
200	0.64	0.61	0.63
300	0.71	0.69	0.70
400	0.77	0.75	0.76
500	0.82	0.80	0.82
600	0.87	0.84	0.86
700	0.91	0.88	0.90

[a] The value of D in this publication was erroneously tabulated as 2.26×10^{-11} m^2/sec instead of 6.45×10^{-10} m^2/sec.

solution to the problem. In addition, the iterative schemes required to solve (3.2-11) for the cohesive zone length d execute faster on the computer if the analytic solution rather than numerical integration is used.

For further discussions about metallurgical aspects of process zones with respect to hydrogen embrittlement, the reader is directed to [GCLL 87, Ger 87].

3.3 A MODIFIED STEFAN PROBLEM RELATED TO STRESS CORROSION CRACKING

We noted previously that three stages of steady-state crack propagation exist for hydrogen-assisted crack propagation. This is true for most forms of environmental cracking.

In stage I crack growth, subcritical crack velocity increases exponentially with an increase in the stress intensity factor K_I. We can see this for the data shown in Fig. 3.3-1, which is taken from a study involving the stress corrosion cracking of glasses [Fre 74]. The glasses 1–4 have various compositions of SiO_2–Na_2O–CaO with the exception of glass 5, which has a composition of SiO_2–BaO. In this first example, the corrodant is water. We recall that data exhibiting exponential behavior appear as a straight line when plotted on semilog paper. Represented by straight lines in the figure, the crack growth rates v may be approximated by the expression,

TABLE 3.2-2
Comparison of Crack Tip Opening Displacements δ

t (sec)	δ (mm)		
	Lee and Unger [LU 88][a]	Seo and Unger [SU 88]	Eq. (3.2-30)
2.5	0.0045	0.0045	0.0045
5.0	0.0048	0.0048	0.0049
7.5	0.0050	0.0051	0.0052
12.5	0.0053	0.0054	0.0055
22.0	0.0058	0.0058	0.0059
32.5	0.0061	0.0061	0.0063
40.0	0.0063	0.0063	0.0064
50.0	0.0065	0.0065	0.0066
60.0	0.0067	0.0067	0.0068
70.0	0.0068	0.0068	0.0070
80.0	0.0070	0.0069	0.0071
90.0	0.0071	0.0070	0.0072
100.0	0.0072	0.0071	0.0073
110.0	0.0073	0.0072	0.0074
120.0	0.0074	0.0073	0.0075
130.0	0.0074	0.0074	0.0076

[a] The value of D in this publication was erroneously tabulated as 2.26×10^{-11} m^2/sec instead of 6.45×10^{-10} m^2/sec.

$v = c_1 \exp(c_2 K_I)$, with c_1, c_2 being constants. Stage II and stage III growth were not recorded for this particular environment. (Interested readers may find a useful account of the physics and chemistry of the fracturing of glass in water in the popular press [MB 87].)

In stage II steady-state crack propagation, the crack velocity becomes relatively insensitive to the stress intensity factor. In cases where the crack velocity becomes virtually independent of the stress intensity factor, the second stage is referred to as the plateau stage. We find in Fig. 3.3-2, which was taken from [Spe 84], experimental data for the stress corrosion cracking of aluminum alloys in humidified air. These data were chosen as an example on the basis of their pronounced plateau stage II crack growth behavior.

This intermediate stage of growth is followed by stage III crack propagation where the crack velocity is again strongly influenced by the stress intensity factor. Stage III growth occurs for loading conditions near the fracture toughness of the specimen, as measured in an inert environment. In Fig. 3.3-3, again drawn from [Fre 74], we see the same five glasses as

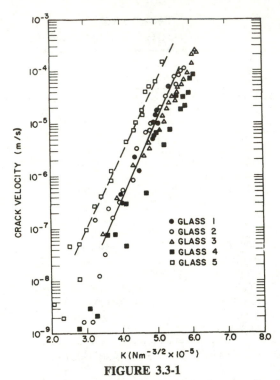

FIGURE 3.3-1

Effect of glass composition on crack propagation behavior in water. Reprinted from S. W. Freiman, Effect of alcohols on crack propagation in glass, *J. Am. Ceram. Soc.* **57**, 350–353 (1974), by permission of The American Ceramic Society.

those in Fig. 3.3-1, subjected to octanol rather than water. In Fig. 3.3-3, we see all three stages of steady-state crack propagation represented.

Different rate-controlling mechanisms can be dominant in each of the three distinct stages of steady-state crack propagation. In this section, we concentrate on the second stage of crack growth for those cases where the controlling mechanism is related to mass transport (Knudsen diffusion). We do not attempt to incorporate into this model the parameters that control stages I and III. Thus the model predicts neither the threshold value of stress intensity factor K_{Iscc} nor the toughness K_C shown in Fig. 3.3-4.

A moving boundary value problem is proposed and analytically solved [Ung 90c] for environmental crack propagation where the transport of the deleterious species is the controlling mechanism of the plateau stage of subcritical crack growth. The concentration of the corrodant diffuses along

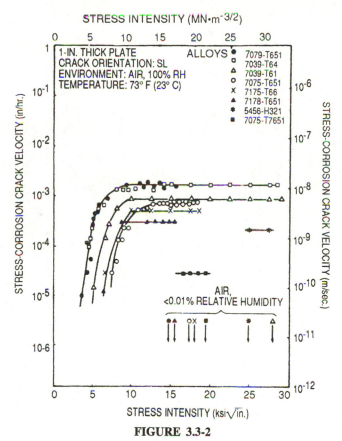

FIGURE 3.3-2

Effect of moisture and stress intensity factor on the subcritical crack growth rates of several high-strength aluminum alloys in air. Reprinted from [Spe 84] by permission of ASM International.

the surfaces of the crack from a stationary environmental reservoir to the moving crack tip. A minimum concentration of gas at the crack tip is required to sustain crack propagation at a given temperature. The magnitude of the crack velocity is proportional to the mass flux at the crack tip, while the diffusivity of the gas is theoretically related to the evolving crack tip opening displacement. Under a transformation of coordinates, this moving boundary value problem is mapped onto the classic Stefan problem and solved. Because the theory is based primarily on gas transport and the mechanical response of the specimen to an applied load, it should be applicable to a wide class of materials and environments.

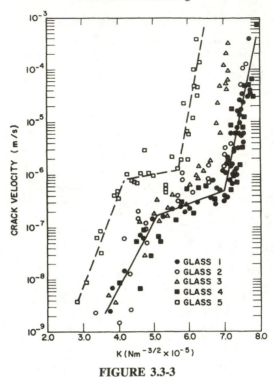

FIGURE 3.3-3

Effect of glass composition on crack propagation behavior in octanol. Reprinted from S. W. Freiman, Effect of alcohols on crack propagation in glass, *J. Am. Ceram. Soc.* **57**, 350–353 (1974), by permission of The American Ceramic Society.

Analysis

The flux $j(x, t)$ of a deleterious species that migrates from a fixed external reservoir ($x = 0$) down the crack surfaces is assumed to follow Fick's first law, i.e.,

$$j(x, t) = -D(a(t))\frac{\partial \rho(x, t)}{\partial x}, \qquad (3.3\text{-}1)$$

where x is the Cartesian coordinate shown in Fig. 3.3-5, t is time, ρ is the density of the diffusing species, D is the diffusivity, and a is the crack length. It is further assumed that the diffusivity in (3.3-1) is a function of the crack length. This is a logical assumption as crack growth is accompanied by an increase in crack surface separation. Consequently, this wider conduit permits faster mass transport which is reflected through the diffusivity $D(a(t))$ in (3.3-1).

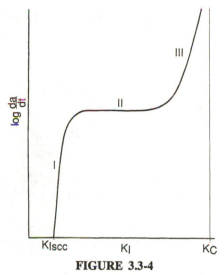

FIGURE 3.3-4

Crack velocity versus stress intensity factor. Reprinted from *Eng. Fract. Mech.*, **37**, D. J. Unger, A modified Stefan problem for transport-controlled stress corrosion cracking, 101–106 (1990), with permission from Pergamon Press, Ltd., Headington Hill Hall, Oxford OX3 OBW, UK.

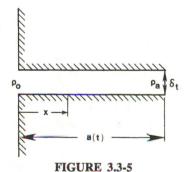

FIGURE 3.3-5

Crack geometry and parameters. Reprinted from *Eng. Fract. Mech.*, **37**, D. J. Unger, A modified Stefan problem for transport-controlled stress corrosion cracking, 101–106 (1990), with permission from Pergamon Press, Ltd., Headington Hill Hall, Oxford OX3 OBW, UK.

Conservation of mass requires equation (3.3-2) be satisfied:

$$\frac{\partial \rho(x,t)}{\partial t} + \frac{\partial j(x,t)}{\partial x} = 0. \tag{3.3-2}$$

Then the substitution of (3.3-1) into (3.3-2) produces the following diffusion equation (Fick's second law):

$$\frac{\partial \rho(x,t)}{\partial t} = D(a(t))\frac{\partial^2 \rho(x,t)}{\partial x^2}. \tag{3.3-3}$$

Equation (3.3-3) ignores diffusion in the antiplane direction, i.e., normal to the plate. This approximation of the diffusion process improves with plate thickness.

We assume that a sufficiently large reservoir of fluid exists to impose a constant concentration of corrodant ρ_0 at the entry point to the specimen ($x = 0$), i.e.,

$$\rho(0,t) = \rho_0. \tag{3.3-4}$$

A critical concentration of gas at the crack tip ρ_a (which is related to pressure by an equation of state) is proposed as a necessary condition for crack propagation. For sustained crack growth, the boundary concentration ρ_0 must be greater than the critical value. These two conditions are expressed mathematically as

$$\rho(a(t),t) = \rho_a, \qquad \rho_0 > \rho_a. \tag{3.3-5}$$

We take our initial crack length to be zero in a mathematical sense, i.e.,

$$a(0) = 0. \tag{3.3-6}$$

Physically, (3.3-6) models a very small surface flaw, i.e., a crack length that is negligible in comparison to the length, width, and thickness of the specimen.

The solution obtained using relationship (3.3-6) can also be applied to problems involving finite initial crack lengths as $a(t)$ grows large; i.e., the two solutions should converge with sufficient crack growth.

The continuity equation of mass at a moving interface $x = a(t)$ requires [Jos 60]

$$\rho_a \frac{da(t)}{dt} = j(x,t)|_{x=a(t)} = -D(a(t))\frac{\partial \rho(x,t)}{\partial x}\bigg|_{x=a(t)}. \tag{3.3-7}$$

We might note the similarity between (3.3-3)–(3.3-7) and the temperature-formulated Stefan problem [Rub 71, Hil 87]. However, the diffusivity appearing in (3.3-3) and (3.3-7) is a function of the interface, whereas the analogous coefficient in the standard Stefan problem is constant.

A transformation of coordinates allows us to map our original moving boundary value problem onto the standard Stefan problem (for which an analytical solution is known) and hence solve it.

To this end, let us define the variable τ as

$$\tau \equiv \int_0^t D(a(\xi)) \, d\xi, \tag{3.3-8}$$

and make a transformation of coordinates from t to τ in (3.3-3)–(3.3-7): i.e.,

$$\frac{\partial \hat{\rho}(x,\tau)}{\partial \tau} = \frac{\partial^2 \hat{\rho}(x,\tau)}{\partial x^2}, \tag{3.3-9}$$

$$\hat{\rho}(0,\tau) = \rho_0, \tag{3.3-10}$$

$$\hat{\rho}(\hat{a}(\tau),\tau) = \rho_a, \qquad \rho_0 > \rho_a, \tag{3.3-11}$$

$$\hat{a}(\tau_0) = 0, \tag{3.3-12}$$

$$\rho_a \frac{d\hat{a}(\tau)}{d\tau} = -\frac{\partial \hat{\rho}(x,\tau)}{\partial x}\bigg|_{x=\hat{a}(\tau)}, \tag{3.3-13}$$

where $\hat{a}$ is the crack length, $\hat{\rho}$ is the concentration, and τ_0 is the value of τ at $t = 0$, i.e., zero by (3.3-8). By introducing τ into the formulation, we map our original problem, defined by (3.3-3)–(3.3-7), onto the classic Stefan problem, (3.3-9)–(3.3-13). The analytic solution to the Stefan problem follows [Jos 60]:

$$\hat{\rho}(x,\tau) = \rho_0 - \pi^{1/2}\gamma\rho_a \exp \gamma^2 \text{erf}\left(x/[4\tau]^{1/2}\right), \tag{3.3-14}$$

$$\hat{a}(\tau) = 2\gamma\tau^{1/2} \tag{3.3-15}$$

where the constant γ is determined by iteration from the expression

$$\rho_0/\rho_a = 1 + \pi^{1/2}\gamma \exp(\gamma^2)\text{erf}\,\gamma. \tag{3.3-16}$$

Returning to our original notation, we find from (3.3-8) and (3.3-15) that

$$a(t) = 2\gamma\left[\int_0^t D(a(\xi)) \, d\xi\right]^{1/2}. \tag{3.3-17}$$

Now by differentiating (3.3-17) with respect to t, we obtain the crack velocity as

$$\frac{da(t)}{dt} = \gamma D(a(t)) \bigg/ \left[\int_0^t D(a(\xi)) \, d\xi \right]^{1/2} = 2\gamma^2 D(a(t))/a(t). \quad (3.3\text{-}18)$$

In order for plateau steady-state crack propagation to occur, we infer from (3.3-18) that the diffusivity must be proportional to $a(t)$; otherwise, da/dt is a function of the crack length.

Now plateau stage II growth is observed for wide classes of materials and corrodants using a variety of conventional specimens where $K_I(a)$ is approximately proportional to $a^{1/2}$. It is also observed for hydrogen-assisted cracking which is considered chemically distinct from stress corrosion cracking (opposite rate response to an applied potential).

One possible explanation for the appearance of the plateau crack propagation in diverse materials and environments is external fluid transport.

As crack surfaces converge, ordinary viscous flow is impeded. Eventually, viscous flow ceases and molecular diffusion or Knudsen flow begins. As we are modeling small surface cracks, the entire transport process might be considered Knudsen flow as a first approximation.

In [LPWSW 81], the stage II crack propagation for 4340 steel exposed to hydrogen sulfide gas at a pressure of 133 Pa was reported to be controlled by Knudsen diffusion. In [WSHW 80], these researchers incorporated Knudsen diffusion into their environmental cracking model which could be applied to both transport-controlled and surface-reaction-controlled growth. Lawn and Wilshaw [LW 75] modeled the data of Wiederhorn [Wie 69] for sapphire in moistened nitrogen gas. This model combined reaction-controlled crack growth, which dominates in stage I crack propagation, with Knudsen-diffusion-controlled growth, which dominates in stage II.

Returning to our problem, the theoretical relationship for Knudsen diffusivity in a circular cylinder [SS 63] is

$$D_K = (4rk/3)[2RT/(\pi M)]^{1/2} \qquad (3.3\text{-}19)$$

where r is the pore radius, R is the universal gas constant, T is absolute temperature, M is the molecular weight of the diffusing species, and k is a phenomenological constant ($k = 1$ for ideal Knudsen flow). For pore geometries other than circular cylinders, an equivalent pore radius r_e [SS 63] is defined for use in (3.3-19).

The ratio of the volume of a cylindrical pore V to its surface area S (neglecting the two ends—one of which would be equal to πr^2) is

$$r = 2V/S. \tag{3.3-20}$$

If we approximate the crack geometry as a rectangular channel, where the width of the channel is equal to the crack tip opening displacement δ_t, then we have a volume V and area S (neglecting the ends—each of area $B\delta$) equal to

$$V = \delta_t Ba, \tag{3.3-21}$$

$$S = 2a(\delta_t + B) \tag{3.3-22}$$

where B is the thickness of the specimen. By substituting (3.3-21) and (3.3-22) into (3.3-20) and defining an equivalent pore geometry r_e, we find

$$r_e = \frac{B\delta_t}{\delta_t + B} \approx \delta_t \quad \text{for } \delta_t \ll B. \tag{3.3-23}$$

The crack tip opening displacement for large-scale yielding [BS 66] (for an infinite plate, with a crack of length $2a$, subject to a tensile traction σ_∞) is

$$\delta_t = 8(A/\pi)\sigma_0 a \ln \sec(\pi\sigma_\infty/[2\sigma_0]), \tag{3.3-24}$$

where

$$A = \begin{cases} (1 - \nu^2)/E & \text{for plane strain,} & (3.3\text{-}25) \\ 1/E & \text{for plane stress,} & (3.3\text{-}26) \end{cases}$$

σ_0 is the yield stress, ν is Poisson's ratio, and E is Young's modulus. For small-scale yielding this expression (3.3-24) reduces to

$$\delta_t = A\sigma_\infty^2 \pi a/\sigma_0 = AK_I^2/\sigma_0. \tag{3.3-27}$$

We see from (3.3-24) and (3.3-27) that the crack tip opening displacement for the most fundamental fracture problem is proportional to the crack length for both large- and small-scale yielding. The edge crack (of length a) in our moving boundary problem, has a K_I value that is 1.12 times higher than the K_I of the internal crack (of length $2a$), by (I.5-18). For small-scale yielding, we can replace $\sigma_\infty(\pi a)^{1/2}$ by $1.12\sigma_\infty(\pi a)^{1/2}$ in (3.3-27) to obtain δ_t for the edge crack. Therefore, δ_t for the edge crack of length a is approximately equal to $5/4$ (because $(1.12)^2 \approx 1.25 = 5/4$) of the value of δ_t of the internal crack of length $2a$.

An equivalent pore geometry for Knudsen diffusion coupled to the crack tip displacement was first used for a model of environmental cracking in [WSHW 80]; however, no moving boundary value problem was solved there.

By substituting (3.3-27) into (3.3-19) via (3.3-23) and multiplying the result by $5/4$, we find the Knudsen diffusion

$$D_K = V_0 a(t) \tag{3.3-28}$$

where the parameter V_0 is defined for small-scale yielding as

$$V_0 \equiv 5k[2\pi RT/M]^{1/2} A \sigma_\infty^2 / (3\sigma_0). \tag{3.3-29}$$

When (3.3-28) is substituted into (3.3-18), the predicted velocity v is constant, i.e.,

$$v \equiv \frac{da}{dt} = 2\gamma^2 V_0, \tag{3.3-30}$$

where γ is related to the ratio ρ_0/ρ_a by (3.3-16). Relationship (3.3-30) is consistent with a state of plateau crack propagation where the crack velocity is independent of the stress intensity factor for a constant load. Other types of diffusion processes may give similar results.

Small and Large Values of v/V_0

If we solve for γ in terms of crack velocity v from (3.3-30) and then substitute this relationship for γ into (3.3-16), we obtain

$$\rho_0/\rho_a = 1 + [\pi v/(2V_0)]^{1/2} \exp[v/(2V_0)] \mathrm{erf}([v/\{2V_0\}]^{1/2}). \tag{3.3-31}$$

A plot of (ρ_0/ρ_a) versus $v/(2V_0)$ on a semilog scale is given in Fig. 3.3-6.

Upon expanding (3.3-31) in a series, we find

$$\rho_0/\rho_a = 1 + [\pi v/(2V_0)]^{1/2}(1 + \cdots)(2/\pi^{1/2})\{[v/(2V_0)]^{1/2} - \cdots\}$$

$$= 1 + v/V_0 + \cdots. \tag{3.3-32}$$

By retaining only the first term of the series expansion, we find for small values of the ratio v/V_0,

$$v \approx V_0(\rho_0/\rho_a - 1) \quad \text{for } v/V_0 \ll 1. \tag{3.3-33}$$

For Knudsen flow [SS 63], concentration is proportional to gas pressure p (ideal gas, $\rho = pM/RT$). Therefore, for small values of v/V_0 our theory predicts a velocity v that is a linear function of the reservoir's concentration ρ_0 and hence its pressure.

For large values of v/V_0 we can see on Fig. 3.3-6 that ρ_0/ρ_a approaches an inclined line on the semilog scale. This is the exponential term (3.3-31) dominating the expression for large values of v/V_0. We can

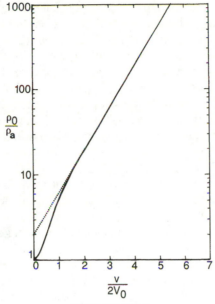

FIGURE 3.3-6

Plot of function (3.3-31), the ratio of boundary values for deleterious species density ρ_0/ρ_a versus normalized stage II crack velocity $v/(2V_0)$.

approximate ρ_0/ρ_a of (3.3-31) for large values of the argument $v/(2V_0)$ by the following:

$$\rho_0/\rho_a \approx c_1 \exp[c_2 v/(2V_0)] \qquad (3.3\text{-}34)$$

where c_1 and c_2 are constants.

Let us select a region of Fig. 3.3-6 where the exponential term outweighs the others. By using the values in Table 3.3-1 and relationship (3.3-34), we find that $c_1 = 1.999$ and $c_2 = 1.137$ approximate the curve (3.3-31) between values of $2 \leq v/(2V_0) \leq 5$.

TABLE 3.3-1

Exact Values from Equation (3.3-31)

$v/(2V_0)$	ρ_0/ρ_a
2	19.435
5	589.21

Even though the line in Fig. 3.3-6 appears nearly straight between the two values of $v/(2V_0)$ given in Table 3.3-1, we should not extrapolate the curve beyond the value of $v/(2V_0) = 5$. There is still a weak distortion of the exponential function due to the leading term $[\pi v/(2V_0)]^{1/2}$ of (3.3-32) which has a significant effect. (The only other term involving the error function $\to 1$.) Therefore, we may interpolate only between the limits on $v/(2V_0)$ that were used to determine c_1 and c_2. Furthermore, the smaller the interval between the limits on $v/(2V_0)$ chosen to determine c_1 and c_2, the better the approximation of ρ_0/ρ_a will be between those limits.

Discussion

Our moving boundary value problem was formulated for a virtual initial crack length. However, our moving boundary value problem should still model the pressure dependence of plateau velocity data, regardless of the initial crack length, as the material response in this stage is independent of crack length (stress intensity factor for constant load).

On the other hand, stage I and stage III data are highly dependent on crack length, and our model should never be applied to these regions, irrespective of the initial condition. In Sections 3.1 and 3.2, a decohesion model of hydrogen-assisted cracking, which is applicable to stages I and III, was analyzed. It was found that behavior similar in shape to regions I and III in Fig. 3.3-4 could be found, but that plateau stage II growth was absent, as no rate-limiting external transport mechanism was incorporated into the computer code.

Temperature may affect several of the parameters of our model simultaneously. One theoretical relationship between temperature and crack velocity is given by (3.3-29). This expression predicts that crack velocity is proportional to $T^{1/2}$. But the parameter ρ_a, which is related to γ and hence v, may have a stronger temperature dependence than the Knudsen diffusivity owing to the thermally activated process to which it is related. For instance, the parameter ρ_a might be associated with a chemical reaction.

Now thermally activated processes often allow an Arrhenius representation of the form

$$\rho_a = \rho_c \exp(Q/[RT]), \qquad (3.3\text{-}35)$$

where Q is the activation energy, and ρ_c is a weak function of temperature (often approximated as a constant). By knowing the activation energy of the process involved, we can in principle determine the temperature-dependent ρ_a through (3.3-34) and thus predict crack velocities as functions of temperature.

As with all models of environmental crack propagation, this model has its simplifications. The geometry is two-dimensional rather than three, and the transport mechanism is restricted to Knudsen flow, to name just two.

Nevertheless, the author believes that it is still a significant achievement because a true moving boundary value problem has never before been solved analytically for transport-controlled environmental crack growth. This one could serve as a benchmark for numerical studies involving more complicated models.

Although the classic moving boundary value problem, the Stefan problem, would seem to find a natural application for transport-controlled crack propagation, it has not been used in this way. The reason is that the unmodified version of the Stefan problem predicts crack velocities that decay proportionately to $1/t^{1/2}$, which are not typically observed. In our modified Stefan problem, however, by coupling the diffusivity to the crack tip opening displacement, we strike a balance between the increasing path of the corrodant from its external reservoir (due to increased crack length) with faster transport of corrodant (due to the widening channel, which increases diffusivity). Thus plateau crack velocities can be sustained.

4

Small-Scale Yielding versus Exact Linear Elastic Solutions

4.1 THE FUNDAMENTAL MODES OF FRACTURE

In this chapter we discuss the differences between exact linear elastic solutions for crack problems and small-scale yielding solutions, using as examples the solutions of the three fundamental modes of fracture for infinite plates. Westergaard potentials are used in the derivation of the solutions [Cor 72].

Westergaard [Wes 39] proposed the following linear elastic solution to the plane strain, mode I crack problem for an infinite plate subjected to a biaxial tensile traction σ_∞ applied at an infinite distance from an internal crack of length $2a$:

$$\sigma_x = \operatorname{Re} Z_{\mathrm{I}} - y \operatorname{Im} Z_{\mathrm{I}}' \tag{4.1-1}$$

$$\sigma_y = \operatorname{Re} Z_{\mathrm{I}} + y \operatorname{Im} Z_{\mathrm{I}}' \tag{4.1-2}$$

$$\tau_{xy} = -y \operatorname{Re} Z_{\mathrm{I}}' \tag{4.1-3}$$

$$u = (1 + \nu)[(1 - 2\nu)\operatorname{Re} Z_{\mathrm{I}}^* - y \operatorname{Im} Z_{\mathrm{I}}]/E \tag{4.1-4}$$

$$v = (1 + \nu)[2(1 - \nu)\operatorname{Im} Z_{\mathrm{I}}^* - y \operatorname{Re} Z_{\mathrm{I}}]/E \tag{4.1-5}$$

where σ_x and σ_y are the normal stresses in a Cartesian coordinate system (x, y); τ_{xy} is the shear stress in the xy plane; u, v are displacement in the

x and y directions, respectively; E is Young's modulus; and ν is Poisson's ratio. The potential Z_I, which appears in (4.1-1)–(4.1-5), is defined in terms of the complex variable $z = x + iy$ by the relationship

$$Z_I(z) = \sigma_\infty z / (z^2 - a^2)^{1/2}. \tag{4.1-6}$$

The derivative and antiderivative of $Z_I(z)$ with respect to z are designated by

$$Z_I' \equiv dZ_I/dz = -\sigma_\infty a^2 / (z^2 - a^2)^{3/2} \tag{4.1-7}$$

$$Z_I^* \equiv \int Z_I dz = \sigma_\infty (z^2 - a^2)^{1/2}. \tag{4.1-8}$$

The symbols Re and Im in (4.1-1)–(4.1-5) denote respectively the real and imaginary parts of complex functions of z.

The following complex variable identity [AS 64, AG 78, UGA 83] allows the separation of the square root of a complex number into real and imaginary parts:

$$(c + id)^{1/2} = \pm \left(\left\{ \left[c + (c^2 + d^2)^{1/2} \right] / 2 \right\}^{1/2} \right.$$
$$\left. + i \operatorname{sgn}(d) \left\{ \left[-c + (c^2 + d^2)^{1/2} \right] / 2 \right\}^{1/2} \right), \tag{4.1-9}$$

where the symbol $\pm$ denotes the positive square root and the negative square root of the complex number, and the function sgn( ) is defined by

$$\operatorname{sgn}(b) = \begin{cases} -1, & b < 0 \\ 0, & b = 0 \\ 1, & b > 0 \end{cases} \tag{4.1-10}$$

where b is a real number.

The substitution of (4.1-9) into (4.1-6)–(4.1-8) yields for $X \geq 0, Y \geq 0$

$$Z_I = \sigma_\infty 2^{-1/2} \{ [X(A + B)^{1/2} + Y(-A + B)^{1/2}]$$
$$+ i[Y(A + B)^{1/2} - X(-A + B)^{1/2}] \} / B \tag{4.1-11}$$

$$Z_I' = \sigma_\infty (2^{1/2} a)^{-1} \{ -A(A + B)^{1/2} + 2XY(-A + B)^{1/2}$$
$$+ i[A(-A + B)^{1/2} + 2XY(A + B)^{1/2}] \} / B^3 \tag{4.1-12}$$

$$Z_I^* = a\sigma_\infty 2^{-1/2} [(A + B)^{1/2} + i(-A + B)^{1/2}] \tag{4.1-13}$$

with the functions A and B defined by the following:

$$A \equiv X^2 - Y^2 - 1 \qquad (4.1\text{-}14)$$

$$B \equiv \left[(X^2 - Y^2 - 1)^2 + 4X^2Y^2\right]^{1/2}. \qquad (4.1\text{-}15)$$

The substitution of (4.1-11)–(4.1-13) into (4.1-1)–(4.1-5) gives an explicit form of the linear elastic solution of the fundamental mode I fracture problem for the first quadrant:
For $X \geq 0$, $Y \geq 0$:

$$T_x = [X(A + B)^{1/2} + Y(-A + B)^{1/2}]/B$$

$$- Y[A(-A + B)^{1/2} + 2XY(A + B)^{1/2}]/B^3 \qquad (4.1\text{-}16)$$

$$T_y = [X(A + B)^{1/2} + Y(-A + B)^{1/2}]/B$$

$$+ Y[A(-A + B)^{1/2} + 2XY(A + B)^{1/2}]/B^3 \qquad (4.1\text{-}17)$$

$$T_{xy} = Y[A(A + B)^{1/2} - 2XY(-A - B)^{1/2}]/B^3 \qquad (4.1\text{-}18)$$

$$U = (1 + \nu)\{[(1 - 2\nu)B - Y^2](A + B)^{1/2} + XY(-A + B)^{1/2}\}/B \qquad (4.1\text{-}19)$$

$$V = (1 + \nu)\{[2(1 - \nu)B - Y^2](-A + B)^{1/2} - XY(A + B)^{1/2}\}/B \qquad (4.1\text{-}20)$$

where the dimensionless stress T_x, T_y, T_{xy} and displacements U, V are defined by

$$T_x \equiv 2^{1/2}\sigma_x/\sigma_\infty, \qquad T_y \equiv 2^{1/2}\sigma_y/\sigma_\infty, \qquad T_{xy} \equiv 2^{1/2}\tau_{xy}/\sigma_\infty \quad (4.1\text{-}21)$$

$$X \equiv x/a, \qquad Y \equiv y/a, \qquad U \equiv 2^{1/2}uE/(a\sigma_\infty), \qquad V \equiv 2^{1/2}vE/(a\sigma_\infty). \qquad (4.1\text{-}22)$$

In the case of small-scale yielding, only the first term of a series expansion about one of the crack tips is retained for Z_I and its derivatives. Let us define ζ as a complex variable whose origin is positioned at the crack tip $z = a$. Polar coordinates (r, θ) that are established at the crack tip $z = a$ are then related to ζ through the following coordinate transformation:

$$\zeta \equiv z - a \equiv r \exp i\theta. \qquad (4.1\text{-}23)$$

In view of (4.1-23), the complex function Z_I may be rewritten as

$$Z_I = \sigma_\infty(\zeta + a)/[(\zeta + 2a)\zeta]^{1/2}. \qquad (4.1\text{-}24)$$

Westergaard's potential assumes asymptotically the following form as ζ approaches zero:

$$Z_I|_{|\zeta| \to 0} \sim \sigma_\infty[a/(2\zeta)]^{1/2} \qquad (4.1\text{-}25)$$

which by (4.1-23) and Euler's relationship $r \exp i\theta = r(\cos\theta + i\sin\theta)$ becomes

$$Z_I|_{|\zeta| \to 0} \sim \sigma_\infty[a/(2r)]^{1/2}[\cos(\theta/2) - i\sin(\theta/2)]. \qquad (4.1\text{-}26)$$

Similarly,

$$Z_I' = -\sigma_\infty a^2/[(\zeta + 2a)\zeta]^{3/2} \qquad (4.1\text{-}27)$$

$$Z_I'|_{|\zeta| \to 0} \sim -(\sigma_\infty/2)(a/2)^{1/2}\zeta^{-3/2} \qquad (4.1\text{-}28)$$

$$\sim -(\sigma_\infty/2)(a/2)^{1/2}r^{-3/2}[\cos(3\theta/2) - i\sin(3\theta/2)] \qquad (4.1\text{-}29)$$

and

$$Z_I^* = \sigma_\infty[(\zeta + 2a)\zeta]^{1/2} \qquad (4.1\text{-}30)$$

$$Z_I^*|_{|\zeta| \to 0} \sim \sigma_\infty(2a\zeta)^{1/2} \qquad (4.1\text{-}31)$$

$$\sim \sigma_\infty(2ar)^{1/2}[\cos(\theta/2) + i\sin(\theta/2)]. \qquad (4.1\text{-}32)$$

Upon substituting (4.1-26), (4.1-29), and (4.1-32) into (4.1-1)–(4.1-5), we obtain the mode I, small-scale yielding, elastic solution as follows. For $-\pi \le \theta \le \pi$:

$$T_x = R^{-1/2}\cos(\theta/2)[1 - \sin(\theta/2)\sin(3\theta/2)] \qquad (4.1\text{-}33)$$

$$T_y = R^{-1/2}\cos(\theta/2)[1 + \sin(\theta/2)\sin(3\theta/2)] \qquad (4.1\text{-}34)$$

$$T_{xy} = R^{-1/2}\cos(\theta/2)\sin(\theta/2)\cos(3\theta/2) \qquad (4.1\text{-}35)$$

$$U = 2(1 + \nu)R^{1/2}\cos(\theta/2)[1 - 2\nu + \sin^2(\theta/2)] \qquad (4.1\text{-}36)$$

$$V = 2(1 + \nu)R^{1/2}\sin(\theta/2)[2 - 2\nu - \cos^2(\theta/2)] \qquad (4.1\text{-}37)$$

where the dimensionless stresses, displacements, and coordinates are defined by (4.1-21)–(4.1-22) and by

$$R \equiv r/a. \qquad (4.1\text{-}38)$$

The two coordinate systems are shown in Figs. 4.1-1a and 4.1-1b.

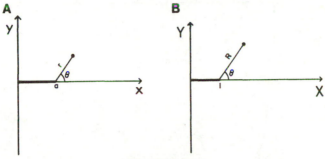

FIGURE 4.1-1

Cartesian and polar coordinate systems. Adapted from *Eng. Fract. Mech.*, **10**, E. C. Aifantis and W. W. Gerberich, A new form of exact solutions for mode I, II, III crack problems and implications, 95–108 (1978), with permission from Pergamon Press Ltd., Headington Hill Hall, Oxford OX3 OBW, UK.

Plots of comparisons between the small-scale yielding (approximate) stresses and exact linear elastic stresses appear in Figs. 4.1-2 through 4.1-4. Corresponding comparisons are made for displacements in Figs. 4.1-5 through 4.1-7.

It can be seen that the deviations between the exact and approximate solutions increase with distance from the crack tip. For the stresses, the exact solution tends toward the remote traction σ_∞, whereas the small-scale yielding solution tends toward zero as $r \to \infty$. Near the crack tip, a

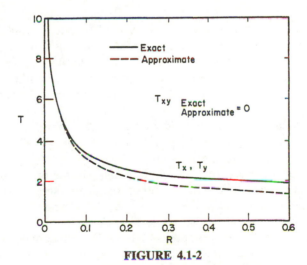

FIGURE 4.1-2

Dimensionless stress field for mode I, $\theta = 0°$.

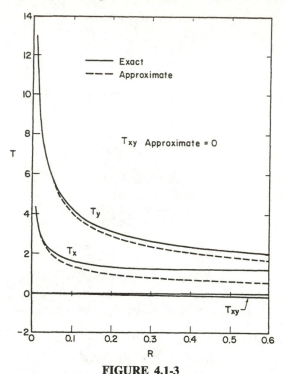

FIGURE 4.1-3

Dimensionless stress field for mode I, $\theta = 60°$.

singularity $O(r^{-1/2})$ dominates the stress field in both solutions. In the case of nonzero displacements, both solutions tend toward the infinite as the distance from the crack increases, but they do so at different rates. Consequently, for brittle materials the small-scale yielding solution is valid only near the crack tip. In the case of a ductile material, it is valid only within an annulus surrounding the crack tip due to formation of a plastic zone. If the plastic deformation is extensive, the purely linear elastic solutions may not characterize the problem at all, owing to elastic unloading and a redistribution of the stresses.

We note that the exact solution requires two parameters (a, σ_∞) to fully characterize the stress field. On the other hand, the small-scale yielding solution requires only one parameter, $a^{1/2}\sigma_\infty$, to characterize the stress field in the neighborhood of the crack tip. [Compare the separability of this product in (4.1-25) as opposed to (4.1-6).] It is customary to multiply this term $a^{1/2}\sigma_\infty$ by the square root of π, and refer to it as the stress intensity factor, $K_I = (\pi a)^{1/2}\sigma_\infty$.

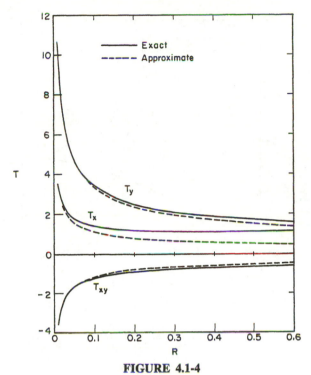

FIGURE 4.1-4

Dimensionless stress field for mode I, $\theta = 90°$. Reprinted from *Eng. Fract. Mech.*, **18**, D. J. Unger, W. W. Gerberich, and E. C. Aifantis, Further remarks on an exact solution for crack problems, 735–741 (1983), with permission from Pergamon Press Ltd., Headington Hill Hall, Oxford OX3 OBW, UK.

The Westergaard potential can also be applied to the mode II problem [PS 65, PM 78] for an infinite plate with an internal crack of length $2a$ which is subjected to a remotely applied shearing traction τ_∞. The solution for plane strain is

$$\sigma_x = 2\,\mathrm{Im}\,Z_{II} + y\,\mathrm{Re}\,Z'_{II} \tag{4.1-39}$$

$$\sigma_y = -y\,\mathrm{Re}\,Z'_{II} \tag{4.1-40}$$

$$\tau_{xy} = \mathrm{Re}\,Z_{II} - y\,\mathrm{Im}\,Z'_{II} \tag{4.1-41}$$

$$u = (1+\nu)[2(1-\nu)\mathrm{Im}\,Z^*_{II} + y\,\mathrm{Re}\,Z_{II}]/E \tag{4.1-42}$$

$$v = -(1+\nu)[(1-2\nu)\mathrm{Re}\,Z^*_{II} + y\,\mathrm{Im}\,\bar{Z}_{II}]/E. \tag{4.1-43}$$

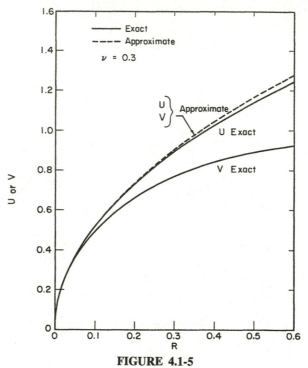

FIGURE 4.1-5

Dimensionless displacement field for mode I, $\theta = 90°$. Reprinted from *Eng. Fract. Mech.*, **18**, D. J. Unger, W. W. Gerberich, and E. C. Aifantis, Further remarks on an exact solution for crack problems, 735–741 (1983), with permission from Pergamon Press Ltd., Headington Hill Hall, Oxford OX3 0BW, UK.

The complex potential Z_{II} is identical to its mode I counterpart Z_I, except that σ_∞ is replaced by a remotely applied, in-plane shearing traction τ_∞; i.e.,

$$Z_{II} = \tau_\infty z / (z^2 - a^2)^{1/2}. \qquad (4.1\text{-}44)$$

Through use of the complex identity (4.1-9), we obtain by (4.1-39)–(4.1-43) the exact solution for the fundamental mode II problem as follows. For $X \geq 0$, $Y \geq 0$:

$$T_x = 2[Y(A + B)^{1/2} - X(-A + B)^{1/2}]/B$$

$$- Y[A(A + B)^{1/2} - 2XY(-A + B)^{1/2}]/B^3 \qquad (4.1\text{-}45)$$

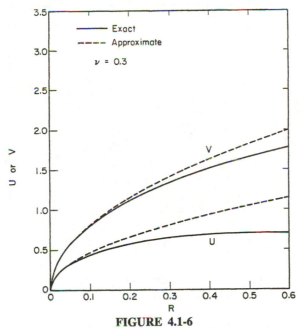

FIGURE 4.1-6

Dimensionless displacement field for mode I, $\theta = 120°$.

$$T_y = Y[A(A + B)^{1/2} - 2XY(-A + B)^{1/2}]/B^3 \qquad (4.1\text{-}46)$$

$$T_{xy} = [X(A + B)^{1/2} + Y(-A + B)^{1/2}]/B$$
$$\qquad - Y[A(-A + B)^{1/2} + 2XY(A + B)^{1/2}]/B^3 \qquad (4.1\text{-}47)$$

$$U = (1 + \nu)\{[2(1 - \nu)B + Y^2](-A + B)^{1/2} + XY(A + B)^{1/2}\}/B \qquad (4.1\text{-}48)$$

$$V = (1 + \nu)\{-[(1 - 2\nu)B + Y^2](A + B)^{1/2} + XY(-A + B)^{1/2}\}/B \qquad (4.1\text{-}49)$$

where dimensionless quantities for mode II are given by

$$T_x \equiv 2^{1/2}\sigma_x/\tau_\infty, \qquad T_y \equiv 2^{1/2}\sigma_y/\tau_\infty, \qquad T_{xy} \equiv 2^{1/2}\tau_{xy}/\tau_\infty \quad (4.1\text{-}50)$$

$$U \equiv 2^{1/2}uE/(a\tau_\infty), \qquad V \equiv 2^{1/2}vE/(a\tau_\infty). \qquad (4.1\text{-}51)$$

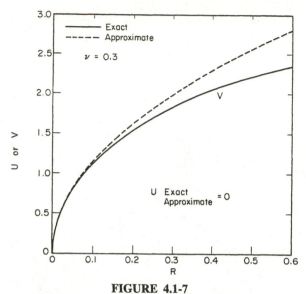

FIGURE 4.1-7

Dimensionless displacement field for mode I, $\theta = 180°$.

The normalized stress and displacement definitions (4.1-50) and (4.1-51) for mode II are identical to the mode I definitions (4.1-21) and (4.1-22) except that τ_∞ replaces σ_∞.

Near the crack tip $z = a$, the small-scale yielding mode II potential approaches asymptotically the following form:

$$Z_{II}|_{|\zeta| \to 0} \sim \tau_\infty [a/(2\zeta)]^{1/2}, \qquad \zeta = z - a = r \exp i\theta. \quad (4.1\text{-}52)$$

The functions Z'_{II} and Z^*_{II} are obtained analogously to (4.1-29) and (4.1-32). After the asymptotic relationships for Z_{II}, Z'_{II}, and Z^*_{II} as $\zeta \to 0$ are substituted into (4.1-39)–(4.1-43), we find the mode II small-scale yielding solution for plane strain as follows:
For $-\pi \le \theta \le \pi$:

$$T_x = -R^{-1/2}\sin(\theta/2)[2 + \cos(\theta/2)\cos(3\theta/2)] \quad (4.1\text{-}53)$$

$$T_y = R^{-1/2}\cos(\theta/2)\sin(\theta/2)\cos(3\theta/2) \quad (4.1\text{-}54)$$

$$T_{xy} = R^{-1/2}\cos(\theta/2)[1 - \sin(\theta/2)\sin(3\theta/2)] \quad (4.1\text{-}55)$$

$$U = 2(1 + \nu)R^{1/2}\sin(\theta/2)[2 - 2\nu + \cos^2(\theta/2)] \quad (4.1\text{-}56)$$

$$V = 2(1 + \nu)R^{1/2}\cos(\theta/2)[-1 + 2\nu + \sin^2(\theta/2)]. \quad (4.1\text{-}57)$$

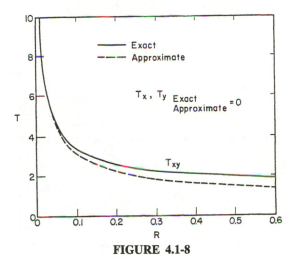

FIGURE 4.1-8

Dimensionless stress field for mode II, $\theta = 0°$.

Comparisons of the mode II small-scale yielding solutions and the exact linear elastic solutions are shown in Figs. 4.1-8 through 4.1-13.

For the third mode of fracture, the Westergaard relationships in terms of the potential $Z_{III}(z)$ are [PA 65, PM 78]

$$\tau_{xz} = \text{Im } Z_{III}, \qquad \tau_{yz} = \text{Re } Z_{III} \qquad (4.1\text{-}58)$$

$$w = (1/G)\text{Im } Z_{III}^* \qquad (4.1\text{-}59)$$

where τ_{xz} and τ_{yz} are the antiplane shear stresses, w is the displacement in the z direction, and G is the shear modulus. All other stresses and displacements are zero. The Westergaard function for mode III assumes the same form as the mode II potential Z_{II} except that τ_∞ represents a remotely applied, out-of-plane (antiplane) shear stress rather than the in-plane shear stress; i.e.,

$$Z_{III} = \tau_\infty z/(z^2 - a^2)^{1/2}. \qquad (4.1\text{-}60)$$

The exact linear elastic solution follows from (4.1-58)–(4.1-60) and (4.1-9). For $X \geq 0$, $Y \geq 0$:

$$T_{xz} = [Y(A + B)^{1/2} - X(-A + B)^{1/2}]/B \qquad (4.1\text{-}61)$$

$$T_{yz} = [X(A + B)^{1/2} + Y(-A + B)^{1/2}]/B \qquad (4.1\text{-}62)$$

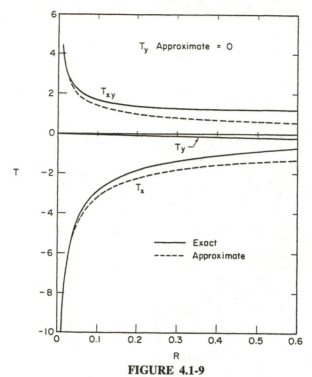

FIGURE 4.1-9

Dimensionless stress field for mode II, $\theta = 60°$.

where for mode III, the normalized relationships are defined by

$$T_{xz} \equiv 2^{1/2}\tau_{xz}/\tau_\infty, \qquad T_{yz} \equiv 2^{1/2}\tau_{yz}/\tau_\infty. \qquad (4.1\text{-}63)$$

The small-scale yielding potential is analogous to the two previous modes, i.e.,

$$Z_{III}|_{|\zeta| \to 0} \sim \tau_\infty[a/(2\zeta)]^{1/2}, \qquad \zeta = z - a = r \exp i\theta \qquad (4.1\text{-}64)$$

and the small-scale yielding solution follows from (4.1-58).
For $-\pi \le \theta \le \pi$:

$$T_{xz} = -R^{-1/2}\sin(\theta/2), \qquad T_{yz} = R^{-1/2}\cos(\theta/2) \qquad (4.1\text{-}65)$$

where T_{xz} and T_{yz} are defined by (4.1-63).

A comparison between the small-scale yielding solution (4.1-65) and the exact linear elastic solution (4.1-61)–(4.1-62) is given in Tables 4.1-1 and 4.1-2. These tables are adapted from data reported in [AG 78].

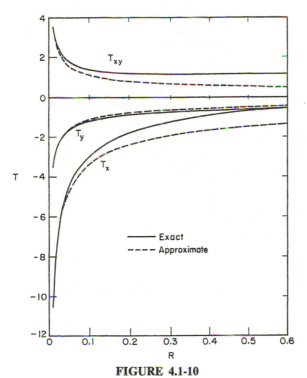

FIGURE 4.1-10

Dimensionless stress field for mode II, $\theta = 90°$. Reprinted from *Eng. Fract. Mech.*, **18**, D. J. Unger, W. W. Gerberich, and E. C. Aifantis, Further remarks on an exact solution for crack problems, 735–741 (1983), with permission from Pergamon Press Ltd., Headington Hill Hall, Oxford OX3 OBW, UK.

The exact mode III linear elastic displacement can be obtained from (4.1-59).
For $X \geq 0, Y \geq 0$:

$$w = (\tau_\infty/G)a[(-A + B)/2]^{1/2}. \tag{4.1-66}$$

The small-scale yielding displacement for mode III follows:
For $-\pi \leq \theta \leq \pi$:

$$w = (\tau_\infty/G)a(2R)^{1/2}\sin(\theta/2). \tag{4.1-67}$$

One final note on the elastic mode III problem: The solution for an edge crack of length a in a semi-infinite plate with a tractionless edge is identical to the solution discussed here for a crack of length $2a$ in an infinite plate [Ric 66].

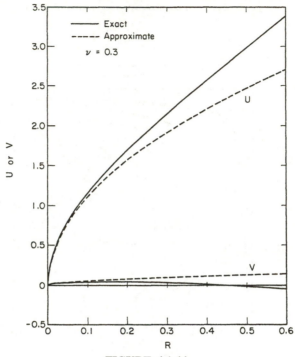

FIGURE 4.1-11

Dimensionless displacement field for mode II, $\theta = 90°$. Reprinted from *Eng. Fract. Mech.*, **18**, D. J. Unger, W. W. Gerberich, and E. C. Aifantis, Further remarks on an exact solution for crack problems, 735–741 (1983), with permission from Pergamon Press Ltd., Headington Hill Hall, Oxford OX3 OBW, UK.

4.2 ELASTIC–PLASTIC LOCI AS PREDICTED BY LINEAR ELASTIC FRACTURE MECHANICS

The Mises yield condition for a perfectly plastic material takes the form

$$(\sigma_1 - \sigma_2)^2 + (\sigma_2 - \sigma_3)^2 + (\sigma_3 - \sigma_1)^2 = 2\sigma_0^2, \qquad (4.2\text{-}1)$$

where σ_1, σ_2, and σ_3 are the principal stresses and σ_0 is the tensile yield stress.

Fundamental relationships among stresses for plane strain are

$$\sigma_3 = \sigma_z = \nu(\sigma_x + \sigma_y) = \nu(\sigma_1 + \sigma_2), \qquad (4.2\text{-}2)$$

where $\sigma_1 \geq \sigma_3$, $\sigma_2 \geq \sigma_3$.

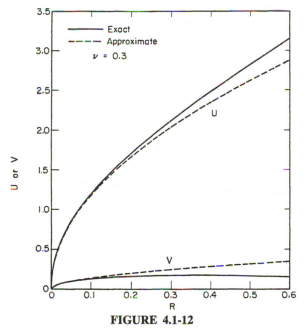

FIGURE 4.1-12

Dimensionless displacement field for mode II, $\theta = 120°$.

By making use of (1.1-33), (1.1-34), (4.2-1), and (4.2-2), we can determine the elastic–plastic boundaries for modes I and II, as predicted by the Mises yield condition for plane strain:

$$3y^2|Z_I'|^2 + (1 - 2\nu)^2(\text{Re } Z_I)^2 = \sigma_0^2 \tag{4.2-3}$$

and

$$3\left[|Z_{II}|^2 + y^2|Z_{II}'|^2 + 2y(\text{Im } Z_{II}\text{Re } Z_{II}' - \text{Re } Z_{II}\text{Im } Z_{II}')\right]$$
$$+ (1 - 2\nu)^2(\text{Im } Z_{II})^2 = \sigma_0^2. \tag{4.2-4}$$

The relationship between the tensile yield stress and the shear yield stress k for the Mises yield condition is

$$\sigma_0^2 = 3k^2. \tag{4.2-5}$$

In light of (4.2-2), the plane stress ($\sigma_z = 0$) loci for the Mises yield condition for modes I and II can be respectively obtained by setting $\nu = 0$ in formulas (4.2-3) and (4.2-4). (Note that the substitution $\nu = 0$ does not work for conversions of displacement from plane strain to plane stress.)

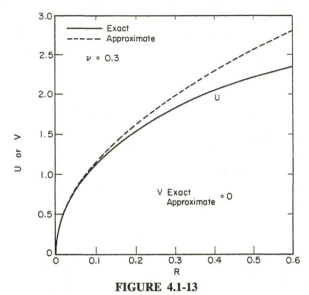

FIGURE 4.1-13

Dimensionless displacement field for mode II, $\theta = 180°$.

The purely elastic estimates of the elastic–plastic boundaries for small-scale boundaries for small-scale yielding for plane strain are (upon substituting $\nu = 0$ in (4.2-6) and (4.2-7) to obtain plane stress)
mode I:

$$R_\mathrm{P} = (1/2)(\sigma_\infty/\sigma_0)^2 \cos^2(\theta/2)\left[3\sin^2(\theta/2) + (1 - 2\nu)^2\right] \quad (4.2\text{-}6)$$

TABLE 4.1-1
Comparison of Mode III Stresses ($\theta = 0°$)

R	T_{xy}		T_{yz}	
	Exact	Approximate	Exact	Approximate
0.000101	0	0	99.951	99.504
0.000501	0	0	44.693	44.677
0.001001	0	0	31.631	31.607
0.005001	0	0	14.194	14.141
0.010001	0	0	10.074	9.9995
0.050001	0	0	4.6381	4.4721
0.100001	0	0	3.3947	3.1622
0.200001	0	0	2.5584	2.2942
0.500001	0	0	1.8974	1.4142
0.990001	0	0	1.6357	1.0050

TABLE 4.1-2
Comparison of Mode III Stresses ($\theta = 60°$)

R	T_{xz}		T_{yz}	
	Exact	Approximate	Exact	Approximate
0.000101	−497.48	−497.52	86.179	86.173
0.000501	−22.330	−22.338	38.706	38.691
0.001001	−15.792	−15.803	27.393	27.372
0.005001	−7.0439	−7.0704	12.292	12.246
0.010001	−4.9624	−4.9998	8.7248	8.6598
0.050001	−2.2361	−2.4262	4.0182	3.8730
0.100001	−1.4674	−1.5811	2.9439	2.7386
0.200001	−0.9638	−1.1180	2.2262	1.9365
0.500001	−0.49174	−0.7071	1.6773	1.2247
0.990001	−0.25276	−0.5025	1.4868	0.8904

mode II:

$$R_P = (1/6)(\tau_\infty/k)^2\left\{3 - \sin^2(\theta/2)\left[9\cos^2(\theta/2) - (1 - 2\nu)^2\right]\right\} \quad (4.2\text{-}7)$$

where the dimensionless plastic radius R_P is measured from the crack tip,

$$R_P = r_P/a. \quad (4.2\text{-}8)$$

Comparisons between "exact" and small-scale yielding (approximate) elastic–plastic boundaries for modes I and II are shown in Figs. 4.2-1 and 4.2-2. The exact boundaries were found numerically [UGA 83] using stresses (4.1-16)–(4.1-18) and (4.1-45)–(4.1-47) in (4.2-1). The approximate boundaries were obtained from (4.2-6) and (4.2-7). Poisson's ratio ν was taken to be 0.3 in all of the calculations.

For mode III the exact elastic–plastic boundary can be obtained [AG 78] from (4.1-61), (4.1-62), and (1.1-6) as

$$R_P^2 + 2R_P\cos\theta + 1 = (k/\tau_\infty)^2\left[R_P^4 + 4R_P^2 + 4R_P^3\cos\theta\right]^{1/2}. \quad (4.2\text{-}9)$$

This locus is geometrically an inverse Cassinian oval with the origin of the Cartesian axes as the site of the center of inversion [Ung 93].

The small-scale yielding solution for mode III reduces the elastic–plastic boundary to a circle.

$$R_P = \tau_\infty^2 a/(2k^2). \quad (4.2\text{-}10)$$

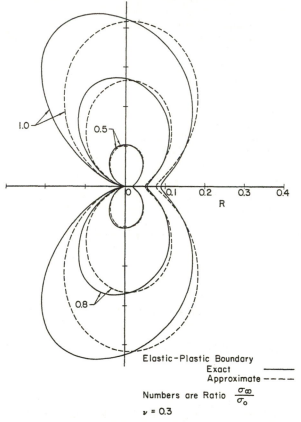

FIGURE 4.2-1

Elastic–plastic boundaries for mode I. Adapted from *Eng. Fract. Mech.*, **18**, D. J. Unger, W. W. Gerberich, and E. C. Aifantis, Further remarks on an exact solution for crack problems, 735–741 (1983), with permission from Pergamon Press Ltd., Headington Hill Hall, Oxford OX3 OBW, UK.

This result was given previously in terms of the stress intensity factor as (1.1-7). (We note that for mode III the Mises and Tresca yield conditions assume a similar form in relationship to the yield stress in pure shear k.)

The exact and small-scale yielding elastic–plastic loci for mode III are shown in Fig. 4.2-3, which was adapted from a figure published in [AG 78].

The boundaries obtained in this section for modes I and II (both exact and small-scale yielding) may be regarded only as gross approximations for elastic–plastic boundaries as determined by numerical elastoplastic solutions (due to elastic unloading). Only the mode III elastic solution (for

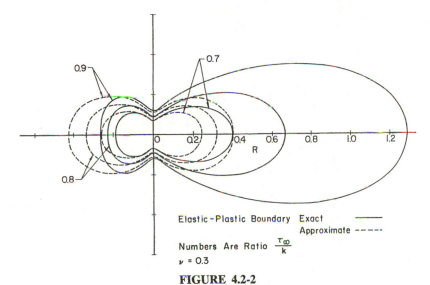

FIGURE 4.2-2

Elastic–plastic boundaries for mode II. Adapted from *Eng. Fract. Mech.*, **18**, D. J. Unger, W. W. Gerberich, and E. C. Aifantis, Further remarks on an exact solution for crack problems, 735–741 (1983), with permission from Pergamon Press Ltd., Headington Hill Hall, Oxford OX3 OBW, UK.

small-scale yielding) provides an elastic–plastic boundary for the statically admissible elastoplastic problem.

The plastic solution associated with the exact elastic–plastic boundary (4.2-9) is not, however, the large-scale yielding Hult–McClintock solution. These investigators [HM 56] imposed the condition that the slip lines should focus at the crack tip, as Fig. 2.1-1d shows for the small-scale yielding solution. The slip lines that are initialized on the boundary (4.2-9) do not focus to a point. Instead, they generate a line of discontinuous stress in a manner that resembles the slip line pattern of Fig. 2.1-1b or 2.1-1c. The Hult–McClintock elastic–plastic boundary must be determined through the use of a contact transformation [HM 56, Ric 66], which is a technique that places no reliance on the completely elastic solution. Nevertheless, the exact linear elastic stress field for the purely elastic problem and its predicted elastic–plastic boundary (4.2-9) might serve as approximations to the Hult–McClintock solution for intermediate levels of τ_∞/k [Ung 93].

For additional small-scale yielding estimates of the elastic–plastic boundaries for mode I and II (see [CZ 91]). There, plane strain and plane stress elastoplastic boundaries are determined for the Mises, Tresca, Rankine, Mohr–Coulomb, and Drucker–Prager yield conditions.

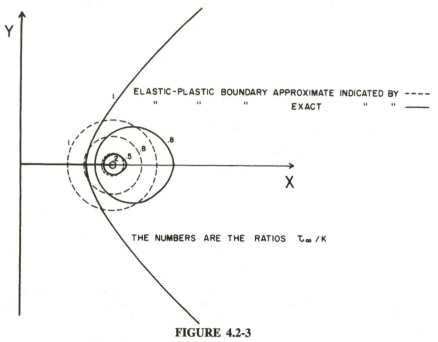

FIGURE 4.2-3

Elastic–plastic boundaries for mode III. Adapted from *Eng. Fract. Mech.*, **10**, E. C. Aifantis and W. W. Gerberich, A new form of exact solutions for mode I, II, III crack problems and implications, 95–108 (1978), with permission from Pergamon Press Ltd., Headington Hill Hall, Oxford OX3 OBW, UK.

4.3 INVERSE CASSINIAN OVAL COORDINATES FOR MODE III

An analytical elastoplastic solution of the mode III fracture problem for the semi-infinite plate was first obtained by Hult and McClintock [HM 56]. These investigators used a contact transformation and a conformal mapping scheme to solve the linear elastic portion of the elastoplastic problem for an arbitrary wedge-shaped notch on the elastic–plastic boundary. The entire elastic solution, however, was not provided.

The complete elastic solution of the small-scale yielding approximation of this problem for a notch reduced to a crack may be found in a number of sources, including Chapters 1 and 2. On the other hand, the large-scale yielding equivalent of this crack problem [Ric 68a, AC 88] is seldom discussed in textbooks because of its complex form and the difficulty of interpreting its physical significance. For example, the exact elastic stresses of this elastoplastic problem for a mode III edge crack are determined implicitly in [AC 88] as

$$z + a_0 = (2/\pi)[(\tau^2 + c^2)(\tau^2 + c^{-2})]^{-1/2}$$

$$\times \left\{ a_0\tau(1 - \tau^2)\left[-(c\tau)^{-2}E(\pi/2; c^2) \right. \right.$$

$$+ c\tau^{-2}(c^{-2} - c^2 - \tau^{-2} - \tau^2 - 1)$$

$$\times F(\pi/2; c^2) + c(1 - \tau^2)^{-1}(c^{-2} + c^2 + \tau^{-2} + \tau^2)$$

$$\left. \left. \times \{\Pi(\pi/2; -c^2\tau^{-2}; c^2) - \tau^{-2}\Pi(\pi/2; -c^2\tau^2; c^2)\} \right] \right\},$$

$$0 < c < 1, \quad (4.3\text{-}1)$$

where $F(\,;\,)$, $E(\,;\,)$, and $\Pi(\,;\,;\,)$ are elliptic integrals [GR 65] of the first, second, and third types, respectively; a_0 is the crack length; and

$$\tau \equiv (\tau_{xz} - i\tau_{yz})/k, \qquad c \equiv \tau_\infty/k, \quad (4.3\text{-}2)$$

where τ is a complex function that is linear in the shear stresses.

These authors [AC 88] readily admit that the above representation is impractical for determining the elastic–plastic boundary directly, and give instead an asymptotic expansion which is valid only for small to intermediate values of c. This asymptotic expansion predicts the length of the plastic zone L_P ahead of the crack tip to be

$$L_P \sim a_0 c^2[1 + (3/4)c^2 + O(c^4)]. \quad (4.3\text{-}3)$$

For comparison, an exact expression for L_P was determined in [BCS 63, Ric 66] as

$$L_P = a_0\{(2/\pi)[(1 + c^2)/(1 - c^2)]E(\pi/2; 2c/[1 + c^2]) - 1\}, \quad (4.3\text{-}4)$$

where

$$E(\pi/2; \epsilon) \equiv \int_0^{\pi/2}(1 - \epsilon^2\sin^2\theta)^{1/2}\,d\theta, \qquad 0 \le \epsilon \le 1. \quad (4.3\text{-}5)$$

It is not surprising that the elastic stress field (4.3-1) of the elastoplastic problem is complicated, considering the complexity of the exact solution for the completely elastic plate (4.1-61)–(4.1-63). Nevertheless, the elastic–plastic boundary as predicted by linear elastic fracture mechanics is relatively simple [AG 78]; i.e.,

$$c^4(x^2 + y^2)^2 = (y^2 - x^2 + a^2)^2 + 4x^2y^2, \quad (4.3\text{-}6)$$

where a is the crack length for the purely elastic problem. The equivalent of (4.3-6) is given in polar coordinates by (4.2-9), when expressed in Cartesian coordinates (4.1-23), which are shown pictorially in Fig. 4.1-1. One should be aware that a shift in origin occurs between the two coordinate systems (4.1-23) and (4.2-9) and that the usual relationships between Cartesian and polar coordinates do not apply.

To the best of the author's knowledge, the shape of (4.3-6) had not been identified geometrically as an inverse Cassinian oval prior to [Ung 93]. Since an inverse Cassinian oval coordinate system is available [MS 71], it would seem only natural to attempt an approximate solution of the mode III elastoplastic problem in this coordinate system as the elastic–plastic boundary will fall on a particular value of one of these coordinates.

Following [MS 71], we define the transformation from Cartesian (x, y) to inverse Cassinian oval coordinates (u, v) as

$$z = a[1 + \exp(u + iv)]^{-1/2}, \tag{4.3-7}$$

where u is a family of inverse Cassinian ovals. We note in [MS 71] that their inverse Cassinian oval coordinates are defined in terms of $\bar{z} = x - iy$ rather than $z = x + iy$ as in (4.3-7). This system differs from ours only by a reflection about the axis $y = 0$. We use z rather than $\bar{z}$ in ours because the coordinate transformation is applied to the Westergaard potential (4.1-60), which is defined in terms of z.

We find from (4.1-58) and (4.3-7) that the Westergaard potential and the exact linear elastic stresses assume particularly simple representations in the inverse Cassinian oval coordinate system; i.e.,

$$Z_{\mathrm{III}} = i\tau_\infty \exp[-(u + iv)/2] \tag{4.3-8}$$

$$\tau_{xz} = \tau_\infty e^{-u/2}\cos(v/2), \qquad \tau_{yz} = \tau_\infty e^{-u/2}\sin(v/2), \qquad -\infty \leq u \leq \infty. \tag{4.3-9}$$

The utility of the compact solution (4.3-9) for the exact linear elastic stresses should be obvious when compared to (4.1-61)–(4.1-62). We may easily apply (4.3-9) to problems involving the semi-infinite or infinite elastic plates when we desire more accuracy than the small-scale yielding solution provides away from the crack tip. Unlike the small-scale yielding solution, (4.3-9) meets the boundary condition on traction at infinity. In the case of the edge crack in a semi-infinite plate, it also reflects the influence of traction-free boundary along $x = 0$.

Now the Mises/Tresca yield condition for a perfectly plastic material is given by (1.1-6) for mode III. Employing (4.3-7) and (4.3-9), we deduce that elastic stresses (4.3-9) may be rewritten as

$$\tau_{xz} = ke^{(u_0-u)/2}\cos(v/2), \qquad \tau_{yz} = ke^{(u_0-u)/2}\sin(v/2), \qquad u_0 \le u \le \infty,$$
$$(4.3\text{-}10)$$

where the coordinate u_0 of the prescribed elastic–plastic boundary, as determined by linear elastic fracture mechanics, is given below:

$$u_0 = 2\ln(\tau_\infty/k) = 2\ln c, \qquad 0 \le c \le 1 \to -\infty \le u_0 \le 0. \quad (4.3\text{-}11)$$

The conversion formulas from inverse Cassinian oval coordinates (u, v) to Cartesian coordinates (x, y) are for the first quadrant $(x \ge 0, y \ge 0)$

$$x = (a/\rho_1)2^{-1/2}[\rho_1 + (e^u\cos v + 1)]^{1/2} \qquad \qquad (4.3\text{-}12)$$
$$y = (a/\rho_1)2^{-1/2}[\rho_1 - (e^u\cos v + 1)]^{1/2} \qquad \pi \le v \le 2\pi. \quad (4.3\text{-}13)$$
$$\text{where} \qquad \rho_1 = [e^{2u} + 2e^u\cos v + 1]^{1/2} \qquad \qquad (4.3\text{-}14)$$

A geometric representation of the coordinates is shown in Fig. 4.3-1. At the origin of the xy coordinate system the value of $u \to \infty$. A heavy line is

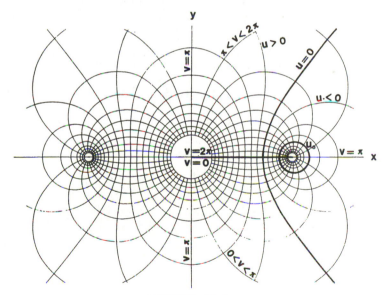

FIGURE 4.3-1

Inverse Cassinian oval coordinates. Adapted from copyrighted material [MS 71] by permission of Springer-Verlag.

TABLE 4.3-1
Mode III Ratio of Plastic Zone Length to Crack Length
(L_P / a_0) versus $c = \tau_\infty / k$

c (4.3-2)	LEFM (4.3-17)	Approximate E–P (4.3-3)	Exact E–P (4.3-4)
0.05	0.00250	0.00251	0.00251
0.1	0.01005	0.01008	0.01013
0.2	0.04083	0.04120	0.04208
0.3	0.09444	0.09608	0.10113
0.4	0.17514	0.17920	0.19811
0.5	0.29099	0.29688	0.35425

drawn along the positive x axis from the origin $(0,0)$ to the point $(a,0)$ where $u \rightarrow -\infty$. The physical crack in the elastoplastic problem in Cartesian coordinates spans from the origin $(0,0)$ to the point $(a_0,0)$ where u_0 intersects the positive x axis. This coordinate x_c is determined from (4.3-12) by substituting u_0 from (4.3-11) and $v = 2\pi$ into it; i.e.,

$$a_0 = x_c(u_0, 2\pi) = a(1 + \exp u_0)^{-1/2} = a(1 + c^2)^{-1/2}. \quad (4.3\text{-}15)$$

Thus the algebraic relationship between a and a_0 is $a = a_0(1 + c^2)^{1/2}$.

Similarly, the x coordinate of the leading edge of the plastic zone x_P is evaluated as

$$x_P(u_0, \pi) = a(1 - \exp u_0)^{-1/2} = a(1 - c^2)^{-1/2}$$
$$= a_0[(1 + c^2)/(1 - c^2)]^{1/2}, \quad (4.3\text{-}16)$$

and the plastic zone length L_P along the crack axis is obtained as follows:

$$L_P = x_P - x_c = a_0\{[(1 + c^2)/(1 - c^2)]^{1/2} - 1\}. \quad (4.3\text{-}17)$$

As can be seen in Table 4.3-1, the length of the plastic zone (4.3-17) from linear elastic fracture mechanics (LEFM) is comparable to the asymptotic expansion (4.3-3) of the elastoplastic (E–P) problem and the exact E–P solution (4.3-17) for the range of values of c provided.

Appendix

Stress across an elastoplastic boundary of a mode I crack: parabolic to hyperbolic plasticity transition

David J. Unger [1]

Department of Mechanical Engineering and Engineering Mechanics, Center for Mechanics of Materials and Instabilities, Michigan Technological University, Houghton, MI 49931, USA

Abstract

In previous work, the stresses of a mode I elastic–plastic fracture mechanics problem were analytically continued across a prescribed elastoplastic boundary for plane stress loading conditions involving a linear elastic/perfectly plastic material obeying the Tresca yield condition. Immediately across the elastic-plastic boundary, a nonlinear parabolic partial differential equation governs the plastic stress field. The present solution deals with stresses extending beyond the parabolic region into the hyperbolic region of the plastic zone. This analytical solution is obtained through a tranformation of the original system of nonlinear partial differential equations into a linear system with constant coefficients. The solution, so obtained, is expressible in terms of elementary transcendental functions. It also exhibits a limiting line which passes through the crack tip. This feature of the solution suggests the formation of a plastic hinge in the material. © 1998 Elsevier Science Ltd. All rights reserved.

1. Introduction

Analytical elastoplastic solutions involving linear elastic and finite-dimensional plastic regions have been confined to various mode III fracture mechanics configurations, originating with [1]. In the case of small scale yielding, the mode III elastic–plastic boundary can be determined by substituting the stresses from the purely linear elastic solution into the Mises or Tresca yield condition. A perfectly plastic solution of the mode III problem can then be obtained by solving an initial value problem for a first-order nonlinear partial differential equation (eikonal equation); see [2]. The mode III problem, however, is not the most important of the three principal modes of

fracture from a practical point of view. Nevertheless, it has by far the simplest governing equations of the three principal modes of fracture, and it has been the basis of many studies where an analytical solution of the mode I problem would have been more appropriate, but was simply unavailable.

Aside from Dugdale-type models [3,4] and wedge-type solutions [5], an exact mode I elastoplastic solution has not been solved by analytical means. Dugdale models have infinitesimallly-thin plastic regions of finite-length as boundary conditions along a portion of the crack faces in what are otherwise linear elastic crack problems. Wedge-type solutions [5] assume infinite sectors composed of individual linear elastic regions and individual plastic regions. The original Dugdale model [3] for a finite-length crack in an infinite plate employed the Tresca yield condition for a perfectly plastic material subject to a plane stress

[1] Tel.: +1 906 487 1647; e-mail: djunger@mtu.edu

loading condition of a uniform tensile traction at infinity. The Dugdale model was later modified to incorporate the Mises yield condition [4] and to accomodate constant, but distinct, biaxial tensile tractions at infinity aligned along the crack axis and its perpendicular. Both the Dugdale model and its modification approach purely linear elastic mode I solutions as one recedes from the crack tip. They do not, however, constitute conventional elastoplastic problems because of the degeneration of the plastic zone to a line segment in the plane. It was also proved for wedge-shaped solutions [5] that the plastic sector must collapse to a line (ray) ahead of the crack tip under the Tresca yield condition for a perfectly plastic material in plane stress; however, unlike the Dugdale model the classical elastic solution is not recoverable as the stress field is independent of r, the distance from the crack tip. For the Mises yield condition, wedge-shaped, plane stress, elastoplastic solutions proved nonexistent [5], unless modified to include a finite plane strain plastic region, which undergoes necking, in place of the unbounded plastic wedge. This additional geometry, however, renders the problem insoluble analytically. The necessity of a change from plane stress to plane strain in the form of a finite-width plastic strip (but of semi-infinite length rather than finite length as in [5]) was also found for the Tresca yield condition [6], assuming a fan of slip lines for a rigid elastic-perfectly plastic material. Necking was also introduced into this model [6] as in [5], but it was limited to a semi-circular band rather than the entire plane strain plastic zone. In Section 2 of this paper some regions of the plastic zone are found inaccessible by the derived hyperbolic plastic solution – another possible indicator of the need for a change from plane stress to plane strain over a portion of the plane. To continue the hyperbolic stress field into these particular regions would violate the yield condition, i.e., normal stresses that exceed the tensile yield stress of the material are predicted. This is impermissible under the Tresca yield condition in plane stress; however, no such restriction applies under plane strain conditions.

Although an exact elastoplastic solution has not been found for a mode I crack problem which asymptotically approaches the classical elastic so-lution away from crack tip, some significant progress toward this goal has been made previously and advanced in this paper. A solution technique amenable to the second-order, nonlinear partial differential equation that governs a portion of the plastic yield surface, MN of Fig. 1, for the Tresca yield condition under plane stress loading conditions was presented in [2,7]. There the elastic stresses from the small scale yielding solution Eqs. (1)–(3) were substituted into the Tresca yield condition (10) to obtain a prescribed elastic–plastic boundary Eq. (11). The initial value problem of the mode I plastic stress function for a non-work-hardening material was then solved analytically. This was accomplished by reducing the governing second-order equation (Monge–Ampere) to first order, i.e. an intermediate integral was found. Then by using differential geometry theory, a mode I plastic stress function was obtained analytically as an integral surface of the first-order partial differential equation. This function circumscribed the Airy stress function of the mode I solution – a geometric property indicating the stress functions and their slopes are continuous at the boundary. This continuity guarantees that equilibrium is satisfied locally across the elastic–plastic boundary $\partial\Omega$. Unfortunately, the stress field Eqs. 13–15, obtained by the partial differen-

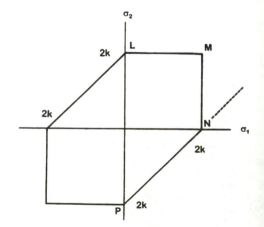

Fig. 1. Tresca yield surface. Adapted from [7].

tiation of the plastic stress function with respect to coordinates, exhibited a disequilibrated discontinuity in the trailing portion of the plastic zone. Thus equilibrium was not established globally even though all stresses were continuous across the entire elastic–plastic boundary. Had this discontinuity not been present, the possibility of a statically-admissible stress field analogous to the small scale yielding mode III elastoplastic solution would have remained open.

The appearance of this stress discontinuity establishes that for this particular problem the elastic–plastic boundary must move from the locus determined exclusively from linear elastic fracture mechanics for equilibrium to be established, i.e., a free boundary value problem must be formulated and solved. A theorem on the uniqueness of the initial value problem for the governing Monge–Ampere equation [2,7] rules out the possibility of an alternative solution for the same elastic–plastic boundary, i.e., a solution where the traction on the boundary would be continuous, but where the stresses tangent to the boundary are discontinous. Further, if a flow theory of plasticity is adopted rather than a deformation theory of plasticity, an elastic unloading accompanied by residual plastic strain in the previously active plastic zone would likely occur.

Nevertheless, the analytical mode I solution of [2,7] for plane stress might serve as an approximation over a limited region of the plastic zone, despite the fact that unloading occurs. A fundamental tenet of small scale yielding is that the asymptotic, linear elastic solution characterizes the stress and strain fields of a ductile material in an annulus removed from the crack tip. If this assumption is correct, then it would also be likely that over a select portion of the plastic zone the elastoplastic solution Eqs. (13)–(15) should approximate the response of a non-work-hardening material. This analytical plastic solution would most probably be appropriate for the leading edge of the plastic zone – seeing that it continues well into the plastic zone from the elastic–plastic boundary, i.e., from $\partial\Omega$ to $\partial\omega$ of Fig. 2. However, near the trailing edge of the plastic zone, the parabolic plastic region extends only a short distance into the plastic zone before changing to

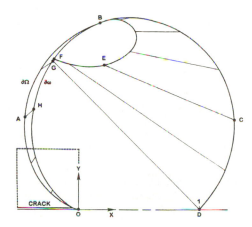

Fig. 2. Parabolic slip lines and the mode I elastic–plastic boundary for plane stress under the Tresca yield condition. Adapted from [7].

a hyperbolic region. Unloading would likely occur in the vicinity of line segment FG on $\partial\omega$, where a disequilibrated stress discontinuity exists [2,7]. This general area is known to unload in finite element solutions [8] of the mode I, plane stress, elastoplastic problem, under the Mises yield condition, for a perfectly plastic material using a flow theory of plasticity (the Prandtl–Reuss equations). However, the extent of the unloading under the Tresca yield condition, and the change in elastic–plastic boundary remain uncertain, due to a lack of numerical studies for this particular case.

In the present analysis, the crack tip is found to fall at the intersection of two limiting lines [9,10] which are envelopes of slip lines emanating from the trailing edges of the plastic zone. This is particularly interesting since limiting lines are line singularities rather than point singularities. This represents a significant departure from previous models of the crack tip based on the point singularity, and it may possibly represent the formation of the plastic hinge that is observed experimentally for cracks in thin steel plates. This experimental phenomenon and its relationship to the analytical solution derived in Section 2 is discussed in Section 3.

1.1. Summary of linear elastic and parabolic plasticity equations

The classical, small scale yielding, linear elastic stresses for the mode I fracture mechanics problems [2] are:

$$\sigma_x^E = cr^{-1/2}\cos(\theta/2)[1 - \sin(\theta/2)\sin(3\theta/2)], \quad (1)$$

$$\sigma_y^E = cr^{-1/2}\cos(\theta/2)[1 + \sin(\theta/2)\sin(3\theta/2)], \quad (2)$$

$$\tau_{xy}^E = cr^{-1/2}\cos(\theta/2)\sin(\theta/2)\cos(3\theta/2), \quad (3)$$

where r and θ are polar coordinates whose origin is at the crack tip with semi-infinite crack faces along $\theta = \pm\pi$; x and y are Cartesian coordinates which are related to the polar as follows

$$x = r\cos\theta, \quad y = r\sin\theta, \quad (4)$$

with z being the third coordinate axis in both systems. The symbols σ_x and σ_y in Eqs. (1)–(3) are normal stresses in the x and y directions respectively; τ_{xy} is the shear stress in the xy plane; and all other stresses are zero because of the plane stress assumption. The constant c appearing in Eqs. (1)–(3) is related to the stress intensity factor K_I by the formula

$$c \equiv K_\mathrm{I}/(2\pi)^{1/2}. \quad (5)$$

For the Tresca condition, yield occurs when the maximum shear stress reaches the critical value k, which is the yield stress of the material in pure shear. The Tresca yield surface is shown in Fig. 1 in terms of the principal stresses σ_1 and σ_2 as σ_3 is zero due to plane stress loading conditions. The algebraic relationships between principal stresses and their Cartesian counterparts are for cases where $\sigma_1 \geqslant \sigma_2$:

$$2\sigma_1 = \sigma_x + \sigma_y + [(\sigma_x - \sigma_y)^2 + 4\tau_{xy}^2]^{1/2}, \quad (6)$$

$$2\sigma_2 = \sigma_x + \sigma_y - [(\sigma_x - \sigma_y)^2 + 4\tau_{xy}^2]^{1/2}, \quad (7)$$

$$\sigma_3 = 0. \quad (8)$$

One finds that the elastic stresses of the mode I problem meet the yield condition along side MN (Fig. 1) of the yield surface where $\sigma_1 = 2k$, i.e.,

$$\sigma_1 = 2k, \quad \sigma_1 \geqslant \sigma_2 \geqslant 0. \quad (9)$$

The yield condition assumes the following form on the elastic–plastic boundary by Eq. (6) and (9),

$$\sigma_x + \sigma_y + [(\sigma_x - \sigma_y)^2 + 4\tau_{xy}^2]^{1/2} = 4k$$

$$\text{for } \sigma_1 \geqslant \sigma_2 \geqslant 0. \quad (10)$$

Upon substitution of the stresses Eqs. (1)–(3) in Eq. (10), one obtains the polar equation of the prescribed elastoplastic boundary $\partial\Omega$,

$$r = [c/(2k)]^2 \cos^2(\theta/2)[1 + \sin(\theta/2)]^2,$$

$$0 \leqslant \theta \leqslant \pi. \quad (11)$$

This curve is shown in Fig. 2 as OABCD for the half plane, $y \geqslant 0$. A similar expression and plot has appeared previously in [11].

The following normalized Cartesian coordinates (X, Y) are now introduced

$$X \equiv 4k^2x/c^2, \quad Y \equiv 4k^2y/c^2. \quad (12)$$

These coordinates are so defined that a dimensionless unit spans the distance OD of Fig. 2, which is the length from the tip of the crack to the leading end of the plastic zone along the crack axis.

In [2,7] it was shown that immediately across $\partial\Omega$ that the stresses assume the parametric form: mode I plastic stresses (parabolic region), $Y \geqslant 0$, $0 \leqslant a \leqslant 1$, $a \neq 2/3$,

$$\sigma_x^P/k = 2$$
$$+ \frac{4a(1+a)(3a-2)(1+2a)^2(1-a^2)}{X(1+4a) + Y(4a^2+a-2)(1-a^2)^{-1/2} + (3-5a)(1+a)^3} \quad (13)$$

$$\sigma_y^P/k = 2$$
$$+ \frac{4a(3a-2)(1-2a)^2(1+a)^3}{X(1+4a) + Y(4a^2+a-2)(1-a^2)^{-1/2} + (3-5a)(1+a)^3} \quad (14)$$

$$\tau_{xy}^P/k$$
$$= \frac{4a(2-3a)(1+a)^2(1-4a^2)(1-a^2)^{1/2}}{X(1+4a) + Y(4a^2+a-2)(1-a^2)^{-1/2} + (3-5a)(1+a)^3} \quad (15)$$

where $a = a(X, Y)$ is a parameter defined in Eq. (16).

Eq. (16) below

$$(1+a)(1-2a)X + (1-a^2)^{1/2}(1+2a)Y$$
$$= (1+a)^4(1-a), \quad y \geqslant 0, \quad 0 \leqslant a \leqslant 1, \quad a \neq 2/3 \quad (16)$$

is the characteristic equation for the governing partial differential equation. It also defines the single family of slip lines present in the parabolic region of the plastic zone. Along a particular slip line in this field the parameter $a(X, Y)$ is constant and Eq. (16) reduces to the equation of a straight line.

Several slip lines, including AH and CE, are shown in the normalized Cartesian plane, Fig. 2. The corresponding slip planes are oriented at an angle of $\pi/4$ to the xy plane. The principal stress σ_1 is perpendicular to a slip line while the second principal stress σ_2 is parallel to a slip line.

Now the following strength of materials formula determines the angles α of two distinct principal stress directions which are separated by $\pi/2$ radians in the plane

$$\cot(2\alpha) = (\sigma_x - \sigma_y)/(2\tau_{xy}). \tag{17}$$

If α is restricted to refer only to those angles that a slip line in the parabolic region makes relative to the x axis (the angle to second principal direction in the plane), then from Eqs. (1)–(3), (11), (16) and (17) and trigonometric identities one can prove, as in [2], that

$$a = \sin(\theta/2)|_{\partial\Omega} = -\cos(2\alpha/3). \tag{18}$$

From Eq. (18) it is deduced for the upper half plane that

$$\alpha = 3(\hat{\theta} + \pi)/4 \quad \text{for } 0 \leqslant \hat{\theta} \leqslant \pi \to 3\pi/4 \leqslant \alpha \leqslant 3\pi/2, \tag{19}$$

where $\hat{\theta}$ is defined as the value of θ on $\partial\Omega$.

The principal stresses in normalized coordinates are determined from Eqs. (6), (7), (13)–(15) to be

$$\sigma_1^P/k = 2, \tag{20}$$

$$\sigma_2^P/k = 2$$

$$+ \frac{8a(3a - 2)(1 + a)^2}{X(1 + 4a) + Y(4a^2 + a - 2)(1 - a^2)^{-1/2} + (3 - 5a)(1 + a)^3}, \tag{21}$$

with parameter $a = a(X, Y)$ again defined by Eq. (16).

The parabolic–hyperbolic plastic boundary $\partial\omega$ is determined by solving the simultaneous Eqs. (16) and (21) with σ_2 set equal to zero. This boundary is located at

$$\partial\omega: \sigma_1 = 2k, \quad \sigma_2 = \sigma_3 = 0; \quad Y \geqslant 0; \tag{22}$$

$$X = (1 + a)^2(1 - a)[1 + a - (2/3)(1 - a)(1 + 2a)$$
$$\times (9a^2 - 4a + 2)]/(1 - 2a)$$
$$0 \leqslant a \leqslant 1, \ a \neq 2/3, \ a \neq 1/2; \tag{23}$$
$$= 15/32, \quad a = 1/2; \tag{24}$$

$$Y = (2/3)(1 - a)(1 + a)^2(1 - a^2)^{1/2}(9a^2 - 4a + 2),$$
$$0 \leqslant a \leqslant 1, \ a \neq 2/3. \tag{25}$$

Note that $a = 2/3$ is excluded from $\partial\omega$ in Eqs. (23) and (25). For $a = 2/3$ the slip line (16) becomes tangent to the elastic–plastic boundary at point B of Fig. 2. Consequently no information about the linear elastic solution is carried into the plastic region from point B making it a singular point. The parabolic–hyperbolic plastic boundary (23)–(25) appears in Fig. 2 as curve OHGFBEF.

2. Plastic analysis in the hyperbolic region

Along $\partial\omega$ the state of stress on the Tresca yield surface moves from region MN to region NP of Fig. 1. Along NP the stress σ_2 is negative and therefore becomes smaller than the third principal stress $\sigma_3 = 0$. As the maximum shear stress is always one half of the greatest difference in principal stresses, the Tresca yield condition governing region NP becomes by Eq. (6) and (7)

$$(\sigma_x - \sigma_y)^2 + 4\tau_{xy}^2 = 4k^2. \tag{26}$$

The following relationships for stress which satisfy Eq. (26) are now introduced

$$\sigma_x = \sigma - k\sin 2\chi, \tag{27}$$
$$\sigma_y = \sigma + k\sin 2\chi, \tag{28}$$
$$\tau_{xy} = k\cos 2\chi, \tag{29}$$

where χ is interpreted as the angle between the x axis and the slip line ξ shown in Fig. 3, and σ is the average normal stress in the xy plane

$$\sigma \equiv (\sigma_x + \sigma_y)/2 = (\sigma_1 + \sigma_2)/2. \tag{30}$$

The in-plane equilibrium equations are

$$\frac{\partial\sigma_x}{\partial x} + \frac{\partial\tau_{xy}}{\partial y} = 0, \quad \frac{\partial\sigma_y}{\partial y} + \frac{\partial\tau_{xy}}{\partial x} = 0. \tag{31}$$

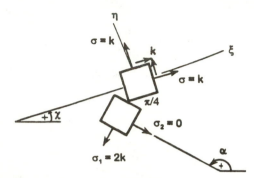

Fig. 3. Stresses and slip line angles on parabolic–hyperbolic plastic boundary.

They become upon substitution of Eqs. (27)–(29), the following system of nonlinear partial differential equations

$$\frac{\partial \sigma}{\partial x} - 2k\left[\cos(2\chi)\frac{\partial \chi}{\partial x} + \sin(2\chi)\frac{\partial \chi}{\partial y}\right] = 0, \qquad (32)$$

$$\frac{\partial \sigma}{\partial y} - 2k\left[\sin(2\chi)\frac{\partial \chi}{\partial x} - \cos(2\chi)\frac{\partial \chi}{\partial y}\right] = 0. \qquad (33)$$

Equations similar to Eqs. (26)–(33) may be found in Chapter 6 of [12], which is dedicated to plane strain problems rather than to plane stress problems. This relationship is merely coincidental. It so happens that along side NP of the plane stress Tresca yield surface that the governing equations for in-plane stresses are identical to those of plane strain slip line theory [13], under the Mises or Tresca yield conditions which are themselves equal (but only when expressed in terms of yield stress in pure shear k rather than the tensile yield stress σ_{YS}, as the relationships between σ_{YS} and k differ between the two yield criteria). Thus, as in plane strain slip line theory, the partial differential equations are hyperbolic and possess two families of characteristics instead of the single family of characteristics found for parabolic partial differential equations.

The number of families of slip lines in the plane change similarly as the number of characteristics as they are coincident with them (This is true for the Tresca yield condition, but not for the Mises yield condition in plane stress.)

On the parabolic–hyperbolic plastic boundary $\partial \omega$

$$\chi_0 \equiv \chi|_{\partial\omega} = \alpha - 3\pi/4, \qquad (34)$$

as the single parabolic slip line bifurcates in the xy plane into ξ and η slip lines at $\pm\pi/4$ radians to the first principal stress direction (Fig. 3).

It is now convenient to formulate the initial value problem for the hyperbolic partial differential equations (32) and (33) in terms of Mikhlin variables $(\bar{X}, \bar{Y})$ [12,14]

$$\bar{X} = X\cos\chi + Y\sin\chi, \quad \bar{Y} = -X\sin\chi + Y\cos\chi. \qquad (35)$$

The nonlinear plastic equilibrium equations for the slip line field can be linearized [12,15] and rewritten as the following system of first order equations

$$\frac{\partial \bar{X}}{\partial \eta} = \bar{Y}, \quad \frac{\partial \bar{Y}}{\partial \xi} = -\bar{X}, \qquad (36)$$

where ξ and η are defined by

$$\xi \equiv (1/2)[\chi + \sigma/(2k)], \quad \eta \equiv (1/2)[\chi - \sigma/(2k)]. \qquad (37)$$

An initial value problem for Eq. (36) can be solved operationally by means of an integral transform. To facilitate solution, two new variables ϕ, ψ are introduced which are defined below

$$\phi \equiv \xi + \eta + 3\pi/4 = \chi + 3\pi/4, \qquad (38)$$

$$\psi \equiv \xi - \eta - 1/2 = 1/2(\sigma/k - 1). \qquad (39)$$

Eq. (36) for $\bar{X}(\phi, \psi)$ and $\bar{Y}(\phi, \psi)$ become the following in terms of the variables defined in Eqs. (38) and (39)

$$\frac{\partial \bar{X}}{\partial \phi} - \frac{\partial \bar{X}}{\partial \psi} = \bar{Y}, \quad \frac{\partial \bar{Y}}{\partial \phi} + \frac{\partial \bar{Y}}{\partial \psi} = -\bar{X}. \qquad (40)$$

Their initial data, $\bar{X}_0(\phi)$ and $\bar{Y}_0(\phi)$ below, are obtained from parametric Eqs. (23)–(25) of the parabolic to hyperbolic plastic boundary,

$$\bar{X}_0(\phi) \equiv \bar{X}(\phi, 0) = (8/3)2^{1/2}\cos^2(\phi/3)\sin^4(\phi/3)$$
$$\times \{3\sin^3(\phi/3) + 5\cos(\phi/3)[1 - 3\cos^2(\phi/3)]\}, \qquad (41)$$

$$\bar{Y}_0(\phi) \equiv \bar{Y}(\phi, 0) = (8/3)2^{1/2}\cos^2(\phi/3)\sin^4(\phi/3)$$
$$\times \{3\sin^3(\phi/3) - 5\cos(\phi/3)[1 - 3\cos^2(\phi/3)]\}. \qquad (42)$$

The above were determined with the aid of Eq. (18) which relates $a(X, Y)$ to α on the boundary $\partial \omega$; Eqs. (34) and (38) which indicate that $\alpha = \phi$ on the boundary $\partial \omega$; and Eq. (34) which defines the relationship between χ and α for use in the Mikhlin coordinates Eq. (35). Initially $\psi = 0$ by Eq. (39) as $\sigma = k$ on $\partial \omega$ by Eqs. (22) and (30). As a consequence of this, the Laplace transform is particularly well-suited for solving this initial value problem with ψ being analogous to the time variable for the many evolution equations which are solved by this technique.

The applicability of the Laplace transform in this problem is fortuitous and is possible only because σ is constant along $\partial \omega$. This situation allows the use of one of the most powerful tools available for solving partial differential equations.

The Laplace transform acting on a function $F(\psi)$ is symbolized as $\mathscr{L}\{F(\psi)\} \rightarrow F_L(s)$ where s is the variable of transformation, ψ is the transformed variable, and the subscript L indicates the transformed function. The variable $\bar{X}(\phi, \psi)$ and its first partial derivative with respect to ψ transform respectively as:

$$\bar{X}_L(\phi, s) \equiv \mathscr{L}\{\bar{X}(\phi, \psi)\} = \int_0^\infty \bar{X}(\phi, \psi)\, e^{-s\psi}\, d\psi, \quad (43)$$

$$\mathscr{L}\{\partial \bar{X}(\phi, \psi)/\partial \psi\} = \int_0^\infty \partial \bar{X}(\phi, \psi)/\partial \psi\, e^{-s\psi}\, d\psi, \quad (44)$$

$$= s\bar{X}_L(\phi, s) - \bar{X}_0(\phi). \quad (45)$$

Using Eqs. (43)–(45) and similar operations on $\bar{Y}(\phi, \psi)$, one transforms Eq. (40) into a system of ordinary differential equations with respect to ϕ, i.e.,

$$\frac{d\bar{X}_L(\phi, s)}{d\phi} - s\bar{X}_L(\phi, s) + \bar{X}_0(\phi) = \bar{Y}_1(\phi, s), \quad (46)$$

$$\frac{d\bar{Y}_L(\phi, s)}{d\phi} + s\bar{Y}_L(\phi, s) - \bar{Y}_0(\phi) = -\bar{X}_L(\phi, s). \quad (47)$$

One of the dependent variables can then be eliminated from the system of Eqs. (46), (47) to obtain in turn:

$$\frac{d^2\bar{X}_L(\phi, s)}{d\phi^2} + (1 - s^2)\bar{X}_L(\phi, s) = \bar{Y}_0(\phi)$$

$$-\frac{d\bar{X}_0(\phi)}{d\phi} - s\bar{X}_0(\phi) \quad (48)$$

$$\frac{d^2\bar{Y}_L(\phi, s)}{d\phi^2} + (1 - s^2)\bar{Y}_L(\phi, s) = \bar{X}_0(\phi)$$

$$+\frac{d\bar{Y}_0(\phi)}{d\phi} - s\bar{Y}_0(\phi). \quad (49)$$

Particular solutions can be obtained for Eqs. (48) and (49) by using formula (18.8) of [16], which can be derived using the variation of parameters solution technique. For the inhomogeneous, linear second-order equation, with constant coefficients,

$$\frac{d^2 Z(\phi)}{d\phi^2} - m^2 Z(\phi) = R(\phi), \quad (50)$$

where ϕ is the independent variable, $Z(\phi)$ is the dependent variable, $R(\phi)$ is an arbitrary function of ϕ, and m is a constant, the particular solution $Z_p(\phi)$ is reduced to quadrature, i.e.,

$$Z_p(\phi) = [e^{m\phi} \int e^{-m\phi} R(\phi)\, d\phi$$

$$- e^{-m\phi} \int e^{m\phi} R(\phi)\, d\phi]/(2m). \quad (51)$$

For Eqs. (48) and (49), the constant m in (51) is identified as

$$m = (s^2 - 1)^{1/2}, \quad (52)$$

with $Z_p(\phi)$ being either $\bar{X}_L(\phi, s)$ or $\bar{Y}_L(\phi, s)$, and $R(\phi)$ corresponding to either the right-hand side of Eq. (48) or Eq. (49).

Only the particular solutions of Eqs. (48) and (49) are needed to fulfill the initial conditions.

What remains to be done, in order to solve the initial value problem, is simple in principle. Calculate the right-hand side of Eqs. (48) and (49) by taking the derivatives of $\bar{X}_0(\phi)$ and $\bar{Y}_0(\phi)$ as indicated, where $\bar{X}_0(\phi)$ and $\bar{Y}_0(\phi)$ are defined by Eqs. (41) and (42). Substitute the resulting expressions for the right-hand sides of Eqs. (48) and (49) into Eq. (51) along with the value of m given by Eq. (52). Perform the integrations and set the constants of integration equal to zero to obtain solutions $\bar{X}_L(\phi,s)$ and $\bar{Y}_L(\phi,s)$ of the system of ordinary differential equations (48) and (49). Take the inverse Laplace transformations of $\bar{X}_L(\phi,s)$ and $\bar{Y}_L(\phi,s)$ to obtain the corresponding solutions $\bar{X}(\phi,\psi)$ and $\bar{Y}(\phi,\psi)$.

Note that some simplification of algebra results by introducing variables $F(\phi,\psi)$ and $G(\phi,\psi)$, defined by (53) and (54), rather than working with $\bar{X}(\phi,\psi)$ and $\bar{Y}(\phi,\psi)$ directly.

The solution of the initial value problem defined by Eqs. (41), (42), (48) and (49) is straightforward but laborious. It is recommended that the reader who wishes to duplicate the solution given here employ one of the symbolic mathematics computer programs such as Mathematica [2], Maple [3] or Macsyma [4], which have both symbolic integration routines for solving indefinite integrals such as Eq. (51), in addition to special routines capable of performing inverse Laplace transformations which involve contour integrations in the complex plane. Mathematica was used in this particular study.

Without the aid of a symbolic processor, the reader will probably find the algebra prohibitive.

Using a symbolic mathematics computer program, one can easily verify by direct substitution, that the following expressions will solve the system of equation (40):

$$\bar{X}(\phi,\psi) = [F(\phi,\psi) + G(\phi,\psi)]/2, \qquad (53)$$
$$\bar{Y}(\phi,\psi) = [F(\phi,\psi) - G(\phi,\psi)]/2, \qquad (54)$$

where the functions $F(\phi,\psi)$ and $G(\phi,\psi)$ are given by

$$
\begin{aligned}
2^{1/2}F(\phi,\psi) \equiv &-(1/16)\{\sin J(\phi,\psi) - \sin L(\phi,\psi)\} \\
&- (2^{1/2}/4)\{\cos J(\phi,\psi) - \cos L(\phi,\psi)\} \\
&+ (5/16)\{\sin M(\phi,\psi) - \sin N(\phi,\psi)\} \\
&+ (10^{1/2}/12)\{\cos M(\phi,\psi) - \cos N(\phi,\psi)\} \\
&- \{\cos P(\psi) + (4/3)\sin P(\psi)\}\sin Q(\phi) \\
&+ \{(7/4)\cosh U(\psi) - 2^{1/2}\sinh U(\psi)\}\sin V(\phi),
\end{aligned}
$$
$$(55)$$

[2] Mathematica, is a registered trademark of Wolfram Research, Inc., Champaign, IL.
[3] Maple, is a registered trademark of Waterloo Maple Software, Inc., Ontario.
[4] Macsyma, is a trademark of Macsyma, Inc., Arlington, MA.

$$
\begin{aligned}
2^{1/2}G(\phi,\psi) \equiv &-(2^{1/2}/8)\{\sin J(\phi,\psi) + \sin L(\phi,\psi)\} \\
&- (5/16)\{\cos J(\phi,\psi) + \cos L(\phi,\psi)\} \\
&+ (10^{1/2}/8)\{\sin M(\phi,\psi) + \sin N(\phi,\psi)\} \\
&+ (5/48)\{\cos M(\phi,\psi) + \cos N(\phi,\psi)\} \\
&+ (5/6)\{\cos[P(\psi) + Q(\phi)] \\
&+ \cos[P(\psi) - Q(\phi)]\} \\
&- (1/2)\{(5/2)\cosh U(\psi) \\
&+ 2^{1/2}\sinh U(\psi)\}\cos V(\phi),
\end{aligned}
$$
$$(56)$$

and the various functions used in Eqs. (55) and (56) are defined by

$$J(\phi,\psi) \equiv 2^{3/2}\psi + 3\phi, \quad L(\phi,\psi) \equiv 2^{3/2}\psi - 3\phi, \qquad (57)$$

$$M(\phi,\psi) \equiv (40^{1/2}\psi + 7\phi)/3,$$
$$N(\phi,\psi) \equiv (40^{1/2}\psi - 7\phi)/3, \qquad (58)$$

$$P(\psi) \equiv 4\psi/3, \quad Q(\phi) \equiv 5\phi/3, \qquad (59)$$

$$U(\psi) \equiv 8^{1/2}\psi/3, \quad V(\phi) \equiv \phi/3. \qquad (60)$$

One may also verify that the solution satisfies the initial conditions (41) and (42) by substituting $\psi = 0$ into the above equations and simplifying.

To return to the original coordinate system (X,Y) from the Mikhlin $(\bar{X}, \bar{Y})$, use the following inversion formulas [12]

$$X = \bar{X}\cos\chi - \bar{Y}\sin\chi, \quad Y = \bar{X}\sin\chi + \bar{Y}\cos\chi. \qquad (61)$$

Now from slip line theory it follows that:

$$\sigma - 2k\chi = \sigma_0 - 2k\chi_0$$
along a ξ line (η constant), $\qquad (62)$

$$\sigma + 2k\chi = \sigma_0 + 2k\chi_0$$
along a η line (ξ constant), $\qquad (63)$

where on the boundary $\partial\omega$, $\sigma_0 = k$, and χ_0 is given by Eq. (34). On substituting χ from one of Eqs. (62) and (63) into Eqs. (53)–(61) via Eqs. (38) and (39), one finds the parametric equations for coordinates (X,Y) of a particular family of slip lines ξ or η in terms of the mean stress σ. By increasing or decreasing σ/k from its initial value of one, the reader can trace the path of a slip line originating on the boundary $\partial\omega$. For an arbitrary point on $\partial\omega$, a slip line will move either into the hyperbolic plastic zone or into the parabolic plastic zone depending on the choice of sign of $\Delta\sigma$. However, $\Delta\sigma$ must be restricted to be negative, otherwise the yield condition would be violated. For positive $\Delta\sigma$, one travels along the dashed line extension of line NP, shown in Fig. 1, which is outside of the yield surface. Consequently some regions interior to $\partial\omega$ are inaccessible by the solution. Fortunately, the near crack-tip region, which is the region where the solution will most likely prove to be a valid approximation, is not affected by this concern.

To summarize, one traces the path of a slip line originating on $\partial\omega$ by making the following substitution for χ into Eq. (61)

$$\chi = \alpha - 3\pi/4 \pm [(\sigma/k) - 1]/2, \qquad (64)$$

together with following substitutions for ϕ and ψ in Eqs. (53)–(60)

$$\phi = \alpha \pm [(\sigma/k) - 1]/2, \quad \psi = [(\sigma/k) - 1]/2. \quad (65)$$

By substituting the resulting expressions for $\bar{X}$ and $\bar{Y}$ from Eqs. (53) and (54) into Eq. (61), one obtains a parametrized solution of X and Y in terms of α and σ.

Now to trace an individual slip line originating on boundary $\partial\omega$, first substitute $\sigma = k$, and choose a value of α between the limits given in Eq. (19). From Eq. (18) together with Eqs. (23)–(25), locate its point of origin in (X, Y) coordinates. If one wishes to trace the path of a ζ slip line emanating from $\partial\omega$, choose the upper signs in Eqs. (64) and (65), and if one wishes to trace the path of an η slip line, choose the lower signs in Eqs. (64) and (65). Finally, decrease σ from its initial value of k to obtain the path of a slip line.

An initial value problem will now be solved using data along $\partial\omega$ near the crack tip where the problem is well-posed.

Starting at the crack tip, one finds that a slip line first becomes tangent to $\partial\omega$ at $\alpha \approx 4.075$. At and beyond this point, the initial value problem for the non-characteristic curve $\partial\omega$ becomes ill-posed, see p. 168 of [13]. One consequently restricts the domain of dependence of the initial data along $\partial\omega$ from $\alpha = 4.075$ to the crack tip $\alpha = 3\pi/2$.

The value of θ on $\partial\Omega$ corresponding to $\alpha \approx 4.075$ is $\hat{\theta} \approx 131.3°$.

Slip lines near the crack tip, obtained from the analytical solution Eqs. (53)–(60), are shown in Fig. 4. Fig. 4 is an enlargement of the region outlined by dashes in Fig. 2.

For completeness, it should be mentioned that a second region also exists where the analytical solution is valid. The initial data for this region lie on $\partial\omega$ between $\alpha \approx 2.852$ and 3.125. The domain of dependence for the initial data of this region lies interior to the loop BEFB of Fig. 2 toward the right-hand side.

2.1. Benchmark

The exact solution, which is both lengthy and partially machine generated, will now be compared with a simple approximate solution. Two points on $\partial\omega$ are U and V whose positions and values of χ are given in Fig. 5. (These two points also appear on Fig. 4 and in the tables.) One also recalls that σ equals k on $\partial\omega$. Consequently, by using Eqs. (62) and (63), one can determine χ and σ where the ζ line from point U intersects the η line from point V (i.e., point W). By solving these simultaneous equations, one finds that the exact value of σ_W is $0.8691\ k$ (to four decimal places) and the exact

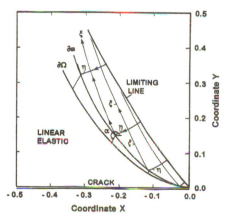

Fig. 4. Near crack-tip slip lines.

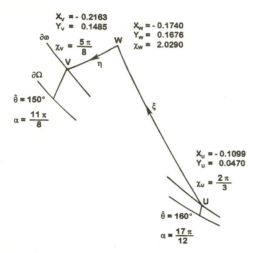

Fig. 5. Slip line data.

value for χ_W is 2.0290 (to four decimal places). The location of point W is all that remains.

Approximate methods of finding (X_W, Y_W) from data on various types of boundaries are discussed in [12,13]. Here, a technique appropriate for a noncharacteristic curve is described.

The slope of the slip lines ξ and η are, respectively

$$\frac{dY}{dX} = \tan \chi, \quad \frac{dY}{dX} = -\cot \chi. \qquad (66)$$

These can be approximated by the following expressions for point W in terms of the positions of points U and V on $\partial\omega$

$$Y_W - Y_U = (X_W - X_U)\tan \frac{1}{2}(\chi_W + \chi_U), \qquad (67)$$

$$Y_W - Y_V = -(X_W - X_V)\cot \frac{1}{2}(\chi_W + \chi_V). \qquad (68)$$

By substituting the known values of χ_U, χ_V, and χ_W, together with the coordinates for points U and V (Fig. 5), one finds an approximate location for W, which is compared below, with the exact location

$$X_W^{\text{Approx}} = -0.1743, \quad Y_W^{\text{Approx}} = 0.1675 \qquad (69)$$

$$X_W^{\text{Exact}} = -0.1740, \quad Y_W^{\text{Exact}} = 0.1676 \qquad (70)$$

As the reader can tell, they are virtually indistinguishable. The reason they agree so closely is that the curvatures of the slip lines are small in this region. Thus straight line approximations (67) and (68) of slip lines coupled with arithmetic averages of the angles χ at their respective end points are a very accurate scheme for this region.

In Tables 1 and 2 additional exact values for principal stresses, positions, and angles along sliplines UW and VW are given. In Tables 3 and 4 are stresses in Cartesian coordinates obtained from Eqs. (27)–(29) by substituting values of χ and σ from Tables 1 and 2.

3. Discussion

Perhaps the most intrigueing feature exhibited by the hyperbolic solution (53) and (54) is the formation of a limiting line (also called rupture line in Russian literature [9]) which passes through the crack tip. A limiting line is a curve that is the envelope of a family of slip lines [9,10]. The envelope here is a family of ξ slip lines as Fig. 4 indicates. Provided the stress ratio σ/k is lowered sufficiently from its initial value of one on $\partial\omega$, the trace of any associated η slip line in this region will eventually form a cusp. The loci of the tips of these individual cusps form collectively the limiting line. Both branches of the cusps meet the limiting line orthogonally; however, only the incoming branches of η lines from $\partial\omega$ are depicted in Fig. 4, as these are the only physically meaningful branches of the solution.

The unique feature of the limiting line in regard to crack problems is that it is a line singularity rather than a point singularity in the plane. This singularity initiates at the crack tip and propagates along two curves whose tangents at the origin make $\pi/4$ radians relative to the crack axis. Along limiting lines the derivatives of the tangential stress with respect to the normal direction are singular [9]. More importantly, singular shear strains form along the entire length of the limiting line [9], rather that at a discrete point. This has significant implications regarding both analytical and numerical elastoplastic solutions of mode I crack problems. For example, singular finite elements are typically

Table 1
Data along plane stress slipline UW (Fig. 5), ξ line, $\sigma_3 = 0$

σ (k)	χ (Radians)	X (Dimensionless)	Y (Dimensionless)	σ_1 (k)	σ_2 (k)
1	2.0944	−0.1099	0.0470	2	0
0.95	2.0690	−0.1321	0.0867	1.95	−0.05
0.9	2.0444	−0.1572	0.1343	1.9	−0.1
0.85	2.0194	−0.1848	0.1897	1.85	−0.15
0.8	1.9944	−0.2143	0.2530	1.8	−0.2

Table 2
Data along plane stress slipline VW (Fig. 5), η line, $\sigma_3 = 0$

σ (k)	χ (Radians)	X (Dimensionless)	Y (Dimensionless)	σ_1 (k)	σ_2 (k)
1	1.9635	−0.2163	0.1485	2	0
0.95	1.9889	−0.1994	0.1557	1.95	−0.05
0.9	2.0135	−0.1833	0.1631	1.9	−0.1
0.85	2.0385	−0.1686	0.1703	1.85	−0.15
0.8	2.0635	−0.1562	0.1768	1.8	−0.2

employed near the crack tip in numerical solutions of crack problems in order to reduce the total number of elements required and to improve the overall accuracy of the analysis. Naturally, if the order or geometry of the singularity is incorrect for these special elements, they would tend to degrade the numerical solution rather than improve it. The line singularity would also have serious consequences for path-independent integral analyses since the tacit assumption is made that their paths do not cross through a singularity.

The limiting line may possibly represent the formation of the experimentally-observed plastic hinge in a material in thin plates. Data from cracked plates of silicon steel [17,18] indicate slip plane patterns of both plane stress and plane strain plastic deformation on single specimens. The plane stress and plane strain region appear, respectively, on the leading and trailing edges of a fully developed plastic zone. This behavior can be interpreted in terms of the analytical solution.

The parabolic solution indicates that in the trailing edge of the plastic zone, the distortion in the z direction is confined to a narrow crescent (OABFGHO of Fig. 2) near the elastic–plastic boundary. This is followed by the hyperbolic plastic region where theoretically no deformation occurs in the z direction, which in this respect resembles plane strain deformation. For plates of silicon steel, at low levels of loading, data show plane strain regions near the crack tip that extend outward in directions normal to the crack line in the plane of the plate. These researchers [17,18] describe this phenomenon, whose path eventually curves forward, as the formation of a plastic hinge (see also [19]), which has slip planes oriented perpendicularly to the plane of the plate. As load levels increase, two wings of plane stress plastic deformation form ahead of the crack tip. This plane stress deformation is marked by slip planes oriented at $\pi/4$ radians to the xy plane of the plate. This agrees with theoretical behavior predicted by

Table 3
In-plane stresses along slipline UW, ξ line

σ (k)	σ_x (k)	σ_y (k)	τ_{xy} (k)
1	1.8660	0.1340	−0.5
0.95	1.7900	0.1101	−0.5427
0.9	1.7118	0.0882	−0.5840
0.85	1.6312	0.0684	−0.6238
0.8	1.5494	0.0506	−0.6621

Table 4
In-plane stresses along slipline VW, η line

σ (k)	σ_x (k)	σ_y (k)	τ_{xy} (k)
1	1.7071	0.2929	−0.7071
0.95	1.6916	0.2084	−0.6709
0.9	1.6742	0.1258	−0.6330
0.85	1.6548	0.0452	−0.5935
0.8	1.6335	−0.0335	−0.5525

the parabolic solution which is dominate near the leading edge of the plastic zone. Forward-swept lobes are also exhibited by isostrain contours of the first and third principal strains [20] that are associated with the parabolic plastic stress solution. (There is no plastic strain in the second principal direction for the Tresca yield condition in plane stress along side MN of Fig. 1.) These contours are obtained by differentiating the parabolic plastic displacement field which was obtained in [2] with the assumption of continuous displacements across the elastic–plastic boundary. These forward-swept strain contours agree qualitatively with plots of experimentally determined plastic strains for a variety of metals; see for example [21].

The parabolic stress field derived for the leading edge of the plastic zone might also serve as an approximation for steadily moving crack problems involving the Tresca yield condition in addition to stationary crack problems. The analogous behavior is known to exist for mode III and mode I plane stress problems involving the Mises yield condition.

To elaborate on this, one finds that the stationary mode III elastoplastic solution of Hult and McClintock (see [2]) for small scale yielding is similar along the leading edge of the plastic zone to the numerical and asymptotic stress fields presented in [22] for the steadily moving crack. Similarly, the stresses from the leading edge of a stationary mode I plane stress solution for a perfectly plastic material [25] agree with the numerical solutions of [23,24] for the steadily moving crack, with the possible exception of the crack axis itself [24]. Along the crack axis in front of the tip, the governing equations of the elastoplastic problem may be elliptic in character rather than parabolic as indicated by the purely plastic solution [25].

It is interesting to note that stresses along the crack axis behind the leading edge of the plastic zone, point D of Fig. 2, also follow from solving an elliptic equation. Along line DG, the parabolic stress solution indicates a biaxial state of stress exists, i.e., $\sigma_x = \sigma_y = 2k$ and $\tau_{xy} = 0$. The governing equation for the plastic stress function changes across DG from the nonlinear parabolic equation (Monge–Ampere), Eq. 125-5 in [2], to a linear elliptic equation (Poisson's equation). The constant

biaxial state of stress found along DG can be continued across the line into the adjoining region. Because of the elliptic nature of the governing equation, there are no mathematical characteristics or slip lines indicated in the sector bounded by line DG and the normalized x axis in Fig. 2.

It can be inferred that a constant biaxial tension $2k$ exists immediately to the left of point D of Fig. 2; however, its actual extent behind this point is unknown because of the uncertainties that remain about the motion of the elastic–plastic boundary from its prescribed position. If the biaxial state of tension were to extend all the way back to the crack tip, one would then have a situation which resembles the stress field along the crack axis in the plastic strip of the Dugdale model. In the case of a steadily moving crack, a plastic strain wake will form behind the crack tip accompanied by an elastic unloading, as indicated from analogous problems.

The state of stress across DG is consistent with a simple lower bound solution of plastic collapse that can be found for the plane stress mode I problem. Suppose a semi-infinite crack exists along the negative x axis in an infinite plate composed of perfectly plastic material under plane stress loading conditions and the Tresca yield condition. Assume in the half plane which contains the crack, $x < 0$, that $\sigma_x = 2k$. Further assume in the remaining half plane, $x > 0$, that $\sigma_x = \sigma_y = 2k$, and that no other stresses exist anywhere in the plane. One notes from this description that a stress discontinuity exists along the y axis in σ_y of magnitude $2k$.

This lower bound solution is another indication that an elliptical region of constant biaxial tension exists in front of the crack tip. Together with the Dugdale model, it reinforces an assumed continuance of the biaxial state of stress found along line DG of Fig. 2 into the fan shaped region behind point D.

It is anticipated that future numerical elastoplastic solutions for the mode I problem under the Tresca yield condition for plane stress loading conditions will reveal regions where this analytical elastoplastic solution is recoverable. Such results are suggested by the recovery of the Hutchinson perfectly plastic solution for the plane stress mode

I crack problem under the Mises yield condition (a lower bound solution) in finite element elasto-plastic studies of the same [8].

One should keep in mind that the plastic stress field obtained here is influenced only by data from a single side of the elastic–plastic boundary, i.e., the leading or trailing edge of the plastic zone which meet at point B of Fig. 2. Whether or not the leading edge solution or the trailing edge solution is a valid approximation has not been established.

Most of the attention in this paper has been focused on the trailing portion of the plastic zone where the hyperbolic solution dominates, as the details of the parabolic solution have previously appeared [2,7,20]. Because data along η lines from the trailing edge of the plastic zone cannot be continued across the plastic hinge (this comes from a general property of limiting lines [9]) the solution is restricted to the crack tip neighborhood, Fig. 4. The passage of the prescribed elastoplastic boundary through the crack tip is in agreement with the finite element analyses [8] of a linear elastic/perfectly plastic material subject to plane stress loading conditions using a flow theory of plasticity for the Mises yield condition. That analysis indicates that virtually no active plastic region remains behind the crack tip along the crack surfaces for a stationary mode I crack. This is in sharp contrast to plane strain finite element analyses of the mode I problem, where the crack tip is completely engulfed by plastic material; see [2], pp. 163–168.

Despite the new information that the analytical solution has to offer, the analysis presented here cannot readily incorporate a failure criterion. It cannot serve as a lower bound solution since equilibrium is not satisfied between the two separate sheets of the plastic solution. Nor can it serve as an upper bound solution because no velocity field or strain rates have been calculated.

The disequilbrated state is a consequence of having solved an initial value problem for the parabolic and hyperbolic stress equations using a prescribed elastoplastic boundary rather than solving a free boundary value problem for equations derived using the compatibility of strains. The leading and trailing edges of the elastic–plastic boundary generate two separate domains of de-

pendence for their initial data which overlap in particular regions. While any contiguous region – say a small circle, confined to any one particular sheet of the plastic solution is in equilibrium, the two separate sheets of the plastic solution are not in equilibrium where they touch [2,7]. For example, along the interfacial curve FG of Fig. 2, two different values of traction are determined on opposite sides of the boundary. As there is no physically-motivated reason to justify this, global equilibrium has not been established.

The relative importance of this work can be assessed properly only after comparisons have been made to numerical elastoplastic solutions of the mode I plane stress problem under the Tresca yield conditon. As none presently exist, one needs new numerical solutions that utilize the Tresca yield condition rather than the Mises yield condition to decide on the regions of applicability of the analytical solution. Despite the questions that have been raised here concerning the very nature of the crack tip strain singularity under the Tresca yield condition for plane stress, it was shown in [8] for the Mises yield condition that if the finite element mesh is kept extremely fine the use of standard elements (4-node isoparametric quadralateral) produce results very similar to those employing singular elements near the crack tip. This indicates that the issue of the line singularity might be circumvented in any first generation finite element solutions by using a sufficiently fine mesh.

The inclusion of elastic strains, the use of compatibility equations for total strain, and the formulation of free boundary value problems for the various interfaces are all necessary in future numerical solutions of the mode I elastoplastic problem under the Tresca yield condition. The possibility of elastic unloading with residual plastic strain would also be included for an incremental theory of plasticity.

In concluding, one should mention that the solution presented here may remain the only available analytical solution for a mode I elastoplastic problem having a finite-dimensional plastic zone which asymptotically approaches the linear elastic solution away from the crack tip. This is a consequence of the difficulties encountered in

solving analytically nonlinear partial differential
equations.

References

[1] J.A. Hult, F.A. McClintock, Elastic–plastic stress and strain distributions around sharp notches under repeated shear, Proceedings of The Ninth Int. Congr. of Applied Mechanics, Brussels, vol. 8, 1956, pp. 51–58.

[2] D.J. Unger, Analytical Fracture Mechanics, Academic Press, San Diego, 1995.

[3] D.S. Dugdale, Yielding of sheets containing slits, J. Mech. Phys. Solids 8 (1960) 100–104.

[4] T.J. Lu, C.L. Chow, A modified Dugdale model for crack tip plasticity and its related problems, Engng Fracture Mech. 37 (1990) 551–568.

[5] Y.C. Gao, Pseudo plane stress plastic field for mode I crack growth, Theor. Appl. Fract. Mech. 27 (1997) 203–212.

[6] D.J. Unger, Plastic hinge formation near the mode I crack tip in thin plates, to be submitted to Theor. Appl. Fract. Mech.

[7] D.J. Unger, Analytic continuation of stresses across a mode I elastoplastic interface, Engng. Fracture Mech. 36 (1990) 763–776.

[8] R. Narasimhan, A.J. Rosakis, A finite element analysis of small-scale yielding near a stationary crack under plane stress, J. of Mech. Phys. Solids 36 (1988) 77–117.

[9] W. Prager, P.G. Hodge, Theory of Perfectly Plastic Solids, Wiley, New York, 1951.

[10] J. Chakrabarty, Theory of Plasticity, McGraw–Hill, New York, 1987.

[11] D. Broek, Elementary Engineering Fracture Mechanics, Kluwer Academic Publishers, Hingham, MA, USA, 1986.

[12] R. Hill, Mathematical Theory of Plasticity, Oxford University Press, London, 1950.

[13] L.M. Kachanov, Fundamentals of the Theory of Plasticity, Mir, Moscow, 1974.

[14] S.G. Mikhlin, Fundamental Equations of the Mathematical Theory of Plasticity, Izd. Akad. Nauk SSSR, Leningrad, 1934 (in Russian).

[15] M. Levy, Sur l'integration des equations aux differences partielles relatives aux mouvements interieurs des corps solides ductiles lorsque ces mouvements ont lieu par plans paralleles, Compt. Rend Acad. Sci. Ser. A 73 (1871) 1098–1103.

[16] M.R. Spiegel, Mathematical Handbook of Formulas and Tables, Shaum's Outline Series, McGraw–Hill, New York, 1968.

[17] G.T. Hahn, R.A. Rosenfield, Local yielding and extension of a crack under plane stress, Acta Metallurgica 13 (1965) 293–306.

[18] R.A. Rosenfield, P.K. Dai, G.T. Hahn, Crack extension and propagation under plane stress, in: T. Yokobori, T. Kawasaki, J.L. Swedlow (Eds.), Proceedings of The First International Conference on Fracture, vol. 1, Sendai, Japan, 1965, pp. 223–258.

[19] V.Z. Parton, E.M. Morozov, Elastic–Plastic Fracture Mechanics, Mir, Moscow, 1978, pp. 151–163.

[20] D.J. Unger, Isostrain contours for a plane stress mode I elastoplastic fracture problem, Int. J. Fract. 82 (1996) R47–R52.

[21] W.W. Gerberich, Plastic strains and energy density in cracked plates, part I – experimental techniques and results, Experimental Mechanics 4 (1964) 335–344.

[22] A.D. Chitaley, F.A. McClintock, Elastic–plastic mechanics of steady crack growth under anti-plane shear, J. Mech. Phys. Solids 19 (1971) 147–163.

[23] R.H. Dean, Elastic–plastic steady crack growth in plane stress, in: C.F. Shih, J.P. Gudas (Eds.), Elastic–Plastic Fracture: Second Symposium, vol. I, Inelastic Crack Analysis, ASTM STP 803, 1983, pp. 39–51.

[24] R. Narasimhan, A.J. Rosakis, J.F. Hall, A finite element study of stable crack growth under plane stress conditions: part I – elastic-perfectly plastic solids, J. of Applied Mechanics 54 (1987) 838–845.

[25] J.W. Hutchinson, Plastic stress and strain fields at a crack tip, J. Mech. Phys. Solids 16 (1968) 337–347.

References

[AC 88] B. D. Annin and G. P. Cherepanov, *Elastic–Plastic Problems*, pp. 27–31, ASME Press, New York (1988).

[AG 78] E. C. Aifantis and W. W. Gerberich, A new form of exact solutions for mode I, II, III crack problems and implications, *Eng. Fract. Mech.* **10**, 95–108 (1978).

[Aif 80] E. C. Aifantis, On the problem of diffusion in solids, *Acta Mech.* **37**, 265–296 (1980).

[AM 88] A. G. Atkins and Y.-W. Mai, *Elastic and Plastic Fracture, Metals, Polymers, Ceramics, Composites, Biological Materials*, Ellis Horwood, West Sussex/Halsted Press/Wiley, New York (1988).

[AS 64] M. Abramowitz and I. A. Stegun, *Handbook of Mathematical Functions with Formulas, Graphs, and Mathematical Tables*, NBS Appl. Mathe. Ser., Vol. 55, U.S. Government Printing Office, Washington, DC (1964).

[Ayr 52] F. Ayres, Jr., *Theory and Problems of Differential Equations*, Shaum's Outline Series, McGraw-Hill, New York (1952).

[Bar 59] G. I. Barenblatt, The formation of equilibrium cracks during brittle fracture. General ideas and hypotheses. Axially Symmetric Cracks, *PMM* **23**, 434–444 (1959).

[BCS 63] B. A. Bilby, A. H. Cottrell, and K. H. Swinden, The spread of plastic yield from a notch, *Proc. R. Soc. London, Ser. A* **272**, 304–314 (1963).

[BH 86] N. Bleistein and R. A. Handelsman, *Asymptotic Expansions of Integrals*, Dover, New York (1986).

[BL 72] J. A. Begley and J. D. Landes, The J integral as a fracture criterion, *ASTM Spec. Tech. Publ.* **STP 514**, 1–20 (1972).

[Bro 79] S. D. Brown, Subcritical crack growth: A treatment based on multibarrier kinetics, In *Environmental Degradation of Engineering Materials* (M. R. Louthen, Jr., and R. P. McNitt, Eds.), pp. 141–149, VPI Press, Blacksburg, VA (1979).

[Bro 82] Broek, D., *Elementary Engineering Fracture Mechanics*, Kluwer Academic Publishers, Hingham, MA (1982).

[BS 66] F. M. Burdekin and D. E. W. Stone, The crack opening displacement approach to fracture mechanics in yielding materials, *J. Strain Anal.* **1**, 145–153 (1966).

[Cal 85] C. R. Calladine, *Plasticity for Engineers*, Ellis Horwood Series, Engineering Science, West Sussex/Wiley, New York (1985).

[CEGB 84] *Assessment of the Integrity of Structures Containing Defects-Addendum for Structures Made of Material with High Capacity for Work Hardening*, CEGB Research Memorandum, Central Electricity Generating Board, London (1984).

299

[CH 62] R. Courant and D. Hilbert, *Methods of Mathematical Physics*, Vol. 2, Wiley, New York (1962).

[Cha 87] J. Chakrabarty, *Theory of Plasticity*, p. 88, McGraw-Hill, New York (1987).

[Chel 77] G. G. Chell, The application of post-yield fracture mechanics to penny-shaped and semi-circular cracks, *Eng. Fract. Mech.* **9**, 55–63 (1977).

[Chel 79] G. G. Chell, Elastic-plastic fracture mechanics, In *Developments in Fracture Mechanics* (G. G. Chell, Ed.), Vol. 1, pp. 67–105, Applied Science Publishers, London (1979).

[Cher 67] G. P. Cherepanov, The propagation of cracks in a continuous media, *PMM* **31** 476–488 (1967).

[Cher 79] G. P. Cherepanov, *Mechanics of Brittle Fracture*, McGraw-Hill, New York (1979).

[CHi 62] R. J. Charles and E. G. Hilig, The kinetics of glass failure by stress corrosion, *Proc. Union Sci. Cont. Verre*, Belgium, pp. 511–527 (1962).

[Chu 60] R. V. Churchill, *Complex Variables and Applications*, 2nd ed., McGraw-Hill, New York (1960).

[CJ 49] A. H. Cottrell and M. A. Jawson, Distribution of solute atom round a slow dislocation, *Proc. R. Soc. London Ser. A* **199**, 104–114 (1949).

[CM 71] A. D. Chitaley and F. A. McClintock, Elastic-plastic mechanics of steady crack growth under anti-plane shear, *J. Mech. Phys. Solids* **19**, 147–163 (1971).

[Cor 72] H. T. Corten, Fracture mechanics of composites, In *Fracture: An Advanced Treatise* (H. Liebowitz, Ed.), Vol. 7, pp. 675–770, Academic Press, New York (1972).

[CP 67] M. Creager and P. C. Paris, Elastic field equations for blunt cracks with reference to stress corrosion cracking, *Int. J. Fract. Mech.* **3**, 247–252 (1967).

[CS 77] G. G. Chell and G. M. Spink, A post-yield fracture mechanics analysis of three-point bend specimens and its implications to fracture toughness testing, *Eng. Fract. Mech.* **9**, 101–121 (1977).

[CZ 91] W. F. Chen and H. Zhang, *Structural Plasticity*, Springer-Verlag, New York (1991).

[DeB 81] N. G. De Bruijn, *Asymptotic Methods in Analysis*, Dover, New York (1981).

[DH 91] Z.-Z. Du and J. W. Hancock, The effect of non-singular stresses on crack-tip constraint, *J. Mech. Phys. Solids* **39**, 555–567 (1991).

[DT 75] A. R. Dowling and C. H. A. Townley, The effects of defects on structural failure: A two-criterion approach, *Int. J. Pressure Vessels Piping* **3**, 77–107 (1975).

[Dug 60] D. S. Dugdale, Yielding of sheets containing slits, *J. Mech. Phys. Solids* **8**, 100–104 (1960).

[For 59] A. R. Forsyth, *Theory of Differential Equations*, Vols. 4–5, Dover, New York (1959).

[Fre 74] S. W. Freiman, Effect of alcohols on crack propagation in glass, *J. Am. Ceram. Soc.* **57**, 350–353 (1974).

[Fuj 85] F. E. Fujita, The iron-hydrogen phase diagram, In *Hydrogen Degradation of Ferrous Alloys* (R. A. Oriani, J. P. Hirth, and M. Smialowski, Eds.), pp. 1–15. Noyes Publications, Park Ridge, NJ (1985).

[Gar 91] Y. S. Garud, Quantitative evaluation of environmentally assisted cracking: A survey of developments and application of modeling concepts, *J. Pressure Vessel Technol.* **113**, 1–9 (1991).

[GCLL 87] W. W. Gerberich, S.-H. Chen, G.-S. Lee, and T. Livine, Brittle fracture: Weakest link or process zone control? *Metall. Trans. A* **18A**, 1861–1875 (1987).

[GCS 75] W. W. Gerberich, Y. T. Chen, and C. St. John, A short-time diffusion correlation for hydrogen-induced crack growth studies, *Metall. Trans. A* **6**, 1485–1498 (1975).

[Gei 53] H. Geiringer, Some recent results in the theory of an ideal plastic body, In *Advances in Applied Mechanics* (R. von Mises and Th. von Kármán, Eds.), Vol. 3, pp. 197–294, Academic Press, New York (1953).

[Ger 87] W. W. Gerberich, Novel techniques as applied to fracture process zone theory, In *Chemistry and Physics of Fracture* (R. M. Latanision and R. H. Jones, Eds.), pp. 419–437, Martinus Nijhoff Publishers, Dordrecht, The Netherlands (1987).

[GR 65] I. S. Gradshteyn and I. M. Ryzhik, *Table of Integrals, Series, and Products*, Academic Press, New York (1965).

[Gri 20] A. A. Griffith, The phenomena of rupture and flow in solids, *Trans. R. Soc. London* **221A**, 163–197 (1920), reprinted with annotations and corrections, *ASM Trans. Q.* **61**, 871–906 (1968).

[GT 84] J. M. Gere and S. P. Timoshenko, *Mechanics of Materials*, 2nd ed., PWS Publishers, Wadsworth, Inc., Belmont, CA (1984).

[GW 77] R. P. Gangloff and R. P. Wei, Gaseous hydrogen embrittlement of high strength steels, *Metall. Trans. A* **8A**, 1043–1053 (1977).

[Han 92] J. W. Hancock, Constraint and stress state effects in ductile fracture. In *Topics in Fracture and Fatigue* (A. S. Argon, Ed.), pp. 99–144, Springer-Verlag, New York (1992).

[Hel 84] K. Hellan, *Introduction to Fracture Mechanics*, McGraw-Hill, New York (1984).

[Hen 23] H. Hencky, Über einige statisch bestimmte Fälle des Gleichgewichts in plastischen Körperr, *Z. Angew. Math Mech.* **3**(4), 241–251 (1923).

[Her 76] R. W. Hertzberg, *Deformation and Fracture Mechanics of Engineering Materials*, Wiley, New York (1976).

[HG 64] W. F. Hughes and E. W. Gaylord, *Basic Equations of Engineering Science*, Schaum's Outline Series, McGraw-Hill, New York (1964).

[Hil 50] R. Hill, *The Mathematical Theory of Plasticity*, Oxford University Press, London (1950).

[Hil 52] R. Hill, On discontinuous plastic states with special reference to localized necking in thin sheets, *J. Mech. Phys. Solids* **1**, 19–30 (1952).

[Hil 87] J. M. Hill, *One-Dimensional Stefan Problems: An Introduction*, Vol. 31, Longmans, London (1987).

[HL 82] J. P. Hirth and J. Lothe, *Theory of Dislocations*, 2nd ed., Wiley, New York (1982).

[HLM 76] R. P. Harrison, K. Loosemore, and I. Milne, *Assessment of the Integrity of Structures Containing Defects*, CEGB Report R/H/R6, Central Electricity Generating Board, London (1976).

[HM 56] J. A. Hult and F. A. McClintock, Elastic–plastic stress and strain distributions around sharp notches under repeated shear, *Appl. Mech.* **8**, pp. 51–58 (1957).

[HM 75] J. P. Hutin and Y. Mizuta, Lehigh University, Bethlehem, PA, unpublished results (1975).

[HM 84] Y. Hirose and T. Mura, Nucleation mechanism of stress corrosion cracking from notches, *Eng. Fract. Mech.* **19**, 317–329 (1984).

[Hut 68a] J. W. Hutchinson, Singular behavior at the end of a tensile crack in a hardening material, *J. Mech. Phys. Solids* **16**, 13–31 (1968).

[Hut 68b] J. W. Hutchinson, Plane stress and strain fields at the crack tip, *J. Mech. Phys. Solids* **16**, 337–347 (1968).

[Hut 79] J. W. Hutchinson, *Nonlinear Fracture Mechanics*, Department of Solid Mechanics, Technical University of Denmark (1979).

[HW 71] S. J. Hudak, Jr., and R. P. Wei, unpublished results.

[HW 81] S. J. Hudak, Jr., and R. P. Wei, Considerations of non-steady-state crack growth in materials evaluation and design, *Int. J. Pressure Vessels Piping* **9**, 63–74 (1981).

[IKS 58] G. R. Irwin, J. A. Kies, and H. L. Smith, Fracture strengths relative to onset and arrest of crack propagation, *Proc. Am. Soc. Mater. Testing* **58**, 640–657 (1958).

[Irw 49] G. R. Irwin, *Fracturing of Metals*, p. 147, American Society of Metals, Cleveland, OH (1949).

[Irw 58] G. R. Irwin, The crack extension force for a crack tip at a free surface boundary, *NRL Rep.* **NRL-MR-5120** (1958).

[Irw 60] G. R. Irwin, Fracture mode transition for a crack traversing a plate, *J. Basic Eng.* **82**, 417–425 (1960).

[Joh 82] R. Johnson, *Resolution of the Reactor Vessel Materials Toughness Safety Issue*, Vols. 1 and 2, Nuclear Reactor Commission Report NURGE 0744, U.S. Nuclear Regulatory Commission, Washington, DC (1982).

[Jos 60] W. Jost, *Diffusion*, Academic Press, New York (1960).

[Kac 74] L. M. Kachanov, *Fundamentals of the Theory of Plasticity*, Mir, Moscow (1974).

[KGS 81] V. Kumar, M. D. German, and C. F. Shih, *An Engineering Approach for Elastic-Plastic Fracture Analysis*, EPRI Project 1237-1, Electric Power Research Institute, Palo Alto, CA (1981).

[Kli 72] M. Kline, *Mathematical Thought from Ancient to Modern Times*, Vol. 2, Oxford University Press, Oxford and New York (1972).

[Kno 73] J. F. Knott, *Fundamentals of Fracture Mechanics*, Butterworth, London (1973).

[Kob 52] H. Kober, *A Dictionary of Conformal Representations*, Dover, New York (1952).

[Koi 65] W. T. Koiter, Discussion of rectangular tensile sheet with symmetric edge cracks by O. L. Bowie, *J. Appl. Mech.* **32**, 237 (1965).

[Köt 03] F. Kötter, Die Bestimmung des Druckes an gekrümmten Gleitflächen, eine Aufgabe aus der Lehre vom Erddruck, *Berl. Ber.* (1903).

[KP 85] M. F. Kanninen and C. H. Popelar, *Advanced Fracture Mechanics*, Oxford University Press, New York (1985).

[KPPC 70a] B. A. Kudryavtsev, V. Z. Parton, Yu. A. Peskov, and G. P. Cherepanov, On a local plastic zone near the tip of a crack, *Mekh. Tverd. Tela* **5**, 61–64 (1970).

[KPPC 70b] B. A. Kudryavtsev, V. Z. Parton, Yu. A. Peskov, and G. P. Cherepanov, On the local plastic zone near the end of a slit (plane strain), *Mekh. Tverd. Tela* **5**, 1132–138 (1970).

[Kra 79] A. S. Krausz, The theory of thermally activated processes in brittle stress corrosion cracking, *Eng. Fract. Mech.* **11**, 33–42 (1979).

[Law 72] J. D. Lawrence, *A Catalog of Special Plane Curves*, Dover, New York (1972).

[LC 73] S. G. Larsson and A. J. Carlsson, Influence of non-singular stress terms and specimen geometry on small-scale yielding at crack tips in elastic–plastic materials *J. Mech. Phys. Solids* **21**, 263–277 (1973).

[LC 90] T. J. Lu and C. L. Chow, A modified Dugdale model for crack tip plasticity and its related problems, *Eng. Fract. Mech.* **37**, 551–568 (1990).

[Lee 86] S. L. Lee, Ph.D. Dissertation, Ohio State University, Columbus (1986).

[Lie 72] H. M. Lieberstein, *Theory of Partial Differential Equations*, Math. Sci. Eng. Ser., Vol. 92, Academic Press, New York (1972).

[Lit 73] R. W. Little, *Elasticity*, Prentice-Hall, Englewood Cliffs, NJ (1973).

[Liu 70] H. W. Liu, Stress-corrosion cracking and the interaction between crack-tip stress field and solute atoms, *J. Basic Eng.* **92**, 633–638 (1970).

[LMOR 71] N. Levy, P. V. Marcal, W. J. Ostergren, and J. R. Rice, Small scale yielding near a crack in plane strain: A finite element approach, *Int. J. Fract. Mech.* **7**, 143–156 (1971).

[Lov 44] A. E. H. Love, *A Treatise on the Mathematical Theory of Elasticity*, 4th ed., Dover, New York (1944).

[LPWSW 81] M. Lu, P. S. Pao, T. W. Weir, G. W. Simmons, and R. P. Wei, Rate controlling processes for crack growth in hydrogen sulfide for an AISI 4340 steel, *Metall. Trans. A* **12A**, 805–811 (1981).

[LSU 79] N. N. Lebedev, I. P. Skalskaya, and Y. S. Uflyand, *Worked Problems in Applied Mathematics*, Dover, New York (1979).

[LU 88] S. L. Lee and D. J. Unger, A decohesion model of hydrogen assisted cracking, *Eng. Fract. Mech.* **31**, 647–660 (1988).

[LW 73] J. D. Landes and R. P. Wei, The kinetics of subcritical crack growth under sustained loading, *Int. J. Fract.* **9**, 227–293 (1973).

[LW 75] B. R. Lawn and T. R. Wilshaw, *Fracture of Brittle Solids*, Cambridge University Press, London (1975).

[LY 58] J. D. Lubahn and S. Yukarra, ASTM Preprint 79 (1958).

[Mal 69] L. E. Malvern, *Introduction to the Mechanics of Continuous Medium*, pp. 510–511, Prentice-Hall, Englewood Cliffs, NJ (1969).

[MB 87] T. A. Michalske and B. C. Bunker, The fracture of glass, *Sci. Am.* **257**, 122–129 (1987).

[McC 58] F. A. McClintock, Ductile fracture instability in shear, *J. Appl. Mech.* **25**, 582–588 (1958).

[McC 89] D. E. McCabe, A viewpoint on the failure assessment diagram, *ASTM Spec. Tech. Publ.* **STP 995**, 261–279 (1989).

[McC 94] D. E. McCabe, private communication (1994).

[Men 68] A. Mendelson, *Plasticity: Theory and Application*, Macmillan, New York (1968).

[Mer 81] J. G. Merkle, *Approximate Analysis of Ductile Crack Growth in a Nozzle Corner Region*, pp. 1–5, NRC Vessel and Piping Review Workshop, Oak Ridge, TN (1981).

[MMc 88] A. J. Markworth and J. K. McCoy, Chaotic dynamics in an atomistic model of environmentally assisted fracture, *J. Mater. Res.* **3**, 675–666 (1988).

[MS 71] P. Moon and D. E. Spencer, *Field Theory Handbook Including Coordinate Systems, Differential Equations and Their Solutions*, 2nd ed., Springer-Verlag, Berlin (1971).

[Mus 53] N. I. Muskhelishvili, *Some Basic Problems of the Mathematical Theory of Elasticity; Fundamental Equations, Plane Theory of Elasticity, Torsion and Bending*, 5th ed., Noordhoff, Gröningen, Leyden, The Netherlands (1953).

[NA 85] A. Neimitz and E. C. Aifantis, On certain fracture mechanics considerations in environmental cracking, In *Time-Dependent Fracture* (A. S. Krausz, Ed.), pp. 189–199. Martinus Nijhoff Publishers, Dordrecht, The Netherlands (1985).

[NA 87a] A. Neimitz and E. C. Aifantis, On the size and shape of the process zone, *Eng. Fract. Mech.* **26**, 491–503 (1987).

[NA 87b] A. Neimitz and E. C. Aifantis, On the length of crack jump during subcritical growth, *Eng. Fract. Mech.* **26**, 505–518 (1987).

[OJ 77] R. A. Oriani and P. H. Josephic, Equilibrium and kinetic studies of the hydrogen-assisted cracking of steel, *Acta Metall.* **25**, 979–988 (1977).

[Ori 72] R. A. Oriani, A mechanistic theory of hydrogen embrittlement of steels, *Ber. Bunsenges. Phys. Chem.* **76**, 848–851 (1972).

[Oro 45] E. Orowan, *Trans. Inst. Eng. Shipbuild. Scotl.* **89**, 165 (1945).

[Oro 50] E. Orowan, *Fatigue and Fracture of Metals*, p. 139, MIT Press, Cambridge, MA (1950).

[Pan 60] V. V. Panasyuk, On the theory of crack extension during the deformation of a brittle body, *Dopov. Akad. Nauk Ukr. RSR* **9**, 1185–1188, (in Ukrainian) (1960).

[PDS 74] M. P. Puls, R. Dutton, and R. N. Stevens, The chemical stress applied to creep and failure theories. II. Application to the growth of sub-critical Griffith cracks, *Acta Metall.* **22**, 639–647 (1974).

[PM 78] V. Z. Parton and E. M. Morozov, *Elastic–Plastic Fracture Mechanics*, Mir, Moscow (1978).

[Pra 21] L. Prandtl, Über die Eindringungsfestigkeit (Härte) plastischer Baustoffe und die Festigkeit von Schneiden, *Z. Angew. Math. Mech.* **1**, 15–20 (1921).

[PS 65] P. C. Paris and G. C. Sih, Fracture toughness testing and its application, *ASTM Spec. Tech. Publ.* **STP 381**, 30 (1965).

[RDS 80] J. R. Rice, W. J. Drugan, and T. L. Sham, Elastic-plastic analysis of growing cracks, *ASTM Spec. Tech. Publ.* **STP 700**, 189–221 (1980).

[Ric 66] J. R. Rice, Contained plastic deformation near cracks and notches under longitudinal shear, *Int. J. Fract. Mech.* **2**, 426–447 (1966).

[Ric 67] J. R. Rice, Stresses due to a sharp notch in a work-hardening elastic-plastic material loaded by a longitudinal shear, *J. Appl. Mech.* **34**, 287–298 (1967).

[Ric 68a] J. R. Rice, Mathematical analysis in the mechanics of fracture, In *Fracture: An Advanced Treatise* (H. Liebowitz, Ed.), Vol. 2, pp. 191–311, Academic Press, New York (1968).

[Ric 68b] J. R. Rice, A path independent integral and the approximate analysis of strain concentration by notches and cracks, *J. Appl. Mech.* **35**, 379–386 (1968).

[Ric 74] J. R. Rice, Limitations to the small scale yielding approximation for crack tip plasticity, *J. Mech. Phys. Solids* **22**, 17–26 (1974).

[Ric 78] J. R. Rice, Thermodynamics of the quasi-static growth of Griffith cracks, *J. Mech. Phys. Solids* **26**, 61–78 (1978).

[RJ 70] J. R. Rice and M. A. Johnson, The role of large crack tip geometry changes in plane strain fracture, In *Inelastic Behavior of Solids* (M. F. Kanninen, W. F. Adler, A. R. Rosenfield, and R. I. Jaffee, Eds.), pp. 641–672, McGraw-Hill, New York (1970).

[RR 68] J. R. Rice and G. F. Rosengren, Plane strain deformation near a crack tip in a power-law hardening material, *J. Mech. Phys. Solids* **16**, 1–12 (1968).

[Rub 71] L. I. Rubenstein, *The Stefan Problem*, Vol. 27, American Mathematical Society, Providence, RI (1971).

[RV 77] R. Raj and V. K. Varadan, The kinetics of hydrogen assisted crack growth, In *Mechanisms of Environmental Sensitive Cracking of Materials*, pp. 426–436, Metals Society, London (1977).

[SC 92] I. H. Shames and F. A. Cozzarelli, *Elastic and Inelastic Stress Analysis*, Prentice-Hall, Englewood Cliffs, NJ (1992).

[SD 53] R. T. Shield and D. C. Drucker, The application of limit analysis to punch-indentation problems, *J. Appl. Mech.* 453–460 (1953).

[SDP 74] R. N. Stevens, R. Dutton, and M. P. Puls, The chemical stress applied to creep and failure theories. I. A general approach, *Acta Metall.* **22**, 629–638 (1974).

[SF 81] K. Sieradski and P. J. Ficalora, The adsorption of hydrogen on iron and hydrogen embrittlement of steel, in *Environmental Degradation of Engineering Materials in Hydrogen* (M. R. Louthen, Jr., R. P. McNitt, and R. D. Sisson, Eds.), pp. 43–54, VPI Press, Blacksburg, VA (1981).

[SG 73] C. St. John and W. W. Gerberich, The effect of loading mode on hydrogen embrittlement, *Metall. Trans.* **4**, 589–594 (1973).

[SL 69] I. N. Sneddon and M. Lowengrub, *Crack Problems in the Classical Theory of Elasticity*, Wiley, New York (1969).

[SM 89] P. Sofronis and R. M. McMeeking, Numerical analysis of hydrogen transport near a blunting crack tip, *J. Mech. Phys. Solids* **57**, 317–350 (1989).

[Sne 57] I. N. Sneddon, *Elements of Partial Differential Equations*, McGraw-Hill, New York (1957).

[Sok 56] I. S. Sokolnikoff, *Mathematical Theory of Elasticity*, pp. 179–180, McGraw-Hill, New York (1956).

[Spe 84] M. O. Speidel, Hydrogen embrittlement and stress corrosion cracking of aluminum alloys, In *Hydrogen Embrittlement and Stress Corrosion Cracking* (R. Gibala and R. F. Hehemann, Eds.), pp. 271–296, American Society of Metals, Metals Park, OH (1984).

[Spi 64] M. R. Spiegel, *Theory and Problems of Complex Variables*, Shaum's Outline Series, McGraw-Hill, New York (1964).

[SPW 78] G. W. Simmons, P. S. Pao, and R. P. Wei, Fracture mechanics and surface chemistry studies of subcritical crack growth, *Metall. Trans A* **9A**, 1147–1158 (1978).

[SS 63] C. N. Satterfield and T. K. Sherwood, *The Role of Diffusion in Catalysis*, Addison-Wesley, Reading, MA (1963).

[Ste 89] H. Stephani, *Differential Equations: Their Solution Using Symmetries*, Cambridge University Press, Cambridge (1989).

[Str 88] D. J. Struik, *Lectures on Classical Differential Geometry*, Dover, New York (1988).

[SU 88] Y. Seo and D. J. Unger, unpublished results (1988).

[TA 77] A. N. Tikhonov and V. Y. Arsenin, *Solutions of Ill-posed Problems*, Winston/Wiley, Washington, DC (1977).

[TF 89] D. M. Tracey and C. E. Freese, Plasticity near a blunt flaw under remote tension, *ASTM Spec. Tech. Publ.* **STP 995**, 93–106 (1989).

[TG 70] S. P. Timoshenko and J. N. Goodier, *Theory of Elasticity*, 3rd ed., McGraw-Hill, New York (1970).

[Tro 60] A. R. Troiano, The role of hydrogen and other interstitials in the mechanical behavior of metals, *Trans. ASME* **52** 54–80 (1960).

[Tub 66] I. S. Tuba, A method of elastic-plastic plane stress and strain, *J. Strain Anal.* **1**, 115–122 (1966).

[UA 83] D. J. Unger and E. C. Aifantis, On the theory of stress-assisted diffusion, II. *Acta Mech.* **47**, 117–151 (1983).

[UGA 83] D. J. Unger, W. W. Gerberich, and E. C. Aifantis, Further remarks on an exact solution for crack problems, *Eng. Fract. Mech.* **18**, 735–742 (1983).

[Ung 86] D. J. Unger, On a decohesion model of hydrogen assisted cracking, *U.S. Natl. Congr. Appl. Mech., 10th*, University of Texas, Austin, Paper M2A (1986).

[Ung 89a] D. J. Unger, A mathematical analysis for impending hydrogen-assisted crack propagation, *Eng. Fract. Mech.* **34**, 657–667 (1989).

[Ung 89b] D. J. Unger, A finite-width Dugdale zone model for mode III, *Eng. Fract. Mech.* **34**, 977–987 (1989).

[Ung 90a] D. J. Unger, Analytic continuation of stresses across a mode I elastoplastic interface, *Eng. Fract. Mech.* **36**, 763–776 (1990).

[Ung 90b] D. J. Unger, A transition model of crack tip plasticity, *Int. J. Fract.* **44** R27-R31 (1990).

[Ung 90c] D. J. Unger, A modified Stefan problem related to transport-controlled stress corrosion cracking, *Eng. Fract. Mech.* **37**, 101–106 (1990).

[Ung 91] D. J. Unger, Developable surfaces in elastoplastic fracture mechanics, *Int. J. Fract.* **50**, R33–R38 (1991).

[Ung 92a] D. J. Unger, An energy dissipation analysis for a transitional model of crack tip plasticity, *Eng. Fract. Mech.* **41**, 457–462 (1992).

[Ung 92b] D. J. Unger, A comparison between mode I and mode III fracture assessment diagrams, *Int. J. Fract.* **53** R37–R41 (1992).

[Ung 93] D. J. Unger, On the utility of inverse Cassinian oval coordinates for the mode III elastoplastic problem, *Int. J. Fract.* **63**, R59–R63 (1993).

[vLe 75] H. P. van Leeuwen, Plateau velocity of SCC in high strength steel—A qualitative approach, *Corrosion* **31**, 42–50 (1975).

[WB 70] S. M. Wiederhorn and L. H. Bolz, Stress corrosion and static fatigue of glass, *J. Am. Ceram. Soc.* **53**, 543–548 (1970).

[Wel 63] A. A. Wells, Application of fracture mechanics at and beyond general yielding, British Welding Research Association Report M13/63, *Bri. Weld. J.* 563–570 (1963).

[Wes 39] H. M. Westergaard, Bearing pressures and cracks, *J. Appl. Mech.* **6**, 49–53 (1939).

[Wie 69] S. M. Wiederhorn, Mechanical and thermal properties of ceramics, *NBS Spec. Publ.* (U.S.) **303**, 217 (1969).

[Wil 57] M. L. Williams, On the stress distribution at the base of a stationary crack, *J. Appl. Mech.* **24**, 109–114 (1957).

[Wil 78] H. S. Wilf, *Mathematics for the Physical Sciences*, Dover, New York (1978).

[WNW 72] R. P. Wei, S. R. Novak, and D. P. Williams, Some important considerations in the development of stress corrosion cracking test methods, *Mater. Res. Stand.* **12**, 25–30 (1972).

[WSHW 80] T. W. Weir, G. W. Simmons, R. G. Hart, and R. P. Wei, A model for surface reaction and transport controlled fatigue crack growth, *Scr. Metall.* **14**, 357–364 (1980).

[ZT 76] E. C. Zachmanoglou and D. W. Thoe, *Introduction to Partial Differential Equations with Applications*, Williams & Wilkins, Baltimore (1976).

[Zwi 89] D. Zwillinger, *Handbook of Differential Equations*, Academic Press, San Diego, CA (1989).

Index

A CATALOG OF SELECTED
DOVER BOOKS
IN ALL FIELDS OF INTEREST

A CATALOG OF SELECTED DOVER
BOOKS IN ALL FIELDS OF INTEREST

CONCERNING THE SPIRITUAL IN ART, Wassily Kandinsky. Pioneering work by father of abstract art. Thoughts on color theory, nature of art. Analysis of earlier masters. 12 illustrations. 80pp. of text. 5⅜ x 8½. 23411-8 Pa. $4.95

ANIMALS: 1,419 Copyright-Free Illustrations of Mammals, Birds, Fish, Insects, etc., Jim Harter (ed.). Clear wood engravings present, in extremely lifelike poses, over 1,000 species of animals. One of the most extensive pictorial sourcebooks of its kind. Captions. Index. 284pp. 9 x 12. 23766-4 Pa. $14.95

CELTIC ART: The Methods of Construction, George Bain. Simple geometric techniques for making Celtic interlacements, spirals, Kells-type initials, animals, humans, etc. Over 500 illustrations. 160pp. 9 x 12. (Available in U.S. only.) 22923-8 Pa. $9.95

AN ATLAS OF ANATOMY FOR ARTISTS, Fritz Schider. Most thorough reference work on art anatomy in the world. Hundreds of illustrations, including selections from works by Vesalius, Leonardo, Goya, Ingres, Michelangelo, others. 593 illustrations. 192pp. 7⅛ x 10¼. 20241-0 Pa. $9.95

CELTIC HAND STROKE-BY-STROKE (Irish Half-Uncial from "The Book of Kells"): An Arthur Baker Calligraphy Manual, Arthur Baker. Complete guide to creating each letter of the alphabet in distinctive Celtic manner. Covers hand position, strokes, pens, inks, paper, more. Illustrated. 48pp. 8¼ x 11. 24336-2 Pa. $3.95

EASY ORIGAMI, John Montroll. Charming collection of 32 projects (hat, cup, pelican, piano, swan, many more) specially designed for the novice origami hobbyist. Clearly illustrated easy-to-follow instructions insure that even beginning papercrafters will achieve successful results. 48pp. 8¼ x 11. 27298-2 Pa. $3.50

THE COMPLETE BOOK OF BIRDHOUSE CONSTRUCTION FOR WOODWORKERS, Scott D. Campbell. Detailed instructions, illustrations, tables. Also data on bird habitat and instinct patterns. Bibliography. 3 tables. 63 illustrations in 15 figures. 48pp. 5¼ x 8½. 24407-5 Pa. $2.50

BLOOMINGDALE'S ILLUSTRATED 1886 CATALOG: Fashions, Dry Goods and Housewares, Bloomingdale Brothers. Famed merchants' extremely rare catalog depicting about 1,700 products: clothing, housewares, firearms, dry goods, jewelry, more. Invaluable for dating, identifying vintage items. Also, copyright-free graphics for artists, designers. Co-published with Henry Ford Museum & Greenfield Village. 160pp. 8¼ x 11. 25780-0 Pa. $10.95

HISTORIC COSTUME IN PICTURES, Braun & Schneider. Over 1,450 costumed figures in clearly detailed engravings–from dawn of civilization to end of 19th century. Captions. Many folk costumes. 256pp. 8⅜ x 11¾. 23150-X Pa. $12.95

MY BONDAGE AND MY FREEDOM, Frederick Douglass. Born a slave, Douglass became outspoken force in antislavery movement. The best of Douglass' autobiographies. Graphic description of slave life. 464pp. 5⅜ x 8½. 22457-0 Pa. $8.95

FOLLOWING THE EQUATOR: A Journey Around the World, Mark Twain. Fascinating humorous account of 1897 voyage to Hawaii, Australia, India, New Zealand, etc. Ironic, bemused reports on peoples, customs, climate, flora and fauna, politics, much more. 197 illustrations. 720pp. 5⅜ x 8½. 26113-1 Pa. $15.95

THE PEOPLE CALLED SHAKERS, Edward D. Andrews. Definitive study of Shakers: origins, beliefs, practices, dances, social organization, furniture and crafts, etc. 33 illustrations. 351pp. 5⅜ x 8½. 21081-2 Pa. $10.95

THE MYTHS OF GREECE AND ROME, H. A. Guerber. A classic of mythology, generously illustrated, long prized for its simple, graphic, accurate retelling of the principal myths of Greece and Rome, and for its commentary on their origins and significance. With 64 illustrations by Michelangelo, Raphael, Titian, Rubens, Canova, Bernini and others. 480pp. 5⅜ x 8½. 27584-1 Pa. $9.95

PSYCHOLOGY OF MUSIC, Carl E. Seashore. Classic work discusses music as a medium from psychological viewpoint. Clear treatment of physical acoustics, auditory apparatus, sound perception, development of musical skills, nature of musical feeling, host of other topics. 88 figures. 408pp. 5⅜ x 8½. 21851-1 Pa. $11.95

THE PHILOSOPHY OF HISTORY, Georg W. Hegel. Great classic of Western thought develops concept that history is not chance but rational process, the evolution of freedom. 457pp. 5⅜ x 8½. 20112-0 Pa. $9.95

THE BOOK OF TEA, Kakuzo Okakura. Minor classic of the Orient: entertaining, charming explanation, interpretation of traditional Japanese culture in terms of tea ceremony. 94pp. 5⅜ x 8½. 20070-1 Pa. $3.95

LIFE IN ANCIENT EGYPT, Adolf Erman. Fullest, most thorough, detailed older account with much not in more recent books, domestic life, religion, magic, medicine, commerce, much more. Many illustrations reproduce tomb paintings, carvings, hieroglyphs, etc. 597pp. 5⅜ x 8½. 22632-8 Pa. $12.95

SUNDIALS, Their Theory and Construction, Albert Waugh. Far and away the best, most thorough coverage of ideas, mathematics concerned, types, construction, adjusting anywhere. Simple, nontechnical treatment allows even children to build several of these dials. Over 100 illustrations. 230pp. 5⅜ x 8½. 22947-5 Pa. $8.95

THEORETICAL HYDRODYNAMICS, L. M. Milne-Thomson. Classic exposition of the mathematical theory of fluid motion, applicable to both hydrodynamics and aerodynamics. Over 600 exercises. 768pp. 6⅛ x 9¼. 68970-0 Pa. $20.95

SONGS OF EXPERIENCE: Facsimile Reproduction with 26 Plates in Full Color, William Blake. 26 full-color plates from a rare 1826 edition. Includes "TheTyger," "London," "Holy Thursday," and other poems. Printed text of poems. 48pp. 5¼ x 7. 24636-1 Pa. $4.95

OLD-TIME VIGNETTES IN FULL COLOR, Carol Belanger Grafton (ed.). Over 390 charming, often sentimental illustrations, selected from archives of Victorian graphics—pretty women posing, children playing, food, flowers, kittens and puppies, smiling cherubs, birds and butterflies, much more. All copyright-free. 48pp. 9¼ x 12¼. 27269-9 Pa. $7.95

CATALOG OF DOVER BOOKS

PERSPECTIVE FOR ARTISTS, Rex Vicat Cole. Depth, perspective of sky and sea, shadows, much more, not usually covered. 391 diagrams, 81 reproductions of drawings and paintings. 279pp. 5⅜ x 8½. 22487-2 Pa. $9.95

DRAWING THE LIVING FIGURE, Joseph Sheppard. Innovative approach to artistic anatomy focuses on specifics of surface anatomy, rather than muscles and bones. Over 170 drawings of live models in front, back and side views, and in widely varying poses. Accompanying diagrams. 177 illustrations. Introduction. Index. 144pp. 8⅜ x11¼. 26723-7 Pa. $9.95

GOTHIC AND OLD ENGLISH ALPHABETS: 100 Complete Fonts, Dan X. Solo. Add power, elegance to posters, signs, other graphics with 100 stunning copyright-free alphabets: Blackstone, Dolbey, Germania, 97 more–including many lower-case, numerals, punctuation marks. 104pp. 8⅛ x 11. 24695-7 Pa. $8.95

HOW TO DO BEADWORK, Mary White. Fundamental book on craft from simple projects to five-bead chains and woven works. 106 illustrations. 142pp. 5⅜ x 8. 20697-1 Pa. $5.95

THE BOOK OF WOOD CARVING, Charles Marshall Sayers. Finest book for beginners discusses fundamentals and offers 34 designs. "Absolutely first rate . . . well thought out and well executed."–E. J. Tangerman. 118pp. 7¾ x 10⅝. 23654-4 Pa. $7.95

ILLUSTRATED CATALOG OF CIVIL WAR MILITARY GOODS: Union Army Weapons, Insignia, Uniform Accessories, and Other Equipment, Schuyler, Hartley, and Graham. Rare, profusely illustrated 1846 catalog includes Union Army uniform and dress regulations, arms and ammunition, coats, insignia, flags, swords, rifles, etc. 226 illustrations. 160pp. 9 x 12. 24939-5 Pa. $10.95

WOMEN'S FASHIONS OF THE EARLY 1900s: An Unabridged Republication of "New York Fashions, 1909," National Cloak & Suit Co. Rare catalog of mail-order fashions documents women's and children's clothing styles shortly after the turn of the century. Captions offer full descriptions, prices. Invaluable resource for fashion, costume historians. Approximately 725 illustrations. 128pp. 8⅜ x 11¼. 27276-1 Pa. $11.95

THE 1912 AND 1915 GUSTAV STICKLEY FURNITURE CATALOGS, Gustav Stickley. With over 200 detailed illustrations and descriptions, these two catalogs are essential reading and reference materials and identification guides for Stickley furniture. Captions cite materials, dimensions and prices. 112pp. 6½ x 9¼. 26676-1 Pa. $9.95

EARLY AMERICAN LOCOMOTIVES, John H. White, Jr. Finest locomotive engravings from early 19th century: historical (1804–74), main-line (after 1870), special, foreign, etc. 147 plates. 142pp. 11⅜ x 8¼. 22772-3 Pa. $12.95

THE TALL SHIPS OF TODAY IN PHOTOGRAPHS, Frank O. Braynard. Lavishly illustrated tribute to nearly 100 majestic contemporary sailing vessels: Amerigo Vespucci, Clearwater, Constitution, Eagle, Mayflower, Sea Cloud, Victory, many more. Authoritative captions provide statistics, background on each ship. 190 black-and-white photographs and illustrations. Introduction. 128pp. 8⅞ x 11¾. 27163-3 Pa. $14.95

THE INFLUENCE OF SEA POWER UPON HISTORY, 1660–1783, A. T. Mahan. Influential classic of naval history and tactics still used as text in war colleges. First paperback edition. 4 maps. 24 battle plans. 640pp. 5⅜ x 8½. 25509-3 Pa. $14.95

THE STORY OF THE TITANIC AS TOLD BY ITS SURVIVORS, Jack Winocour (ed.). What it was really like. Panic, despair, shocking inefficiency, and a little heroism. More thrilling than any fictional account. 26 illustrations. 320pp. 5⅜ x 8½. 20610-6 Pa. $8.95

FAIRY AND FOLK TALES OF THE IRISH PEASANTRY, William Butler Yeats (ed.). Treasury of 64 tales from the twilight world of Celtic myth and legend: "The Soul Cages," "The Kildare Pooka," "King O'Toole and his Goose," many more. Introduction and Notes by W. B. Yeats. 352pp. 5⅜ x 8½. 26941-8 Pa. $8.95

BUDDHIST MAHAYANA TEXTS, E. B. Cowell and others (eds.). Superb, accurate translations of basic documents in Mahayana Buddhism, highly important in history of religions. The Buddha-karita of Asvaghosha, Larger Sukhavativyuha, more. 448pp. 5⅜ x 8½. 25552-2 Pa. $12.95

ONE TWO THREE . . . INFINITY: Facts and Speculations of Science, George Gamow. Great physicist's fascinating, readable overview of contemporary science: number theory, relativity, fourth dimension, entropy, genes, atomic structure, much more. 128 illustrations. Index. 352pp. 5⅜ x 8½. 25664-2 Pa. $9.95

EXPERIMENTATION AND MEASUREMENT, W. J. Youden. Introductory manual explains laws of measurement in simple terms and offers tips for achieving accuracy and minimizing errors. Mathematics of measurement, use of instruments, experimenting with machines. 1994 edition. Foreword. Preface. Introduction. Epilogue. Selected Readings. Glossary. Index. Tables and figures. 128pp. 5³⁄₈ x 8¹⁄₂. 40451-X Pa. $6.95

DALÍ ON MODERN ART: The Cuckolds of Antiquated Modern Art, Salvador Dalí. Influential painter skewers modern art and its practitioners. Outrageous evaluations of Picasso, Cézanne, Turner, more. 15 renderings of paintings discussed. 44 calligraphic decorations by Dalí. 96pp. 5⅜ x 8½. (Available in U.S. only.) 29220-7 Pa. $5.95

ANTIQUE PLAYING CARDS: A Pictorial History, Henry René D'Allemagne. Over 900 elaborate, decorative images from rare playing cards (14th–20th centuries): Bacchus, death, dancing dogs, hunting scenes, royal coats of arms, players cheating, much more. 96pp. 9¼ x 12¼. 29265-7 Pa. $12.95

MAKING FURNITURE MASTERPIECES: 30 Projects with Measured Drawings, Franklin H. Gottshall. Step-by-step instructions, illustrations for constructing handsome, useful pieces, among them a Sheraton desk, Chippendale chair, Spanish desk, Queen Anne table and a William and Mary dressing mirror. 224pp. 8⅛ x 11¼. 29338-6 Pa. $13.95

THE FOSSIL BOOK: A Record of Prehistoric Life, Patricia V. Rich et al. Profusely illustrated definitive guide covers everything from single-celled organisms and dinosaurs to birds and mammals and the interplay between climate and man. Over 1,500 illustrations. 760pp. 7½ x 10⅛. 29371-8 Pa. $29.95

Prices subject to change without notice.

Available at your book dealer or write for free catalog to Dept. GI, Dover Publications, Inc., 31 East 2nd St., Mineola, N.Y. 11501. Dover publishes more than 500 books each year on science, elementary and advanced mathematics, biology, music, art, literary history, social sciences and other areas.